Laboratory Experiments and Exercises for Organic Chemistry

Dr. Chase C. Smith
Dr. David Kurtz

Department of Chemistry
Ohio Northern University

WILEY

CUSTOM SERVICES

This custom textbook includes materials submitted by the Author for publication by John Wiley & Sons, Inc. The material has not been edited by Wiley and the Author is solely responsible for its content.

Printed in the United States of America.

ISBN 0-471-31786-1

Table of Contents

Table of Contents - continued.

ONU Department of Chemistry Safety Plan
Students' Guide to Standard Operating Procedures for Course Laboratories

General Safety

It is your responsibility to make sure that you are sufficiently well informed to be able to work safely in a laboratory. You need to consider how your work affects not only yourself, but the others working in the laboratory.

1. All laboratory operations should be planned carefully beforehand. Review and understand the written procedure for the experiment before coming to the laboratory. Your instructor will demonstrate how to use equipment and instruments, as well as alerting you to any special hazards and how to deal with them. Follow directions and pay close attention to instructions.

2. Your laboratory instructor will show you the location of the following items and instruct you how to use them. Be sure you know their location and proper use of the following:

Eye Wash Fountain	Fire Blanket
Safety Shower	First Aid Kit & Supplies
Fire Extinguisher	Emergency Exits
First Aid Manual	Biohazards
Emergency Phone Nos.	Sinks
Nearest Phone	Chemical Hygiene Plan
Material Safety Data Sheets	Broken Glass Receptacle

3. Consult your lab instructor if you are unsure of the hazards or proper use of any reagent or equipment. Ask questions about use, technique or disposal when you have any doubt as to proper procedure. **There are NO dumb safety questions.**

4. Perform only the assigned experiments. Unauthorized experiments are strictly forbidden. Maintain a serious working atmosphere. **Do not engage in horseplay.**

5. Do not store equipment, backpacks, coats, chemicals or other materials on the floor or in other places where

laboratory workers can trip or knock over the item, or in places that would block fire exits.

6. Do not work alone in laboratories except under the supervision of a faculty member. Permission from the laboratory instructor is required for after hours work.

7. Get approval from the lab instructor if you intend to leave experiments unattended for a short time. Leave a note by the apparatus identifying the experimenter and back-up personnel.

8. Report any accidents, injuries or close calls to the lab instructor or teaching assistant immediately. To ensure appropriate treatment, report minor injuries, no matter how trivial they seem.

9. Do not consume or store any food or beverages in the laboratory. If the laboratory experiment involves food or beverages, clearly label them "Not for human consumption" or equivalent.

10. Keep your work area safe and clean.

11. After completing an experiment, turn off, unplug, and properly store all electrical equipment. Turn off all gas and water valves.

12. Wash hands, face, and arms thoroughly if contaminated and always wash your hands before leaving the building. Always wash before eating, drinking, smoking or applying make-up after working in the laboratory. Shower after working with chemicals.

Lab Attire & Protective Clothing

Proper attire and use of approved safety goggles are simple but effective ways of protecting oneself from laboratory hazards.

1. Wear approved eye protection at all times when working in the laboratory. Eye protection must have "ANSI Z87" stamped on it. The use of contact lenses (especially soft contacts) in the laboratory is not recommended. Chemicals can become entrapped in, absorbed by or caught behind the lens, promoting eye irritation or causing damage to the eye. If you do wear contact lenses in the laboratory, use a good set of safety goggles over them. Goggles are required by the second laboratory period.

2. Use face shields or safety shields in laboratory operations that have the potential to result in fires or explosions or which utilize pressurized or high vacuum operations. Authorization of the lab supervisor is required before carrying out any of the above operations. Prior to such operations, check the safety equipment (fire extinguishers, shields, safety showers, etc.)

3. Wear protective gloves for some procedures. The type of glove selected should protect against the chemical that you are using, or against heat, cold, or sharp objects. Wear gloves for work with strong corrosives or with acutely toxic chemicals. As noted above, special procedures may require special protective equipment on a case by case basis. Consult your lab instructor.

4. Wear clothing that is comfortable, covers exposed skin, and does not restrict motion yet is not so loose (especially sleeves) as to catch on equipment. Shorts and miniskirts are not recommended. Consider the flammability of the clothing fabric. The use of lab coats is strongly recommended.

5. Wear sturdy shoes that cover your feet. Sandals and open-toed shoes are dangerous footwear in the lab. Canvas shoes do not provide the necessary protection from laboratory accidents.
    A. If you have long hair, tie it back to keep it away from flames and chemicals.
    B. Have your personal clothing and protective equipment, such as lab coats, laundered or cleaned
        regularly. Immediately clean your personal clothing and protective equipment after contamination.

Working with Equipment & Glassware

A little forethought in the use of and assembly of equipment and glassware can prevent major accidents. Be careful with Bunsen burners, hot plates, hot plate-stirrers and other hot objects. Be especially careful around equipment with moving parts. These items can catch your clothing or open up suddenly, showering you with dangerous material.

1. Whenever possible, use a broom and dustpan to handle broken glassware. Do not use damaged, cracked or broken glassware.

2. Dispose of broken glassware and dangerous items such as syringe needles in special containers as directed by your laboratory instructor. Do not place in the regular trash. These items should be as free of chemical contamination as possible before disposal.

3. When inserting thermometers or glass tubing into stoppers or corks, lubricate them with water or glycerin and twist, using short strokes and minimum pressure. Covering the thermometer or tubing with a towel protects hands and fingers from injury in case the article being inserted breaks.

4. Treat a test tube as you would a gun. Never point a test tube at anyone, especially when it is being heated. Never look down into a test tube or flask in which an experiment is being conducted.

5. Never take equipment or glassware out of the chemistry laboratory.

6. Report broken thermometers to the lab supervisor. The mercury must be cleaned up thoroughly under the direction of the laboratory supervisor to avoid contamination of the lab with poisonous mercury vapor.

Working Safely with Chemicals

Knowledge, caution and common sense add up to chemical safety. Assume any unfamiliar chemical is hazardous. Consider a mixture to be at least as hazardous as its most hazardous component. Know the hazards before you handle the material. Treat all chemicals with respect. Check your lab write-up for special hazards. Follow all chemical safety instructions and procedures to the letter. Minimize chemical exposure by careful use and good housekeeping.

1. Laboratory operations that have the potential to produce hazardous levels of fumes, gases, or volatile solvent vapors in excess of recommended exposure levels require fume hoods.

2. Do not (a) use unlabeled chemicals, (b) taste a chemical, (c) pipet by mouth, (d) smell a chemical. Check odors only if instructed to do so. Check by gently wafting the vapor towards your nose with your hand. Avoid skin contact with reagents.

3. Never combine substances unless you have been explicitly instructed to do so.

4. Clean up any spilled reagents immediately, especially near the balances or reagent shelf. Before clean-up, neutralize acid spills with solid sodium bicarbonate, $NaHCO_3$; neutralize base spills with boric acid. You are responsible for neutralizing, if necessary, and cleaning up your own spills.

5. Read the chemical labels very carefully to ensure that you have the correct chemical. Read labels 3 times:

when you pick it up; just before you use it; and after finishing. Match name, formula and concentration on the label to lab directions.

6. Use particular care to avoid skin and eye contact when working with corrosive agents such as acids and bases. If you spill any corrosive chemical on yourself, rinse the affected area with water for a minimum of 15 minutes. If the outside of a reagent bottle is contaminated, handle with gloves and rinse the bottle before using the reagent. Remove contaminated clothing immediately. Notify your lab supervisor.

7. Always add acid to water. Pour water and acid into the mixing container in the order of the spelling of "water". The "w" for water precedes the "a" for acid. **Always mix acids and water slowly and carefully.**

8. Do not light Bunsen burners or strike matches unless instructed to do so. Do not risk electrical sparks when flammable vapors are present.

9. Do not insert pipets, spatulas, or medicine droppers from your own lab kit into the reagent bottle. Dispense solids by tapping out and take only what you need.

10. Never return unused reagents to the reagent bottle. Do not contaminate reagents by exchanging caps or stoppers or by laying stoppers on the desk top. Contact your lab instructor for proper disposal of excess reagent.

11. Do not place reagents directly on the balance pan. Use a tared weighing container or paper.

12. Clean up your work area prior to leaving the laboratory.

Working with Electrical Equipment

Electrical equipment always means the chance of shock or fire. Do not touch with wet hands or while standing on a wet floor.

1. Do not use any electrically powered equipment that is not wired with a safety ground and 3-prong plug.

2. Report any shocks, defective or worn equipment, such as frayed wires, or undue heating to your laboratory

instructor.   Do not attempt to repair the equipment yourself.

3. Extension cords are not appropriate.

4. Never use electrical wires as supports, nor pull live wires.

Working with Pressurized Materials

Handle cylinders of compressed gases as high-energy sources and therefore as potential explosives.   Be aware that non-toxic gases can act as asphyxiates should they displace enough air.

1. Toxic gases should be used and stored in ventilation hoods.

2. Except when being moved, compressed gas cylinders must be securely strapped or chained to a bench-top or wall at all times.

3. Whenever moving a gas cylinder, remove the regulator and replace with the protective cap.

4. If a cylinder is moved more than a few feet, a properly-designed wheeled cart must be used, with the cylinder strapped down and the protective cap in place.

5. Never use cylinders whenever uncertain of the contents.

6. Always use the appropriate regulator on each gas cylinder. The threads on the regulators are designed to avoid improper use. Do not use adapters or homemade modifications!

7. Do not expose cylinders to temperatures higher than 50(C.

8. Never lubricate, modify, force, or tamper with cylinder valves.

9. Never bleed cylinders completely empty. Leave a slight pressure to keep out contaminants

10. Never direct high pressure gases at anyone, nor use compressed gas or air to blow away dust or dirt or residual solvent; the resultant flying particles are dangerous. Be aware that rapid release of compressed gas

will cause an unsecured gas hose to whip dangerously.

11. Wrap evacuated or pressurized glass containers with tape or enclose in a box or approved shielding to protect against implosion whenever possible.

12. When reducing pressure, use specifically designed equipment only. To avoid the danger of implosion, never evacuate a thin-walled, flat-bottomed flask.

Working with Cryogens

Use of low temperature chemicals and operations require special procedures. Such operations require the prior approval of your lab instructor. Be aware that the primary hazards of cryogenic liquids are fire, explosion, pressure build-up, embrittlement of materials, asphyxiation, and contact with and destruction of living tissue.

1. Use gloves and face shield for handling cryogenic liquids or chipping or handling dry ice.

2. Use only properly-vented containers for cryogenic liquids. Avoid pouring cold liquid onto the edge of a glass Dewar flask when filling to prevent implosion.

3. Immerse objects to be cooled slowly to prevent boil-over.

4. When finished tapping cryogens, check to ensure that the safety valve is open.

Working with High Energy Radiation

Ultraviolet Radiation

Consider all radiation of wavelengths shorter than 300 nm dangerous.

1. Protective goggles with UV-absorbing lenses should be worn when eyes might be exposed to light in this range.

Dealing with Injury

EYES: Flush with water for 15 minutes

INGESTION: Follow the label and MSDS instructions

SKIN CONTACT: Stand under the emergency shower and remove contaminated clothing immediately for major spills. For minor spills, flush with water for 15 minutes and remove contaminated clothing.

INHALATION: Get to fresh air and get prompt medical attention.

1. If you become overexposed to a hazardous substance, inform your laboratory instructor and get medical attention. For first-aid instructions, check the First Aid Manual (Meyer Hall Room 264), or the MSDS information found in Meyer Hall 226.

2. Remove any clothing on which a chemical has been spilled.

3. Treat burns immediately by placing the burned area under cold water for at least 15 minutes. Cold water markedly reduces the subsequent pain and blisters.

4. If an individual's clothing or hair is on fire, use the safety shower first. If a shower is not readily available, then use a blanket or coat to smother the fire by rolling the individual on the floor. Then get medical help promptly.

5. Report allergies to your lab supervisor.

Dealing with Fire

1. Suffocate a small fire in a vessel by covering it. Do not pick up the vessel. Remove nearby flammable objects. Inform the instructor or TA immediately.

2. If it is not practical to cover the fire, but the fire is small and does not involve metals, then use a CO_2 or dry extinguisher. Fight the fire from a position from which you can escape and only if you are confident that it can be extinguished. Remember that it is easy to underestimate a fire.

3. If the fire cannot be extinguished quickly and simply, all persons should evacuate the laboratory, close the doors, and leave the building using the stairs.

4. Activate the fire alarm located at the intersections of the hallways if instructed to do so.

Laboratory Notebooks

Lab records in **CHEM 254 - 256 & CHEM 264 - 266** are to be written in a bound, quadrille-ruled lab notebook, which is kept up to date. The records that you write must be sufficiently detailed to allow a competent second person to repeat exactly what you have done without your being present to explain. This record must be signed in ink and dated at the end of each lab period. There are two principal reasons for keeping this record. First, in the event that your work produces an unusual result (better or worse than ordinary) you and your instructor will need to know why. If an accurate record of the procedure is not kept there is no way to repeat the procedure or to figure out why the result was out of the ordinary. Both physical and biological scientists are required by the terms of their employment to maintain accurate lab records in order to ensure repeatability and establish legal priority. The only way to get used to keeping such records is to get in the habit now. Second, doing organic chemistry in the lab is not like following a recipe in a cookbook. Good results will come only when you thoroughly plan your experiment and understand the reason for each step. Preparing an up-to-date lab notebook is an organized way to do this planning.

You should set up your notebook as follows:

1. The first five pages of the volume are reserved for a table of contents, and entries are made in the table as each lab is written up. Entries in the table of contents refer to the page numbers on which the experiment/procedure is recorded. Pages in the notebook are numbered consecutively on each side of the page.

2. All entries are made in ball point pen, not pencil. Errors are crossed out with a single stroke, not erased. Writing should be tidy and legible.

3. Before you come to lab format your write-up in this way:
    a. List an experiment title.
    b. State briefly the purpose of the procedure or experiment in one or two simple sentences.
    c. Write balanced equations for any reactions the experiment requires.
    d. Write out the entire experimental procedure. **Do not simply reference this laboratory manual!**

e. Finally, you must record your results after the procedure and before you sign the notebook. This includes all calculations needed to determine the results such as the weight, moles, and percent yield of your product obtained. Also include all observations such as color of the material, evolution of vapor or gas, production of heat, etc.

Melting Point & Chromatography Lab

Discussion

This lab will introduce you to the practice of observing melting point (**mp**) ranges as a way of determining the purity of solid organic compounds. In addition, you will begin to learn about two forms of chromatography; thin-layer chromatography (**tlc**) and column chromatography. A discussion of column chromatography, as well as the experimental procedure, follows the mp and tlc procedure.

All drug substances are chemicals. Analgesics, or pain killers, are among the most common drugs in every culture. In pre-technical cultures, pain killers were often mixtures of natural materials and alcohol. Early in the nineteenth century, when European chemists were isolating the pure active ingredients from these natural sources, the identification and characterization of the analgesic compounds were put on a systematic basis. Caffeine and its relatives were isolated from plant sources in both the old and new worlds, as were the salicylates. As these pure chemical compounds were made available, doctors were able to test their physiological properties. Many discoveries resulted; for example, the fact that many of the analgesics also reduce fevers (antipyretics.) By the 1880's, not only purified chemicals from plants, but pure derivatized compounds were undergoing medical evaluation. Acetanilide, acetominophen, and phenacetin are three examples used as commercial pain relievers. (**Figure 1**) You will be using the compounds shown as knowns and unknowns in order to learn about compound identification through melting point determination and compound purification and identification through tlc and column chromatography.

A. Melting Point Determination

The melting point of an organic compound is one of its characteristic physical properties. During your organic laboratory experience you will use physical properties of organic molecules, such as melting point, density, boiling point and refractive index, to identify and characterize the compounds that you use. Typical organic compounds melt below 300° C and, if pure, melt over a narrow 1° - 2° range. Impurities in the compound being melted can lower the melting point of the material under study. This is known as the melting point depression. It is also why people put salt on the roads and sidewalks during the winter to melt the ice and prevent refreezing.

When a compound melts, it is the intermolecular types of bonds that are being broken. Forces such as hydrogen bonding, van der Waals forces, dipole-dipole interactions, and ionic attractions are being overcome to allow the highly ordered solid state to give way to the less ordered liquid state. (Please note: some organic compounds do decompose when heated to their melting point. This type of event will not be considered in this lab.)

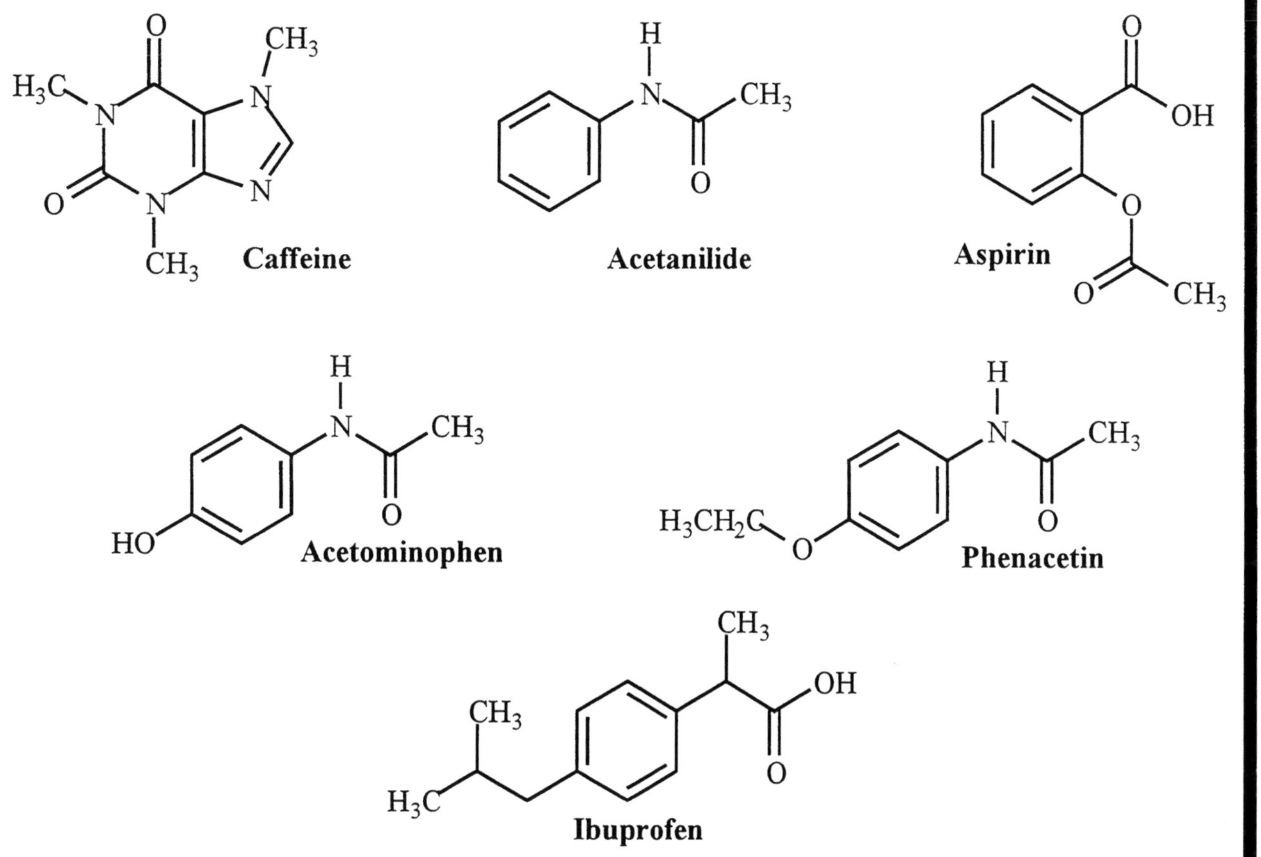

Figure 1: Structures of Analgesics

B. Chromatography

Chromatography is based on the principles of distributing materials between differing phases. Chromatography involves the selective removal of certain components of a mobile phase as it is flowing through a secondary stationary phase. The partitioning of components between the mobile and stationary phases is an equilibrium process, so that molecules that have entered the stationary phase will eventually return to the mobile phase. Separation of two or more components in the mobile phase will result when the equilibrium constants for the partitioning of these components between the two phases differ. In other words, the more strongly one component is retained by the stationary phase, the greater the percentage of molecules of that component that will be held immobile. The second component, which would be less strongly held, will provide a higher percentage of molecules in the mobile phase than will the first component. Therefore, on the average, the molecules of the component that is held less strongly will move over the stationary phase, in the direction of flow, at a higher rate than the other, resulting in a migration of the components into separate regions, or bands, of the stationary phase, as shown in **Figure 2**. This lab will use an organic solvent (ethyl acetate) as the mobile phase for both the thin-layer and column chromatography sections. The solid phase in both sections will also be the same. The solid phase will be silica gel. In the tlc part, the silica gel will be pasted to a plastic backing to make a thin plate. In the

11

column chromatography section, the silica gel will be used in a powder form held in a glass tube.

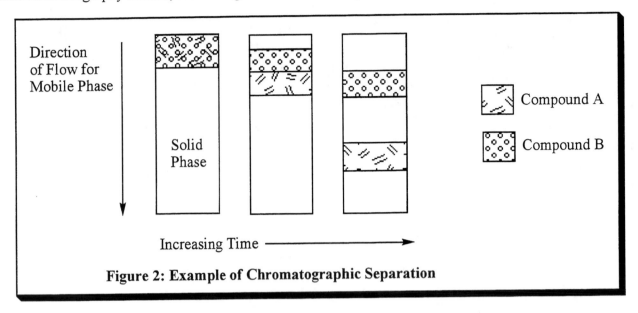

Figure 2: Example of Chromatographic Separation

B. Chromatography - Column Chromatography

In column chromatography the stationary phase is a solid, which separates the components of a liquid passing through it by selective adsorption on its surface. The types of interactions that cause adsorption are the same as those that cause attractions between any molecules, that is, electrostatic attraction, hydrogen bonding, dipole-dipole interaction, complexation, hydrogen bonding, and van der Waals forces. The column is packed with a finely divided solid such as alumina or silica gel, which serves as the stationary phase, and a sample of the mixture to be separated is applied at the top. If the mixture is solid, it must be dissolved in a solvent and then applied. The sample will initially be adsorbed at the top of the column, but when an eluting solvent, the mobile phase, is allowed to flow through the column, it will carry with it the components of the mixture. Owing to the selective adsorption power of the solid phase, the components ideally will move down the column at different rates. A more weakly adsorbed compound will be eluted more rapidly than a more strongly adsorbed compound, because the former will have a higher percentage of molecules in the mobile phase. The progressive separation of the components will appear as in Figure 2. The separated components are usually recovered by collecting the solvent that passes through the column in different containers, since they will be eluted at different times.

With colored materials the band may be directly observed as they pass down the column. The word chromatography (Gr. chromatos, a color) was originally coined to describe this technique from such observations. With colorless materials the changes cannot be observed directly. Many materials fluoresce when irradiated with ultraviolet light, however, and this provides a method of observing the bands in these cases. Usually the progress of a column chromatographic experiment is followed by collecting a series of fractions of eluent of equal volume, for example, 25 mL. The solvent is then evaporated from each to see if any solute is present. If the volume of each fraction is kept relatively small—for example, less than 10% of the volume of the column—the different bands will usually be obtained in different flasks, although each component may be distributed among several flasks. Another convenient method of following the separation is to analyze the eluent at intervals by thin layer chromatography.

A few of the solid adsorbents commonly used include alumina, silica gel, Florisil, charcoal, magnesia, calcium carbonate, starch, and sugar. The organic chemist usually finds alumina, silica gel, and Florisil (activated magnesium silicate) of the greatest utility. Alumina (Al_2O_3) is a highly active, strongly adsorbing, polar compound coming in three forms: neutral, base and acid washed. Basic and acidic alumina offer good separating power for acids and bases, respectively. For compounds sensitive to chemical reaction under acidic or basic conditions, neutral alumina should be used. Being highly polar itself, alumina adsorbs polar compounds quite tenaciously, so that they may be difficult to elute from the column. The activity (absorptivity) of alumina may be reduced by the addition of small amounts of water; the weight percentage of water present determines the activity grade of the alumina. Silica gel and Florisil are also polar, but less so than alumina. For the greatest effectiveness, the solid adsorbent should be of uniform particle size and of high specific area, a property that promotes more rapid equilibrium of the solute between the two phases. This is important for producing narrow bands. Good grades of alumina and silica gel have very high specific areas, on the order of several hundred m^2/g. The strength of adsorption depends on the adsorbate as well as on the adsorbent. It has been found that the strength of adsorption for compounds having the following types of polar functional groups increases on any given adsorbent in the following order:

Cl—, Br—, I— < C=C < —OCH$_3$ <—CO$_2$R < C=O <—CHO < —SH < —NH$_2$ < —OH < —CO$_2$H

The nature of the liquid phases (solvents) to be used is an important consideration when designing a chromatographic experiment. The solvent may also be adsorbed on the solid, thereby competing with the solute for the adsorptive sites on the surface. If the solvent is more polar and more strongly adsorbed than the components of the mixture, these components will remain almost entirely in the mobile liquid phase, and little separation will occur during the experiment. For effective separation, the eluting solvent must be significantly less polar than the components of the mixture. Furthermore, the components must be soluble in the solvent; if they are not, they will remain permanently adsorbed on the stationary phase of the column. The eluting powers of various solvents, that is, their ability to move a given substance down a column, are generally found to occur in the order shown.

B. Chromatography - Thin-Layer Chromatography (tlc)

Thin-layer chromatography follows the same principles of chromatography as already stated, but its purpose is different. Column chromatography is typically used to purify organic molecules, whereas tlc is typically used to identify the purity of a material or to monitor the completeness of an organic reaction. Thin-layer chromatography relies on the use of a thin plate covered with silica gel (solid phase). A small drop of compound (usually diluted with solvent) is then placed on the bottom of the plate. The plate is then placed in a jar containing a small pool of organic solvent (mobile phase) at the bottom of the jar. As the solvent moves up the plate, it will pull the organic components with it over the stationary phase (**Figure 3**). When the solvent reaches the top of the plate, it is removed from the jar and examined under ultraviolet light.

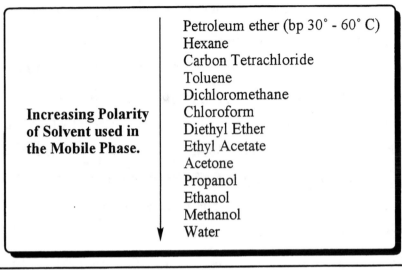

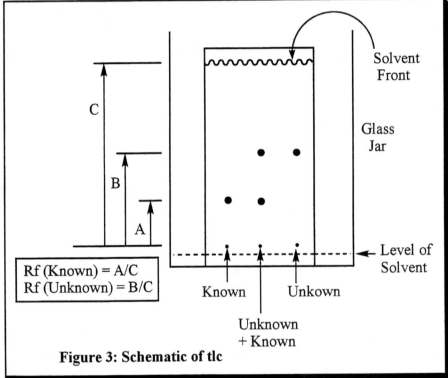

Figure 3: Schematic of tlc

Procedure (mp & tlc)

When you begin work, samples of pure solid acetanilide, aspirin (acetylsalicylic acid), phenacetin, acetaminophen, caffeine, and ibuprofen will be on the lab benches. Please take care with the ibuprofen sample; it is unusually expensive and we need to conserve the material. You are to take a melting range of each of the pure samples (this should require less than 10 milligrams of the solid). After you are confident that you do this, you will receive an unknown which will be either a pure sample of one of the six analgesics listed above, or else a mixture of two of them. Your task will be to determine what is in the sample. You will begin by taking the melting range of the unknown sample. Next you will run a thin layer chromatogram of your unknown; your instructor will give specific directions. This will allow you to compare the components of the unknown directly with samples of the six analgesics. If you find that your unknown is a single pure substance, you will then prove its identity by mixing a small sample of the unknown with the pure solid you think it is, and taking a "mixed melting point." (What will this tell you?) If your unknown proves to be a binary mixture, you will prepare a small amount of the binary from the pure solids available and run a thin layer chromatogram of that mixture against your unknown.

Procedure (Column Chromatography)

Take 100 mg of an acetaminophen / caffeine mixture and dissolve it in 2 mL of ethyl acetate. Analyze the sample by tlc. Prepare a microscale column by taking a Pasteur pipette and placing a wad of cotton where the tip joins the pipette. Fill the pipette half-full with silica gel and then cap it off with a small amount of sand (1/8"). Set-up six micro test tubes in a test tube holder and label them 1 through 6. Also prepare a dry condenser hose that is attached to the air spigot and start a **very slow** stream of air flowing through the tube.

Place the 2 mL of ethyl acetate, containing the mixture, in to the pipette and let it soak on to the silica gel. Add more ethyl acetate and then force the liquid through the pipette using the slow air stream (add more ethyl acetate as needed). Drip approximately 0.5 mL of the ethyl acetate eluent into each of the six micro test tubes. Once this is complete, perform tlc on each of the test tube samples to analyze their chemical composition.

Questions

1. In general chemistry you learned that impurities alter the phase diagram of a solid substance by changing the liquid-solid transition temperature. From your experience in this lab, explain what alterations usually occur in the phase diagram due to addition of a contaminant. Will all contaminants have an identical effect? Why?

2. Next week you are going to synthesize acetaminophen and purify it by recrystallization from water. Pure acetaminophen melts at 169° - 171° C. If you get your product chemically pure in all respects but not quite dry it will melt at 146° - 162° C. What might cause this low, broad melting range?

3. Identify the functional groups present in (a) caffeine, (b) phenacetin and (c) acetaminophen.

4. Rewrite the structural formulas of the following compounds showing explicitly all nonbonding valence electron pairs: (a) caffeine, (b) acetominophen and (c) phenacetin.

5. Polar functional groups generally cause organic molecules to stick more tightly to the silica gel stationary phase in chromatographic procedures. If acetanilide, acetaminophen, and phenacetin are spotted on the origin of a silica gel tlc plate, which do you expect to have the largest Rf? The smallest Rf?

6. Using your answer from question 5, which of the three compounds (acetanilide, acetaminophen, and phenacetin) would elute first during column chromatography?

The Formation and Purification of Acetaminophen (4-Hydroxyacetanilide); An Introduction to the Technique of Recrystallization

Reaction

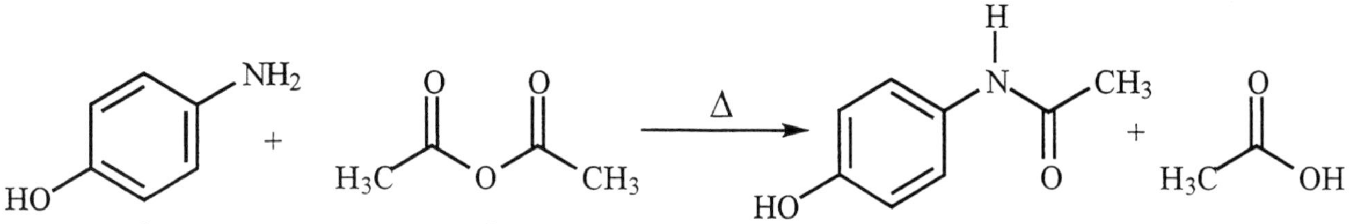

1	2	3	4
4-Aminophenol	**Acetic Anhydride**	**Acetaminophen**	**Acetic Acid**
MW 109.13	MW 102.09	MW 151.17	
mp 188° - 190° C	bp 138° - 140° C	mp 169° - 171° C	

Discussion

The equation above shows the reaction of 4-aminophenol (**1**), an industrial waste product, with acetic anhydride to produce acetaminophen (**3**), a widely used over-the-counter analgesic. This is a straightforward organic reaction with a 1:1 reactant to product stoichiometry, yet there are some practical differences between typical reactions encountered in your freshman chemistry labs and the organic reaction shown above.

One major difference between the reactions you used in freshman lab and those you will encounter this year is that organic reactants, due to their complex structures, often have more than one reaction path available to them under a given set of conditions. This means that products other than the one desired can form and use up reactant, thus reducing the molar efficiency (% yield) of the reaction. For example, in this reaction we want the primary amine functional group to do a substitution reaction with the acid anhydride functional group of reactant **2**, giving us an amide functional group. However, another reaction can occur, a similar substitution reaction between the OH group of reactant **1** and the anhydride group of **2** to give an ester (compound **5** shown below in **Scheme 1**.)

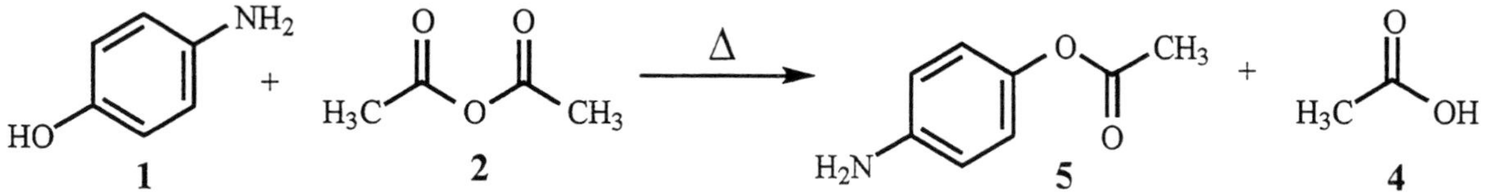

1	2		5	4
4-Aminophenol	Acetic Anhydride			Acetic Acid

Scheme 1: Possible Side Reaction

Adding water to the reaction mixture prevents this side reaction from becoming a serious diversion, but nonetheless it does occur to a small extent. Thus we see that side reactions can reduce the efficiency of a desired reaction even when the equilibrium constant for the desired reaction is very favorable, because the equilibrium constant for the side reaction might also be pretty large.

It is also true that many organic reactions have $K_{eq} < 100$. This means that appreciable amounts of unreacted starting materials will remain in the reaction vessel even after the reaction is "complete." This unreacted starting material will reduce the amount of pure product recovered in two ways; first, 1.00 mole of reactant will give perhaps 0.90 mol of product if 0.10 mole of the starting material remains unreacted, and second, the product which is recovered will have to be made free from unreacted starting material in some way, and such purification processes always remove some of the good product in addition to the impurities.

Finally, since the cost of organic chemicals rises exponentially with their purity, the reactants employed in organic lab often have 1-5% of various impurities in them. Not all of the reactant you add to your reaction mixture is really the correct starting material! Once again, these impurities in your starting material reduce the amount of product you will eventually get.

The starting material for acetaminophen, 4-aminophenol, is pale yellow when pure. However when you weigh it out it will be black because its electron-rich benzene ring is easily oxidized, and although little of the oxidation products are present in commercially produced **1**, the oxidized products are strongly colored and mask the color of it.

Recrystallization

The cheapest and most effective method for purifying most organic solids is recrystallization, which is the process of totally dissolving impure crystals in a boiling hot solvent, then cooling the solvent so that it becomes supersaturated with product and allowing crystals of pure product to precipitate out of solution while leaving impurities behind. [If some of the crude crystals remain undissolved in the hot solvent they will carry impurities through into the recovered even though their surfaces may be clean.] Choosing a good solvent for recrystallization is tricky, since the product must be fairly soluble in the solvent when it is hot, but only slightly soluble when the solvent is cold, so that most of the product will precipitate when the solvent is cooled. Furthermore, the impurities must remain dissolved when the solvent is cooled, so the solvent must be a good solvent for them.

No matter what solvent is chosen, recrystallization always looses some of the "good" product. The reason for this can be seen from **Table 1**. Suppose you have produced 5.0 g of crude acetaminophen and recrystallize it by dissolving it in the minimum amount of boiling hot CH_3OH (~20 mL), then cooling the solution to 0° C. Note that 20 mL x 0.05 g / ml) = 1.0 grams of the product will remain dissolved in the methanol even at 0° C. This is in addition to the impurities which remain in the solvent (dirty recrystallization solvent which contains product and impurities after crystals have formed is called the mother liquor.) If the chemist uses 50% CH_3OH / 50% H_2O, it will require 25 mL of boiling hot solvent to dissolve the crude crystals, and 25 mL x 0.02 g / mL = 0.50 g of the product will remain dissolved when the solution is cooled to 0° C. This is clearly better than pure CH_3OH, since only half as much of the product will remain in the mother liquor. Use of pure ethanol would give similar results. What defines a good solvent for recrystallization is the spread between the hot solubility and cold solubility of the product.

Table 1: Solubility of Acetaminophen in Various Solvents

Solvent	Temp °C	Solubility of Acetaminophen (g / mL)
CH_3OH	0°	0.05
	65° (bp)	0.25
CH_3OH/H_2O 50%/50% by volume.	0° C	0.02
	76° (bp)	0.20
CH_3CH_2OH	0° C	0.10
	78° (bp)	0.60

One further purification procedure which is often done during a recrystallization involves the use of decolorizing carbon, or activated charcoal. It is a fact that colored compounds are more polarizable than those without visible color; it is also true that polarizable compounds are preferentially adsorbed onto the surface of activated carbon, which of course is not soluble in any common solvent. Thus, one easy way to remove colored impurities (such as those in reactant **1**) is to add a teaspoon of activated carbon to the hot recrystallization solvent at the stage when the product is dissolved, boil for a few minutes to allow the carbon surface to adsorb the colored impurities, and filter the boiling hot solution to remove the insoluble carbon which has captured the colored impurities on its surface. Care must be taken to filter the hot liquor rapidly and without cooling, so that the product doesn't begin to crystallize in the hot filter and thus get mixed up with the carbon, which is discarded. This kind of rapid filtration, aimed at removing insoluble impurities (in this case the carbon is the insoluble impurity), is called hot filtration. Hot filtration is done using a stemless crystallization funnel so crystallization does not commence in the stem!), and a fluted filter paper (for speed.) It is never done using a Büchner filter.

Procedure

Part 1. Cleaning up the starting material by recrystallization:

Recrystallize four grams of 4-aminophenol from water (about 100 mL will be necessary.) Dissolve in a 250 mL Erlenmeyer flask of boiling hot water on your hot plate, remove from the hot plate (tongs!), then add about half a teaspoon of activated carbon and reheat for a few minutes; hot filter through a fluted filter paper taking care not to allow crystallization in the filter (**Diagram 1**). It will probably be a good idea to preheat your filter paper and funnel with hot water before you hot filter your material. Chill the filtrate in an ice bath, scratching the sides to induce crystallization. When the mixture is ice cold pour it into a Büchner filter (with a piece of filter paper inside) and vacuum filter (**Diagram 2**). **Note: Always clamp your filter flask before attaching the vacuum hose and Büchner funnel.** Draw air through the crystals for ten minutes to dry them and weigh. Compare the recrystallized material with the crude 4-aminophenol.

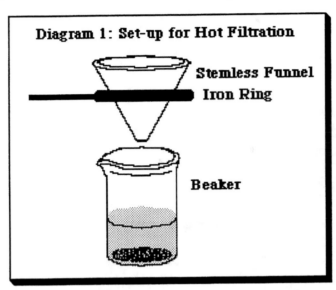

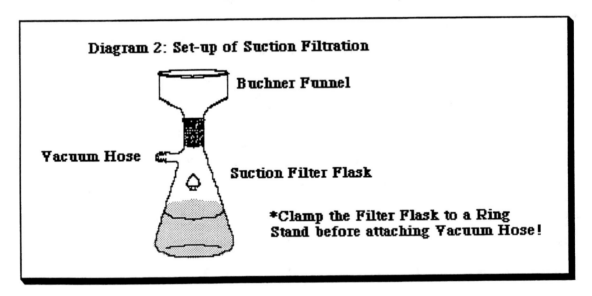

Part 2. Turning the amine into an amide:

Place the recrystallized 4-aminophenol in 30 mL of deionized water in an Erlenmeyer flask, warm on a hotplate to dissolve, and add 3.8 mL of acetic anhydride (4.10 g, 4.02×10^{-2} mol) about 10 drops at a time with stirring. When all the acetic anhydride is in, heat the mixture to boiling for ten minutes, then cool in an ice bath and induce crystallization. When the mixture is at 10° C and crystallization has ceased, filter on a clean Büchner. Recrystallize the crude crystals from water by heating them in about 20 mL of water on your hot plate, and adding more water until all the crystals dissolve. Then add about half a teaspoon of activated carbon, hot filter, cool, and isolate the acetaminophen on the Büchner funnel. (If the 4-aminophenol used was not recrystallized prior to reaction use 1 teaspoon of activated carbon.) Allow the crystals to dry in your drawer for a week, then weigh, take their melting point, and calculate the percent yield using the 4.00 g of crude 4-aminophenol as your starting point.

A small sample of the crystals and a sample of the mother liquor are chromatographed against 4-aminophenol (eluent is 3 mL of methylene chloride with 10 drops of ethanol added) on alumina plates. The bulk of the product is air dried for one week and its m.p. measured.

Questions

1) What is the reason for using activated charcoal (carbon) during a crystallization.

2) Why is gravity filtration and not suction filtration used to remove suspended impurities and charcoal from a hot solution during a hot filtration?

Measurement of Acid Strength

Discussion

Since the relative strengths of acids is so important in predicting chemical reactivity, it is essential to be able to measure the relative strengths of Brønsted-Lowry acids with reasonable accuracy. Once the numerical acid strength of a series of acids has been determined, they can be placed in order from most acidic to least acidic. The usual measure of an acid's strength is its K_a, which is frequently listed in logarithmic form as a pK_a. (Solomons, Organic Chemistry, Table 3.1, p.98) It is worth taking a minute to review what a pK_a is and why it is a measure of acid strength. Acetic acid will be used as an example since it is familiar to you from freshman chemistry.

$$CH_3CO_2H + H_2O \rightleftharpoons CH_3CO_2^- + H$$

$$K_{eq} = \frac{[CH_3CO_2^-][H_3O^+]}{[CH_3CO_2H][H_2O]}$$

-It is then assumed that the concentration of H_2O will be 1 due to the fact that its mole fraction in the equilibrium approaches 1.

$$K_a = \frac{[CH_3CO_2^-][H_3O^+]}{[CH_3CO_2H][1]}$$

$$pK_a = -log_{10}K_a = -log_{10}\left(\frac{[CH_3CO_2^-][H_3O^+]}{[CH_3CO_2H]}\right)$$

$$pK_a = -log_{10}K_a = -log_{10}\left(\frac{[CH_3CO_2^-]}{[CH_3CO_2H]}\right) + -log_{10}[H_3O^+]$$

-Therefore the pK_a equals the pH at the midpoint (halfway to the endpoint) of the titration. Also, since the pK_a scale is logarithmic, the stronger the acid, the smaller its pK_a.

Strong acids have small pK_a's, while weak ones have large pK_a's. When a weak acid is titrated with a strong base, the pH rises rapidly near the beginning of the titration and at the end of the titration. That is, when almost all of the acid is present in its acid form, adding small amounts of the base makes the pH rise rapidly. The same is true when almost all of the acid is present in its conjugate base form. But in the middle of the titration, when half the acid has reacted and the acid and its conjugate base are present in nearly equal proportions, the pH changes very little as more base is added. That is why the weak acid is a buffer, where addition of extra base or acid causes only small changes in the pH near the half way point in the titration. The center of this slow change zone, the pK_a, is easily measured and is characteristic for each acid. An acid with a low pH at the midpoint of its titration is stronger than one which has a high pH at the midpoint.

It is important to notice is that the pK_a for an acid can be determined by conducting a titration and measuring the pH at the halfway point. (Note the final equation shown on the previous page.) That is precisely what we will do for each of a series of acids. You will work in teams of two students, each team titrating one particular acid with 0.2000 M NaOH solution. When the titrations are complete and the pK_a values for the series of acids are calculated, you will share information among all the teams so that each of you can compile a list of the acids studied from strongest to weakest in order of their acidity.

Since this is a quantitative lab problem, you will have to work accurately using the same techniques you learned for titrations in freshman chemistry. The samples of acid to be titrated must be weighed on an analytical balance and the weight must be accurate to 0.0001 g. Most of the acids are solids and may best be weighed by difference from the supply vial on your bench, but some are liquids and must be weighed by first weighing the titration vessel (a beaker), adding acid from a dropper, and then weighing it again.

The NaOH (or KOH) we will provide for you is accurately standardized to 0.2000 M; this means it is expensive, so use what you need but do not waste it by pouring more than you need into one of your beakers or Erlenmeyer flasks "just in case". Titrant exposed to the air evaporates and soon changes concentration. Your burette must be rinsed with titrant prior to filling (at least three times with ~5-7 mL's per rinse) and no air bubbles may be trapped under the stopcock. Burettes must be read to 0.01 of a mL; that is, to one decimal beyond the finest marking on the burette barrel. The titration must be smoothly stirred before and during the addition of titrant without splashing, to completely dissolve the acid before adding titrant, and during base addition so that the pH read from the meter will be accurate at each stage. The pH meter must be calibrated with buffer before beginning, and the electrode quadruply rinsed with good deionized water before placing it in the titration vessel so that none of the standard buffer gets into the titration. (This would make a large error!)

Most of the discussion so far has dealt with the quantitative measurement of acidity. We must also examine the effects that cause certain molecules to be more or less acidic than another. Since all of the compounds that are to be used in the lab are either carboxylic acids or phenols (aromatic rings substituted with an -OH group), it will can make some generalizations about their relative acidities. The foremost generalization is that in order to understand why one compound is more acidic than another, we must examine the structure of their conjugate bases. Whichever conjugate base is better able to stabilize the negative charge that has developed from being deprotonated, will have the stronger corresponding acid. It will be assumed that the two dominant factors that effect anion stability of the conjugate bases are the **Resonance Effect** and the **Inductive Effect**.

The inductive effect can be thought of as an electron attracting (or repelling) force generated by an adjacent dipole in the molecule. For instance, 2,2,2-trinitroethanol has a $pK_a=2.36$, whereas ethanol itself has a $pK_a=16$. The strongly electron withdrawing nitro- groups cause a large dipole between themselves and the carbon they are attached. When the alcohol is deprotonated, the negative charge of the alkoxide can be stabilized through the sigma-bonding framework via the inductive effect (**Figure 1**.)

Figure 1: Inductive Effect

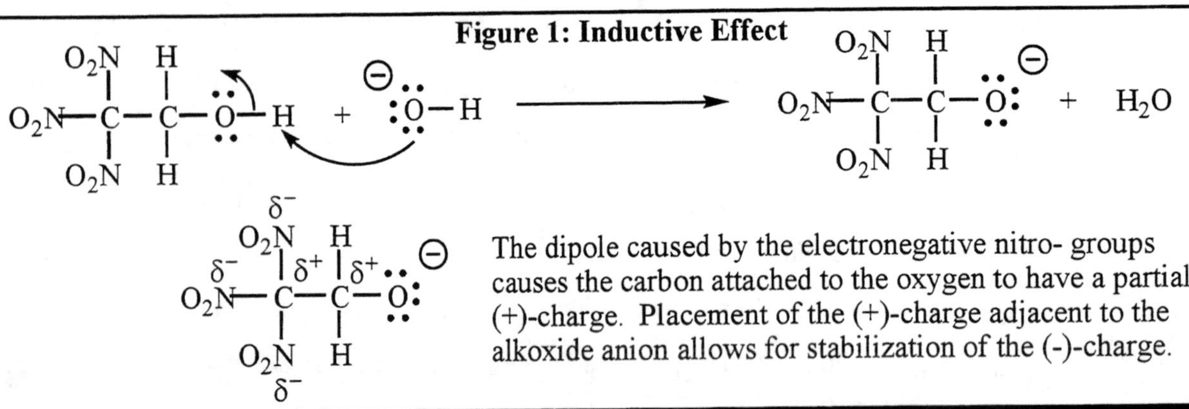

The dipole caused by the electronegative nitro- groups causes the carbon attached to the oxygen to have a partial (+)-charge. Placement of the (+)-charge adjacent to the alkoxide anion allows for stabilization of the (-)-charge.

Resonance is also important when considering the stability of the conjugate base. As a rough estimate, it can be assumed that a resonance stabilized anions are going to be at relatively lower energies, hence more stable and less reactive, than the non-resonance stabilized anions. This can be seen by comparing the pk_a values of ethanol, phenol, and acetic acid (**Figure 2**.)

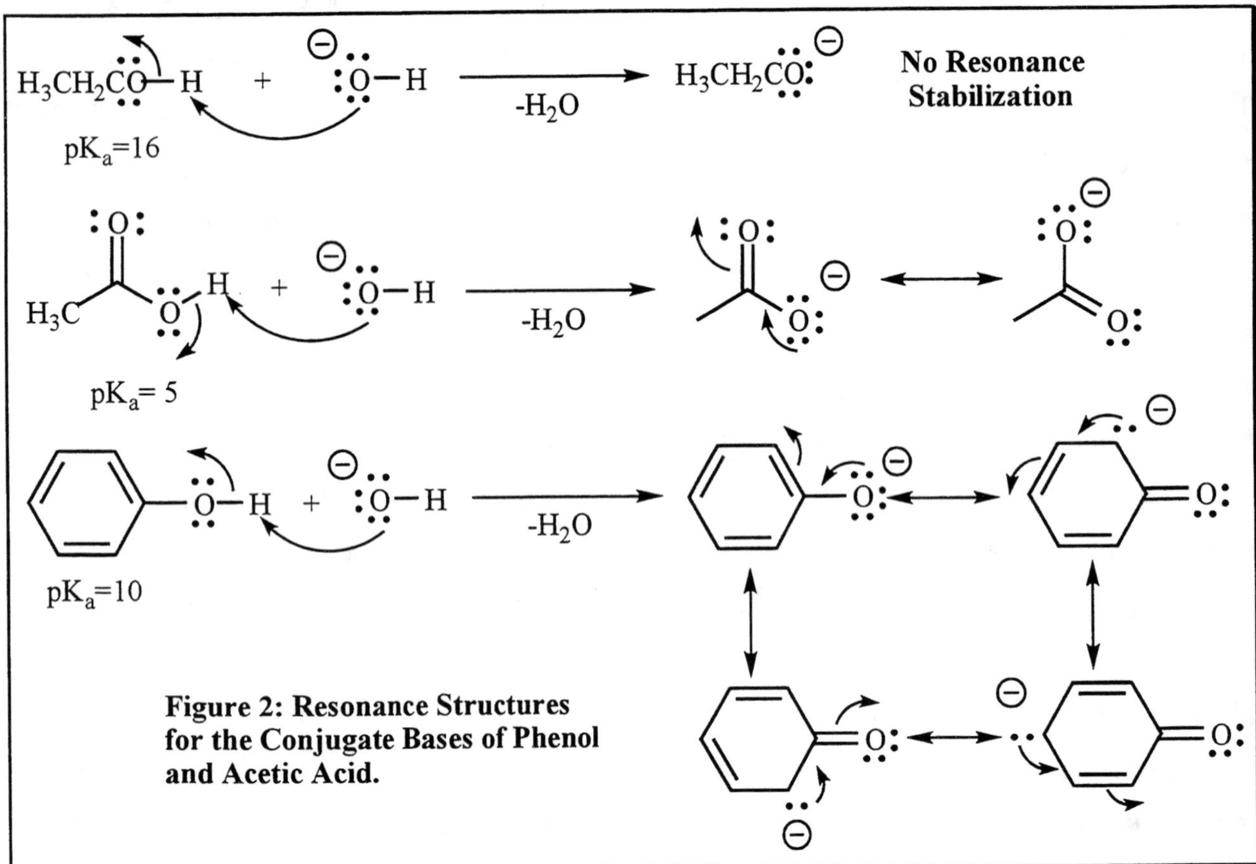

Figure 2: Resonance Structures for the Conjugate Bases of Phenol and Acetic Acid.

24

Procedure

You will be told which of the listed acids to titrate and who your partner will be. Since you don't want to refill your burette during the titration you need just the right amount of acid to react exactly with 30 to 40 mL's of 0.2000 M NaOH. That's approximately $(3.0 \times 10^{-2}$ Liter$) \times 0.2$ mol/Liter $= 6.0 \times 10^{-3}$ mols of acid. Similarly 40 mL of 0.2 M base corresponds to 8.00×10^{-3} mols of acid. So you need to weigh somewhere between six and eight millimoles of your acid into the titration vessel, but the weight you get must be accurate to 0.0001 g. Let's suppose you were assigned to do propanoic acid ($CH_3CH_2CO_2H$). Its molecular weight is 74.01 g/mol. (74.01 g/mol) $\times$ (6.0×10^{-3} mols of acid) $= 0.4441$ g of acid is the minimum needed and 0.5921 g is the maximum. By weighing an amount in this range you know your titration volume ought to be between 30 and 40 mL, but still you can't run in the first 25 mL fast, because you need to observe the pH accurately as the titrant is added. Fast addition of the titrant will not allow you to read the pH and volume of base added for every two mL of titrant.

So you add the propanoic acid to the titration beaker, dilute with 25 mL of good deionized water, put a magnetic stir bar in, commence stirring, immerse the electrode tip in the solution, read the initial pH before adding any titrant, read the initial burette titrant level, and commence adding 0.2000 M NaOH solution from the burette (**Figure 3**.) You do not need to remove the pH electrode after each reading. Every 2.00 mL you stop to read the pH and the burette, so that you get a table that looks like this:

Burette volume (mL)	pH
00.00	2.16
01.94	2.42
03.96	2.86

et cetera

You stop at endpoint to get the reading, but then continue until you have added 40 mL of titrant total. This means your table will have 21 data points. Let's suppose that you finish your titration with these data:

0.5194 g of propanoic acid used; 35.12 mL of 0.2000 M NaOH used to end point.

How do you treat these data to get the pK_a? First of all you need to know how many millimoles of acid you added, which must be calculated from its mass:

(0.5914 g / 74.01 g / mol) x 10³ millimoles / mole = 7.991 millimoles of acid.

Next you need to know how much base this should have required:

7.991 mmols acid x (1 mmol NaOH / 1 mmol acid) x (1.0 ml / 0.2 mmol NaOH) = 39.95 mL

So if the sample was absolutely pure and your technique was flawless, the titration would have required 39.95 ml of 0.2000 M base. Therefore the pK_a is the pH at exactly half that volume added. In order to do the analysis you need to prepare a graph from your data table, since you are unlikely to have stopped to take a burette reading precisely at 19.43 ml of titrant added.

Prepare the graph by plotting pH on the Y-axis vs. volume of titrant on the X-axis. Your X-axis should initially be marked in mL from zero to 40. Next remark the X-axis in centi-equivalents - that is, since 39.95 mL of base is one equivalent, 0.3995 mL would be one centi-equivalent, and 3.995 ml (actually you would use 4.00 mL as you can't read to thousandths of a mL) would be ten centi-equivalents. Mark the X-axis at 2.00 mL (5 centi-equivalents , actually 1.997 rounded to nearest readable mark), at 4.00 mL (10 centi-equivalents) at 6.00 mL (15 centi-equivalents), and so forth. The point you are seeking, the pK_a, is the pH read from the graph at 50 centi-equivalents.

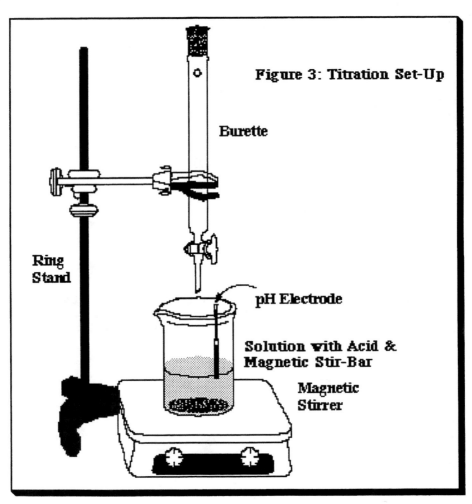

Figure 3: Titration Set-Up

Burette

Ring Stand

pH Electrode

Solution with Acid & Magnetic Stir-Bar

Magnetic Stirrer

Completing the report:

Each student will turn in a three page (1 inch margins at top, bottom, left and right), typed report on the results from this lab. The report is due the first week after the lab has been completed, and will include a clean copy of the graph from which the pK_a was interpolated, with the X-axis marked both in mL of titrant and centi-equivalents; all 21 data points should show and be connected with a smooth curve (not a straight line). Also included will be the observed acidity order for the lab. The bulk of the report will be explanation relating to why the observed order of acidity is as found. This will be further explained by your instructor. Be sure to discuss the specific structural features which make one acid stronger than others of similar type, listing specific effects derived from the structural variations.

Functional Group Interconversion by Redox

Reaction

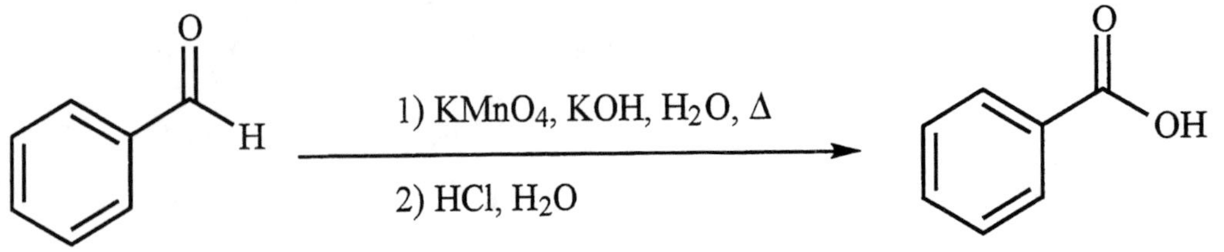

$$\text{(benzaldehyde)} \xrightarrow[\text{2) HCl, H}_2\text{O}]{\text{1) KMnO}_4\text{, KOH, H}_2\text{O, } \Delta} \text{(benzoic acid)}$$

Discussion

There are many examples of organic reactions that convert one functional group into another without altering the carbon skeleton of the molecule. Such reactions are known as "Functional Group Interconversions" or FGI's. You will learn at least seventy of them during your year of sophomore Organic Chemistry. One such FGI is the oxidation reaction. In this lab, we will examine the conversion (**Equation 1**) of an aldehyde (benzaldehyde) to a carboxylic acid (benzoic acid).

Equation 1

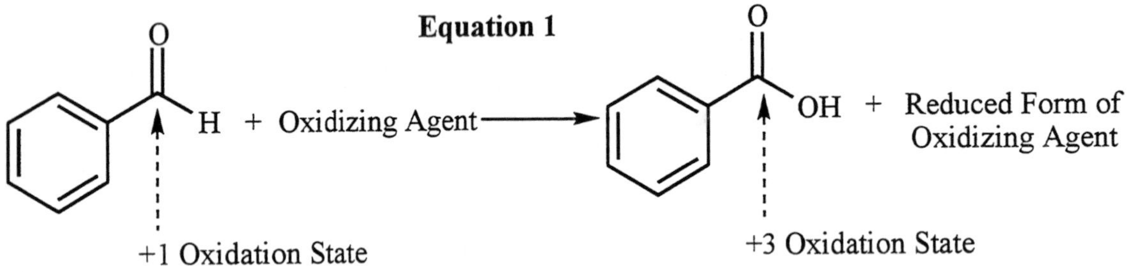

H + Oxidizing Agent ⟶ OH + Reduced Form of Oxidizing Agent

+1 Oxidation State   +3 Oxidation State

Equation 1 is incomplete because it does not specify the oxidizing agent or the reaction conditions. You will encounter a number of reagents that are capable of carrying out the above reaction. Instead of trying to just memorize reagents without understanding what their function is, you should inspect the starting material and product and try to deduce what changes have occurred. In this case, you can use the knowledge that you learned in Freshman Chemistry to determine that the oxidation state of the carbon in question has changed from +1 to +3 (it has been oxidized.) In this lab we will examine two oxidizers which can be used to effect the FGI shown in **Equation 1**. One of them is the permanganate (MnO_4^-) ion, which you should recognize, and the other is the silver (I) diamine ion, $[Ag(NH_3)_2]^+$.

If you examine the reaction shown at the heading of this laboratory, you will see that two steps will actually be necessary in order to isolate the carboxylic acid product. In the first reaction, the permanganate ion oxidizes the aldehyde to the carboxylic acid. The problem is that the oxidizing conditions used in this experiment are basic, therefore causing the carboxylic acid product to be deprotonated and become the carboxylate ion (**Figure 1**). Typically, organic products are isolated and purified using organic solvents such as ethers, alkanes, or alcohols, because they can be removed easily. The carboxylate salt however, prefers to remain in the aqueous (water) solvent because it is highly ionic (polar). In order to cause the carboxylate ion to not want to exist in the aqueous environment, you must protonate it, thereby making it less polar. When the molecule is in its acid form, it becomes insoluble in water. You will encounter this type of problem many times throughout the year.

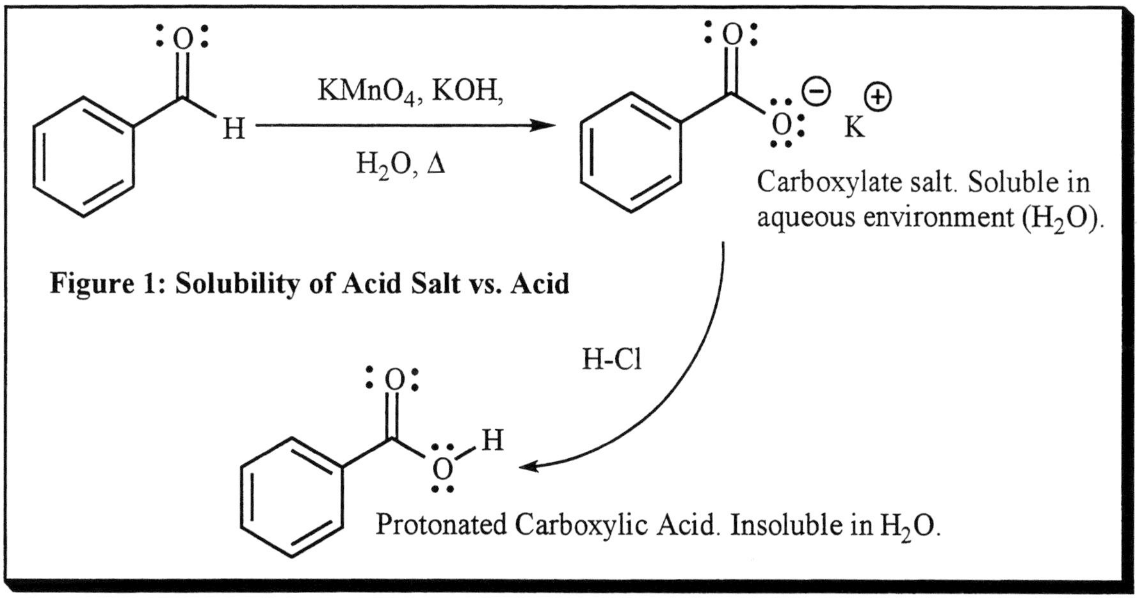

Figure 1: Solubility of Acid Salt vs. Acid

Procedure

Part A. Purification of Starting Material

Assemble a simple distillation apparatus (**Figure 2**). Use a 50 mL round bottom flask as the pot and a 25 mL round bottom as the receiver. Using a funnel with a stem extending below the side arm of the distilling head, pour 10 mL of crude benzaldehyde into the pot. Put your thermometer through the rubber grommet of the straight thermometer adapter and position the adapter and thermometer so that the entire mercury containing head is below the level of the distilling side arm. Plug the heating mantle into the variable voltage transformer and turn it to about 80 volts. It will take a few minutes to bring the flask to a boil. When the first distillate begins to drip into the receiver, capture about ten drops into a clean, dry micro test tube. Replace the receiver and allow the distillation to continue while you obtain a refractive index of the clean, freshly distilled benzaldehyde captured in the micro test tube. (Your instructor will demonstrate how to operate the refractometer.) Continue your distillation until you have collected 5 mL of clean benzaldehyde.

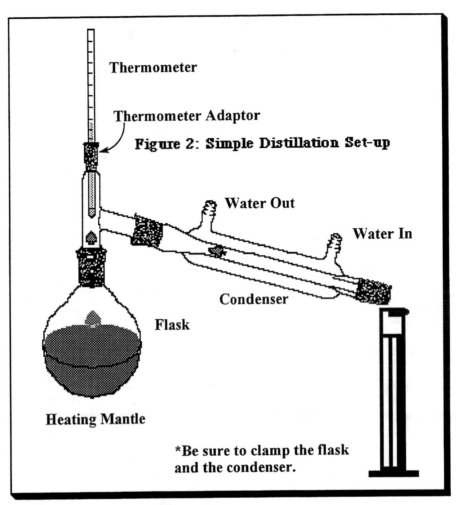

Thermometer

Thermometer Adaptor

Figure 2: Simple Distillation Set-up

Water Out

Water In

Condenser

Flask

Heating Mantle

*Be sure to clamp the flask
and the condenser.

Part B. Oxidation of benzaldehyde with potassium permanganate.

Place your steam bath on a magnetic stirrer. Turn your steam bath on and place a 250 ml beaker containing 40 mL of a 0.65 M $KMnO_4$, 4.0 mL of freshly distilled benzaldehyde, 10 mL of 2M NaOH and a Stir-Bar in the steam bath and heat for 15 minutes. Make sure that the solution is stirred vigorously or the reaction will not go to completion and your product will be contaminated with MnO_2. Observe any color changes carefully. After ten minutes filter off the brown precipitate (what is it?) on a Büchner funnel coated with about 1 cm of celite. Next, pour the filtrate, which contains the product, into a 250 mL Erlenmeyer flask and acidify it with 6 M HCl; check with litmus paper to ensure that the solution is fully acidic. Cool the solution to 5° C (ice bath) and filter the precipitate on a 4.5 cm Büchner. Dry it by pulling air through it for 15 minutes (while this is happening do Part C.) Hand in this product in a vial after determining its melting point. Make sure your label includes your name, the name of the product, its weight, melting point, and percent yield.

Part C. Oxidation of formaldehyde with Tollen's Reagent (silver (I) diamine).

Clean a standard test tube by adding dilute nitric acid to it, heating the solution in the steam jet briefly, discarding the solution, and rinsing the tube four times with deionized water to ensure that no acid residue is present (check with litmus paper.) Prepare Tollen's Reagent by adding 2 drops of 1 M NaOH to 5 mL of 5% $AgNO_3$ solution in your 50 mL beaker; add 2 M NH3 solution dropwise with stirring until the brown precipitate (what is it?) just disappears. Place 1.0 mL (20 drops) of formaldehyde in the clean standard test tube, add 5 mL of the Tollen's reagent, and warm in the steam jet. Observe the reaction. What is the shiny substance which appears in the tube? What is its oxidation state? You may test benzaldehyde with the remainder of the Tollen's reagent, but after adding the aldehyde to the clean test tube, add 3 mL of methanol and then 3 mL of Tollen's Reagent, then heat in the steam jet for 10 minutes. Methanol is necessary in order to cause benzaldehyde to dissolve in an aqueous solution.

Questions

1. Write ion-electron half reactions and balanced gross ionic equation for (a) the reaction of benzaldehyde with $[Ag(NH_3)_2]^+$; (b) with $KMnO_4$.

2. What is the purpose of taking a refractive index?

3. Why is the benzaldehyde distilled before taking its refractive index?

4. In the reaction of $KMnO_4$ with benzaldehyde the reaction is purple to begin with, but the purple color disappears entirely as the reaction disappears. What causes the purple color, and why does it disappear? What is the brown precipitate which is filtered off?

5. Why does the product of part B remain soluble in the basic filtrate after the removal of the brown precipitate? Why does acidification of the solution precipitate the product?

6. In Part C Silver[I] ion is reduced (converted to metallic silver.) What is the reducing agent

Functional Group Interconversion by Hydrolysis:

Preparation and Isolation of an Ester by Simple Distillation

Reaction

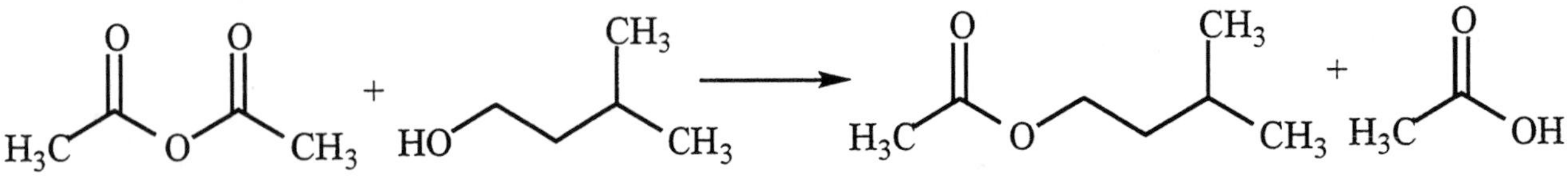

Acetic Anhydride
MW 102.09
bp 138° C - 140° C

Isoamyl Alcohol
MW 88.15
bp 130° C
n_D^{25} 1.4060

Isoamyl Acetate
MW 130.19
bp 142° C
n_D^{25} 1.4000

Acetic Acid
MW 60.05
bp 125° C

Discussion

Many functional groups can be interconverted by adding water or water-like compounds to particular chemical bonds. Such reactions do not augment the carbon skeleton(s) of compounds involved in the reaction, but simply change the functional group(s) of the reacting molecules. An example is shown in **Reaction 1** below, in which a water molecule substitutes the C-Cl bond of tert -butylchloride; the -H of water substitutes on the -Cl, and the -OH of water to the carbon. The formal reaction type is called a substitution.

Reaction 1: Substitution of an Alkyl Halide

The reaction for this lab is very similar in form (a simple molecule substituting across a breakable bond in an organic molecule) except that the simple molecule which substitutes is not water, but an alcohol, which is a water-like organic molecule. The general form of the reaction is shown in **Reaction 2**.

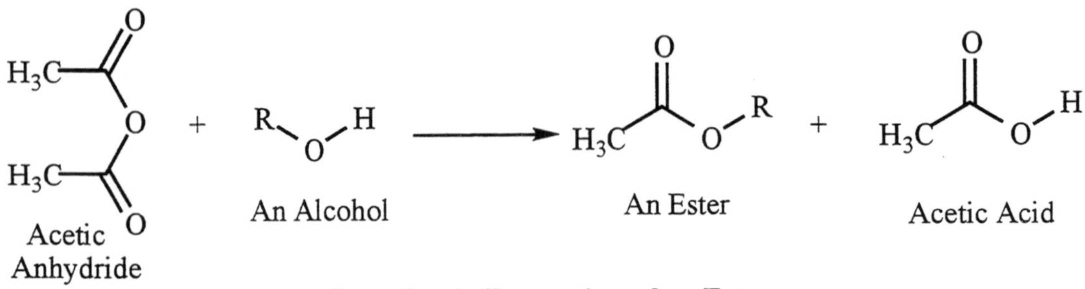

Reaction 2: Formation of an Ester

The alcohol substitutes on the C-O single bond of acetic anhydride with the RO- attaching to the carbon and the H- attaching to the single bonded oxygen. The alcohol is shown in general form to emphasize that a wide variety of alcohols will react with acetic anhydride in the same way regardless of what alkyl group R they bear. Strictly speaking, this reaction is an alcoholysis , since it is an alcohol that breaks the C-O bond of the acetic anhydride; nevertheless, since it is so similar to a hydrolysis it is usually counted among hydrolytic substitutions.

The specific alcohol we are using is iso-amyl alcohol and the specific ester we will isolate is iso-amyl acetate. Iso-amyl is the common name for the 3-methyl-1-butyl alkyl group; iso-amyl acetate is the main fragrance of banana oil. Our reaction involves substitution of the alcohol on acetic anhydride. Notice that one equivalent of acetic acid is formed as a by-product for every equivalent of ester formed. In order to remove this byproduct, we dissolve the entire reaction mixture in an easily removable organic solvent (ethyl ether in this procedure), then "wash" the acetic acid out by using a weak base (sodium bicarbonate solution) to convert it to sodium acetate, a salt, which is soluble in water rather than in the organic solvent. Drying the organic solvent with an inert drying agent, distilling off the organic solvent , and finally distilling the residual crude ester and collecting only the material which boils in the boiling range of the ester complete the procedure.

Gas Chromatography

The theory of chromatography has already been developed during the melting point/thin-layer chromatography lab. Gas chromatography (gc) follows the same principles discussed earlier, but the mobile phase has been changed from a liquid to a gas. In gc, the material under study is heated as it is injected in to the gas chromatograph in order to vaporize it into the gas phase (**Figure 1**). A carrier gas, usually helium because it is inert, then carries the vaporized material into a chromatography column. The carrier gas is the **mobile phase** and the material packed into the chromatography column is the **stationary phase**. The stationary phase is also heated, or else the material being carried by the carrier gas would simply condense, in order to allow an equilibrium to be established between the mobile and solid phases. Different materials will have different equilibria established between the two phases resulting in a difference in time it takes for the materials to flow through the gc. As each material exits the heated gc column, a detector signals its presence on some type of recorder.

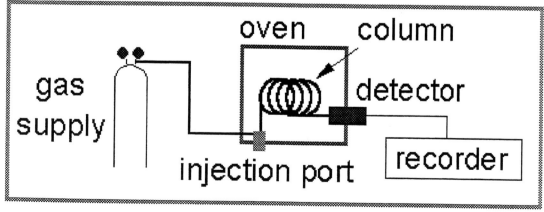

Figure 1: Schematic of a Gas Chromatograph

Procedure

3-Methyl-1-butanol (20.0g, 2.27×10^{-1} mol, d = 0.809g/mL) and acetic anhydride (23.15 g, 2.27×10^{-1} mol, d = 1.08 g/mL) are added to a 250 mL round-bottom flask with several boiling chips, and the flask boiled at reflux for 30 minutes. See **Figure 2** for an example of the glassware set-up for a reflux. The mixture is then cooled to 20° C (ice bath) and added to 50 mL of ether in a separatory funnel. See **Figure 3** for an example of a separatory funnel. The organic layer is washed five times with 20 mL of 10% sodium bicarbonate (caution: CO_2 evolution), then dried over one teaspoon of anhydrous Na_2SO_4. When dry, the organic layer, consisting of diethyl ether and 3-methyl-1-butyl acetate, is filtered through a cotton plug into a 100 mL round bottom flask and assembled for a simple distillation. MAKE SURE THAT THE MERCURY CONTAINING BULB OF THE THERMOMETER IS ENTIRELY BELOW THE SIDE ARM OF THE THREE-WAY HEAD!!!

The distillation is conducted taking care to collect separately all liquid boiling 34° C - 40° C, 125° - 131° C, and finally 140° - 144° C. The last fraction boiling above 140° C is checked for purity by taking its refractive index and a gas chromatogram run against iso-amyl alcohol standard. See **Figure 4** for the glassware needed for a simple distillation.

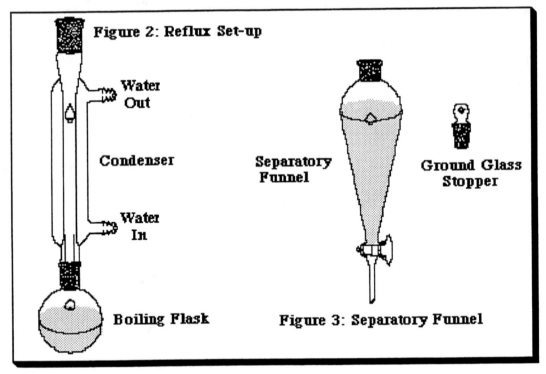

Figure 2: Reflux Set-up

Water Out

Condenser

Water In

Boiling Flask

Separatory Funnel

Ground Glass Stopper

Figure 3: Separatory Funnel

Questions

1. What is the purpose of shaking the ether layer with sodium bicarbonate solution five times after the main reaction is finished?

2. Why is ether added after the reaction is complete? Would it make any difference if the ether was added before the reaction mixture is heated? Why or why not?

3. Explain the difference between reflux and distillation.

4. How does Na_2SO_4 remove water from the ether solution? How much Na_2SO_4 dissolves in the ether/ester solution? Why?

5. What impurities are visible in the gas chromatogram of the fraction boiling above 140° C?

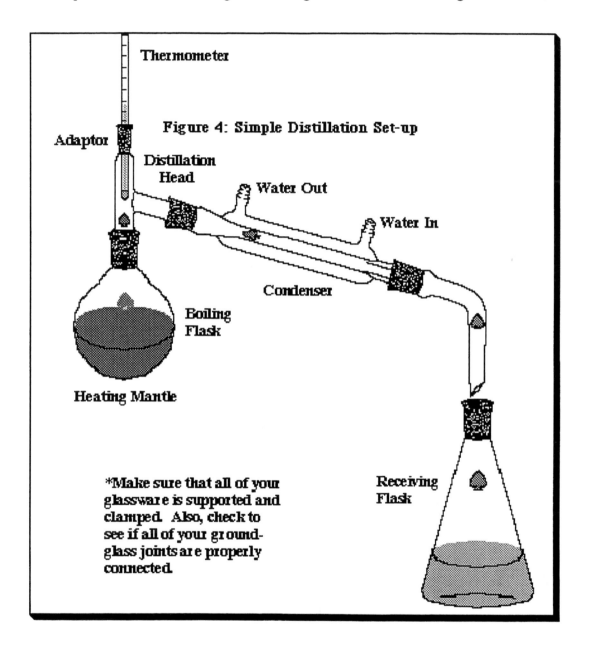

Figure 4: Simple Distillation Set-up

Thermometer

Adaptor

Distillation Head

Water Out

Water In

Condenser

Boiling Flask

Heating Mantle

Receiving Flask

*Make sure that all of your glassware is supported and clamped. Also, check to see if all of your ground-glass joints are properly connected.

Liquid-Vapor Phase Diagrams: Simple, Fractional, and Azeotropic Distillations

Discussion

During the last two labs, you have become familiar with simple distillation as a means of purifying organic chemicals which are liquids at room temperature. You distilled benzaldehyde in order to remove benzoic acid (formed in the bottle by oxidation with O_2), and you distilled your iso-amyl acetate (b.p. 142° C) in order to remove diethyl ether (b.p. 35° C) and iso-amyl alcohol (b.p. 130° C). In the latter case, however, the gas chromatogram should have demonstrated that there was still a substantial amount of the alcohol left in the final ester; that is, simple distillation is effective in separating materials which have very different boiling points, but does not effectively separate two liquids with rather close boiling points, such as the alcohol-ester pair from last week.

The reason for this problem can be seen from the "normal" phase diagram of the benzene/toluene mixture (**Figure 1**). The X axis of the figure is composition in mole percent, and the Y axis is temperature in ° C. We see in the diagram that if you start with a liquid which is 58% benzene and 42% toluene and heat it until boiling starts (vertical dashed line) when the liquid boils isothermally at about 90° C (horizontal line) the vapor it produces has 78% benzene and 22% toluene, that is, the vapor is enriched in the lower boiling component. If the vapor is cooled down from 90° C it will liquefy, and you have done one simple distillation. Note that although simple distillation has enriched the mixture in benzene (it was originally only 58% benzene, but is now almost 80% benzene) the distillate is not nearly pure.

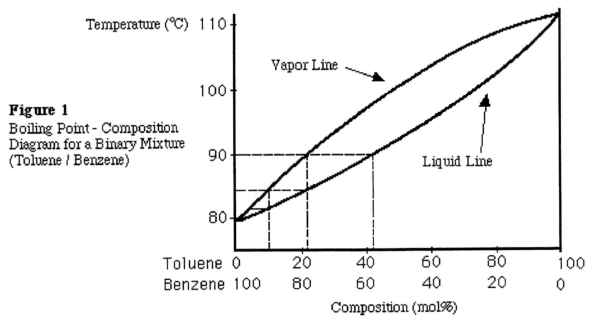

Figure 1
Boiling Point - Composition
Diagram for a Binary Mixture
(Toluene / Benzene)

This is caused by the shape of the lens-shaped area in the phase diagram where both vapor and liquid exist simultaneously. If that area were "fatter" and more horizontal, perhaps a single simple distillation would be enough to take the vapor from a 58/42 mixture the whole way back to a distillate which is 100% benzene.

Although the initial composition of the liquid mixture does influence how effectively a simple distillation can separate the components, the shape of the phase diagram is far more important. A narrow lens-shaped liquid-vapor region means that the vapor will not be much enriched in the lower boiling component, and consequently a simple distillation will not effectively separate the components of the mixture.

It is also possible to have "weird" phase diagrams (**Figure 2** & **Figure 3**). In most phase diagrams the lowest possible boiling point corresponds to the pure lower boiling component, usually shown on the left of the composition axis. In Figure 2 for example, 100% of compound A boils right at 85° C. If compound B is added to the mixture, the boiling point actually begins to decrease to a minimum of 82° C, which corresponds to approximately a 80/20 ratio of A to B. Such a phase diagram describes an azeotrope, a mixture which boils lower than either pure component.

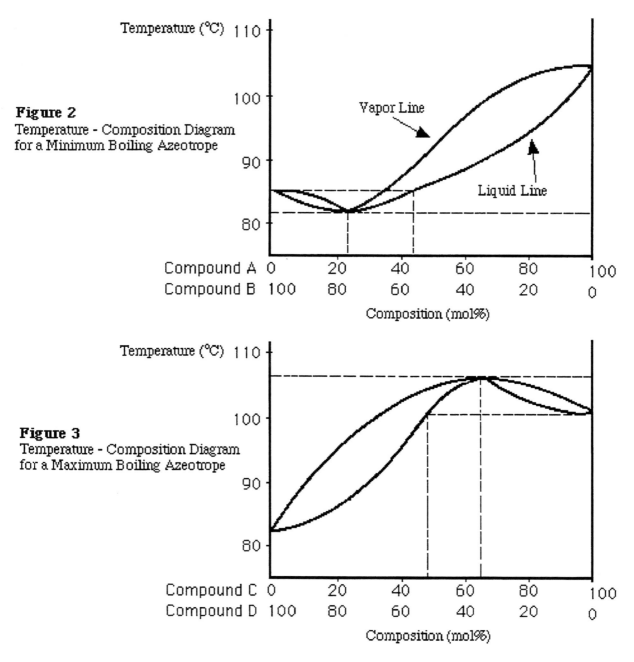

Figure 2
Temperature - Composition Diagram
for a Minimum Boiling Azeotrope

Figure 3
Temperature - Composition Diagram
for a Maximum Boiling Azeotrope

The phase diagram shown in **Figure 3** shows another type of azeotropic distillation known as a Maximum Boiling Azeotrope, where at a certain ratio, a binary mixture will boil at above the boiling point of either of the pure materials.

Fractional Distillation Theory

The separation of two liquids of similar boiling points by simple distillation is time consuming and tedious. It would require many simple distillations where only the first and last distillate portions of each distillation would be relatively pure. A majority of the distillate would be a mixture of the two materials, and hence, would require yet another distillation to purify. A far simpler and more efficient method to purify such a mixture would be to use what is called a Fractional Distillation (**Figure 4**). This process is equivalent to a simple distillation, but adds a new piece of equipment called a fractionating column in between the distilling pot and the distilling head. The fractionating column is packed with material, such as steel wool or glass beads, that allow for multiple simple distillations to occur prior to the vapor entering the condensing column. Each of the simple distillations that occurs in the fractionating column is referred to as a theoretical plate. The more theoretical plates, the better the overall distillation will be. For the same length fractionating column, different packing materials in the fractionating column will allow for different numbers of theoretical plates. The packing material contained in the fractionating column is therefore evaluated according to the number of theoretical plates per unit of height of the column. Usually this is referred to as the height equivalent to a theoretical plate (HETP.)

Procedure

You will be assigned to a group of three students in order to complete this two-week, three part lab. In each group one student (a) will be given 30 mL of a 50%/50% by mole fraction mixture of hexane and ethanol; the other two students (b and c) will be given 60 mL of a mixture of methyl ethyl ketone (MEK) and toluene.

(a)   Hexane/ethanol distillation: Use the hexane/ethanol mixture to set up a fractional distillation apparatus (**Figure 4**) using a distilling column packed with steel wool. Don't forget to add a boiling chip. Start the mantle transformer at 65 or 70 volts; adjust this as needed after distillation starts to achieve a 10 drop per minute distillation. Distill into the 10 mL graduated cylinder, and record the head temperature every 2 mL. Be especially careful to note the temperature at which the first distillate is collected. Save the first 2 mL and last 2 mL of distillate in two tightly stoppered micro test tubes. Obtain gas chromatograms and refractive indices of these samples in order to determine whether they are pure, and if not how much ethanol and how much hexane each contains.

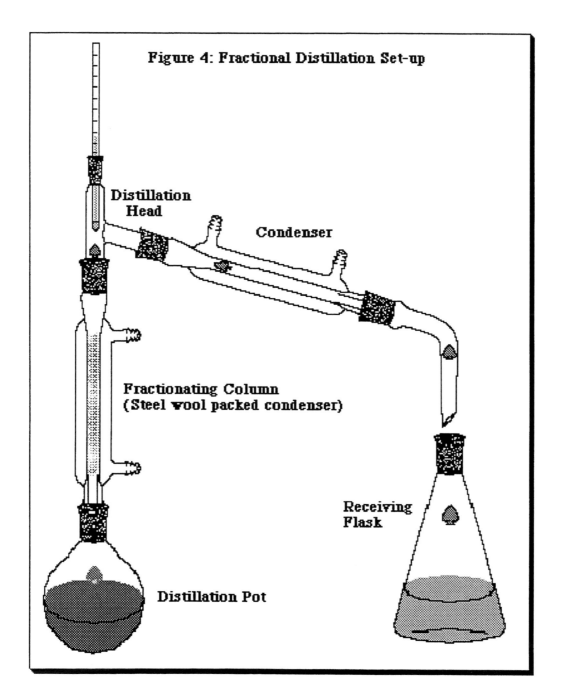

Figure 4: Fractional Distillation Set-up

Distillation Head

Condenser

Fractionating Column
(Steel wool packed condenser)

Receiving Flask

Distillation Pot

(b)   MEK/Toluene distillation: Take 30 mL of the original MEK/Toluene mixture; save 1 mL in a tightly stoppered micro test tube; distill the remaining 29 mL in a simple distillation apparatus (**Figure 5**). Add a boiling chip to the pot and start with a transformer setting of 75 volts, adjusting as necessary after distillation has started. Record the head temperature every 2 mL. Save the first 2 mL and last 2 mL of distillate in two tightly stoppered micro test tubes. When the distillation is finished obtain gas chromatograms and refractive indices of the original mixture and the first and last distillate samples.

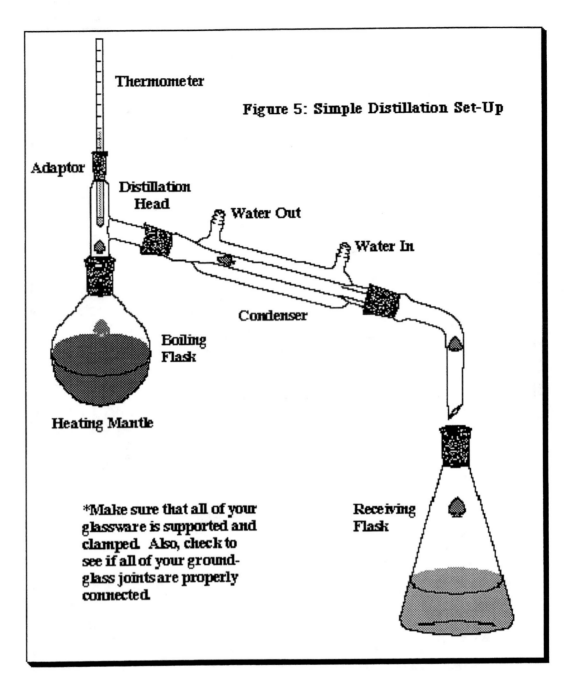

Thermometer

Figure 5: Simple Distillation Set-Up

Adaptor

Distillation
Head

Water Out

Water In

Condenser

Boiling
Flask

Heating Mantle

*Make sure that all of your glassware is supported and clamped. Also, check to see if all of your ground-glass joints are properly connected.

Receiving
Flask

(c)   MEK/Toluene distillation: Use the other 30 mL of the MEK/Toluene solution given to your group. Set up a fractional distillation apparatus, but use the special 3 necked 100 mL pot and extra thermometer and straight thermometer adapter obtained from the TA (**Figure 6**). Remember to add a boiling chip to the pot. Since you are using the same composition mixture as (b), you need not save the original mixture, but fit the distillation pot with a side-arm thermometer (use the extra thermometer and straight adapter), stopper the other side arm, and set up the packed distilling column and head as shown in **Figure 6**. Start the distillation at about 70 volts, and adjust the voltage as needed to maintain about 10 drops per minute distillation after the collection starts. Record both the head and pot temperatures every 2 mL; save one mL of the first and last distillate in tightly stoppered micro test tubes (be sure to label them clearly.) Obtain gas chromatograms and refractive indices of the first and last distillate samples.

40

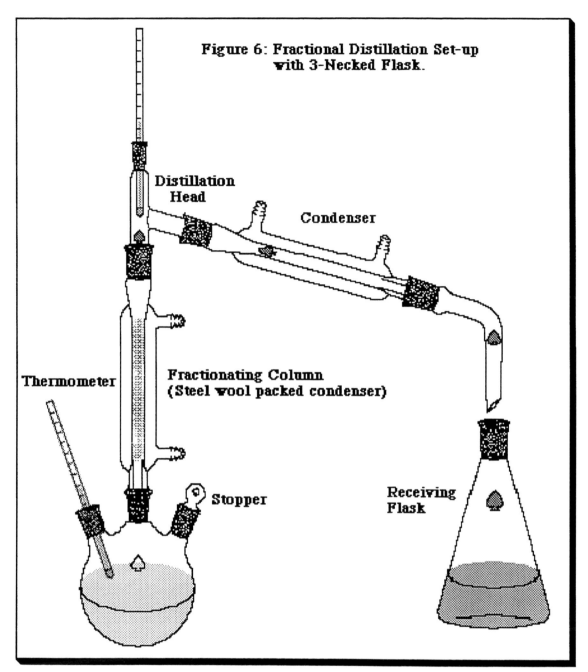

Figure 6: Fractional Distillation Set-up with 3-Necked Flask.

Distillation Head

Condenser

Thermometer

Fractionating Column (Steel wool packed condenser)

Stopper

Receiving Flask

Completing the lab:

This two week lab will be evaluated with a formal report of your data due at the beginning of your lab period in the third week. Follow the following guidelines for submitting the data for each group.

I. Names of Group Members

II. Tables of Data for Each Experiment

    A. Hexane / Ethanol Mixture

        1. Gas Chromatograph Data
            i. Mole percent of components in 1st fraction
            ii. Mole percent of components in last fraction

Nucleophilic Substitution Reactions of Alkyl Halides

Discussion

Nucleophilic substitution reactions of alkyl halides take place by mechanisms related to two limiting models. One, the S_N1 mechanism, has the halide break away in a first step leaving behind a carbocation, which later bonds to the nucleophile in a second step. This mechanism forms a highly polar intermediate (a carbocation) in the rate limiting step, and so is favored by polar solvents and by having the halide leave from a tertiary carbon which can form a stable carbocation. The other, the S_N2 reaction, requires the nucleophile to collide with and bond to the substituted carbon at the same time the C-Halide bond breaks. In this mechanism there is no intermediate of any kind, since the entire reaction takes place "in one fell swoop." Thus polar solvents do not aid, and actually retard the S_N2 reaction, but nonpolar solvents and good nucleophiles accelerate reactions which happen by this mechanism. Both mechanisms need to be studied, because in principle nucleophilic substitution reactions may happen by either pathway. In order to study them separately it was necessary to devise one set of conditions which allow S_N1 reactions to happen but suppress S_N2 reactions and another set of conditions which do the reverse.

Two reagents have been developed for this purpose. The first, devised in order to favor S_N1 reactions while suppressing S_N2, is $AgNO_3$ dissolved in aqueous ethyl alcohol. This very polar, hydroxylic solvent stabilizes the developing charge in the transition state leading to halide loss (see **Figure 1**) and assists halide loss by incorporating the incipient halide ion in a silver halide precipitate. Thus, the Ag^+ ion actually helps "pull" the leaving group off the a carbon. The polar solvent, in addition to encouraging charge development at transition state, stabilizes the reactant rather than the transition state in the S_N2 reaction and thus discourages it.

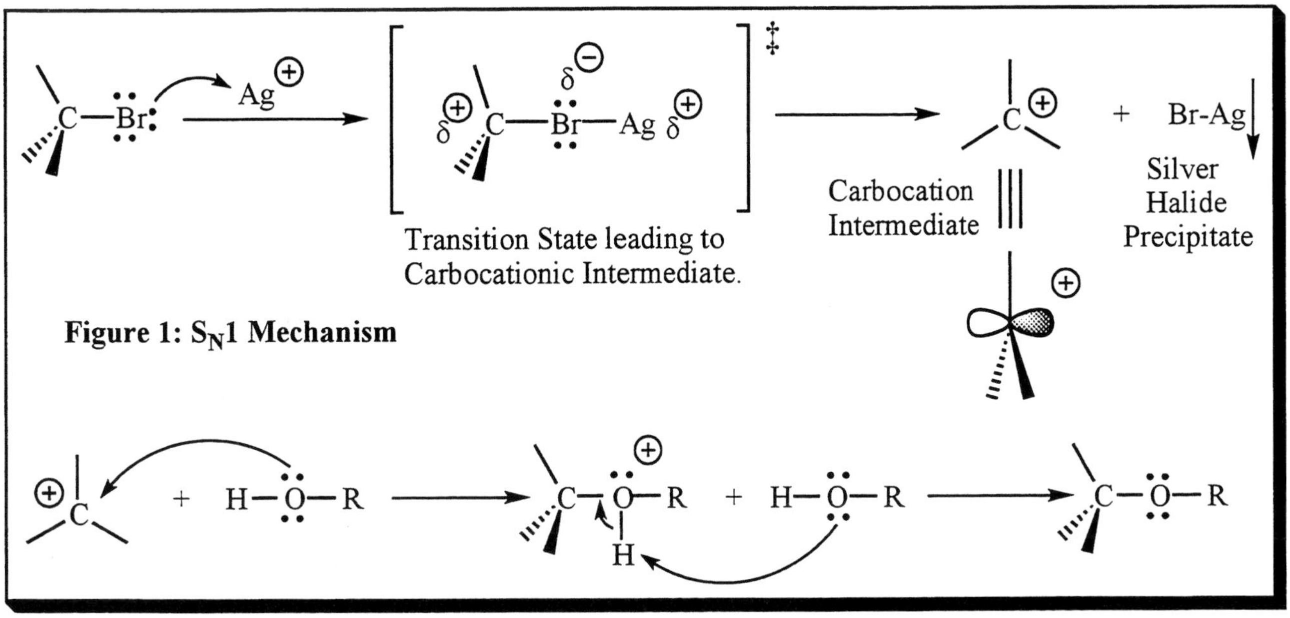

Figure 1: S_N1 Mechanism

Transition State leading to Carbocationic Intermediate.

Carbocation Intermediate

Silver Halide Precipitate

Visual evidence that an S_N1 reaction is taking place in this reaction is the formation of a silver halide precipitate, which is often seen as a dusty appearance at first. (Recall that silver bromide and silver iodide are even more insoluble than silver chloride.) Color change during the reaction means nothing. If a precipitate forms when an organic halide is added to $AgNO_3$ dissolved in 85% ethanol / 15% water, the reaction is assumed to have happened through an S_N1 mechanism.

The reagent devised to test for S_N2 reactions is sodium iodide dissolved in acetone (a relatively non-polar solvent.) The iodide ion is a very good nucleophile and therefore accelerates S_N2 reactions while the non-polar solvent suppresses S_N1 reactions by failing to stabilize the rate limiting transition state (see **Figure 1**) in which there is substantial charge buildup. While sodium iodide is very soluble in acetone, neither sodium bromide nor sodium chloride is; consequently, visual evidence that a reaction is taking place in this reagent is the formation of a NaBr or NaCl precipitate. Since both of these salts are very water soluble, S_N2 tests must be conducted in glassware which is absolutely dry! Once again, the precipitate may at first appear as a faint dusty powder, and once again color changes don't mean anything. (**Figure 2**)

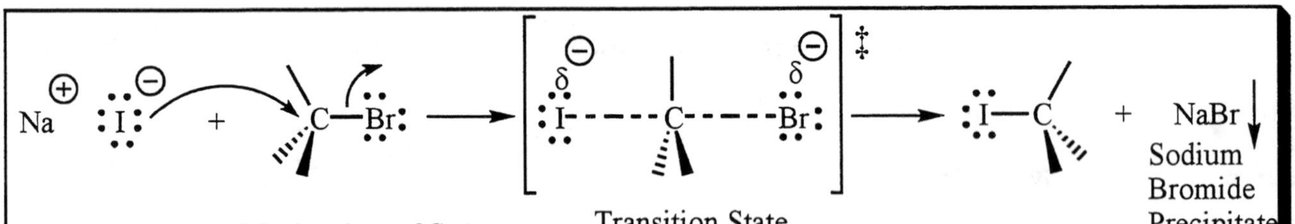

Figure 2: Mechanism of S_N2 Transition State

When nucleophilic substitution reactions are conducted using this reagent system and the precipitate appears, the reaction is assumed to have occurred through an S_N2 mechanism. It may seem odd that sodium iodide dissolves in the nonpolar solvent acetone. You have been taught in freshman chemistry to regard sodium iodide as ionic, and ionic compounds are generally soluble in water, but not in nonpolar solvents like acetone. However, NaI is more covalent than a good freshman chemistry professor would lead you to believe, and dissolves readily in acetone, while the more ionic NaBr and NaCl do not. This is the chemical basis of the test.

Lab organization:

You will be asked to test the organic halides in **Table 1** with both the S_N1 and the S_N2 reagent system and record how quickly you see a precipitate form. In some cases you may see no precipitate form in the first five minutes; for such cases you will heat the test gently to see if you can get a positive test by raising the temperature of the reaction. When you heat either the S_N1 or S_N2 reagents however, you must take care not to boil off the solvent (ethanol for the S_N1 reagent or acetone for the S_N2 test). Both organic solvents boil far below 100° C and if they boil away will leave a precipitate ($AgNO_3$ or NaI) which you will mistake for a positive test. Furthermore, please remember that the S_N2 test must be run in dry test tubes. If you run the $AgNO_3$ / water / ethanol tests first, you will have to wash out the tubes five times with deionized water before using them with NaI; this would mean that you would have to dry them after washing. On the other hand, if you do the NaI / acetone tests first, then you must still wash out the tubes five times with deionized water before moving on to the $AgNO_3$ / water / ethanol tests, but it would not be necessary to dry them rigorously before doing the second set of tests.

Procedure

Place a 400 mL beaker containing 2 inches of warm water on your hotplate; put the thermometer in and turn the plate on low so that the water in the beaker stays at about 50° C. Prepare 11 tubes for testing, and all six medicine droppers (they must be clean and dry.) Add 1.0 mL of 15% NaI in anhydrous acetone to the first four tubes, then add 2 drops of n-butylchloride to the first tube and vortex. Momentary cloudiness as the drops of halide go into the tube but which disappears on shaking does not constitute a positive test. Record when a precipitate forms to the nearest ten seconds; if no precipitate has formed after three minutes place the tube in the beaker of warm water on your hot plate. **Warning: point the test tubes toward the back of the hood when heating. Never point a test tube at yourself or someone else while heating. If the solvent in the test tube begins to boil, it may shoot out of the tube and cause a burn**. Record the time when the first precipitate appears; if no precipitate is present after three minutes of heating, you may write the test off as "no reaction." See **Table 2** for an example of how to set up your notebook for taking data. Test n-butylbromide next; then sec-butyl chloride, sec-butylbromide, etc. It may be possible to conduct two or more tests simultaneously if you are careful to keep track of the times separately. Once you are done with the first four tubes, prepare another group of four and keep testing until all halides have been tested with NaI / acetone. At that point clean the tubes thoroughly and begin testing with $AgNO_3$ / water / ethanol in the same way.

Questions

1) What would happen in you ran the NaI/Acetone test first, and then tried the $AgNO_3$ / H_2O / EtOH conditions without washing your test tubes well?

2) If *sec* -butyl bromide is a primary halide, why does it work so well during an S_N1 reaction?

3) Why doesn't chlorobenzene react either through an S_N1 or an S_N2?

Table 1: Halides Tested

n-Butylbromide

n-Butylchloride

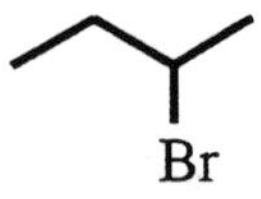

sec-Butylbromide

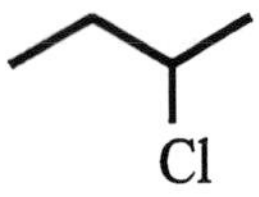

sec-Butylchloride

tert-Butylchloride

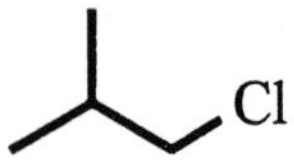

iso-Butylchloride

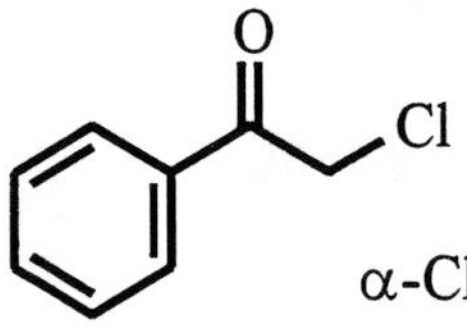

α-Chloroacetophenone

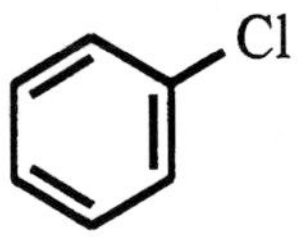

Chlorobenzene

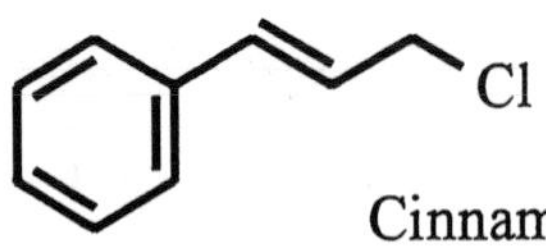

Cinnamylchloride

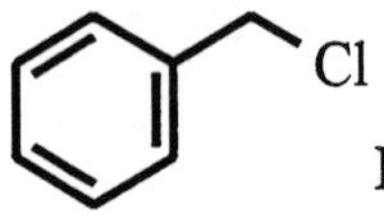

Benzylchloride

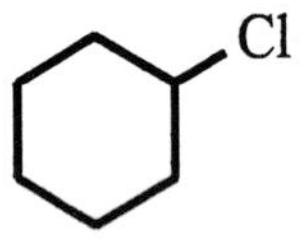

Cyclohexylchloride

46

Table 2: Organization of Data from Experiment

Halide	NaI/Acetone Time for ppt.	AgNO$_3$/water/ethanol Time for ppt.
n-Butylchloride	_____	_____
n-Butylbromide	_____	_____
sec-Butylchloride	_____	_____
sec-Butylbromide	_____	_____
t-Butylchloride	_____	_____
Isobutylchloride	_____	_____
α-Chloroacetophenone	_____	_____
Chlorobenzene	_____	_____
Benzylchloride	_____	_____
Cinnamylchloride	_____	_____
Cyclohexylchloride	_____	_____

Bromination and Debromination of Cholesterol

Reaction

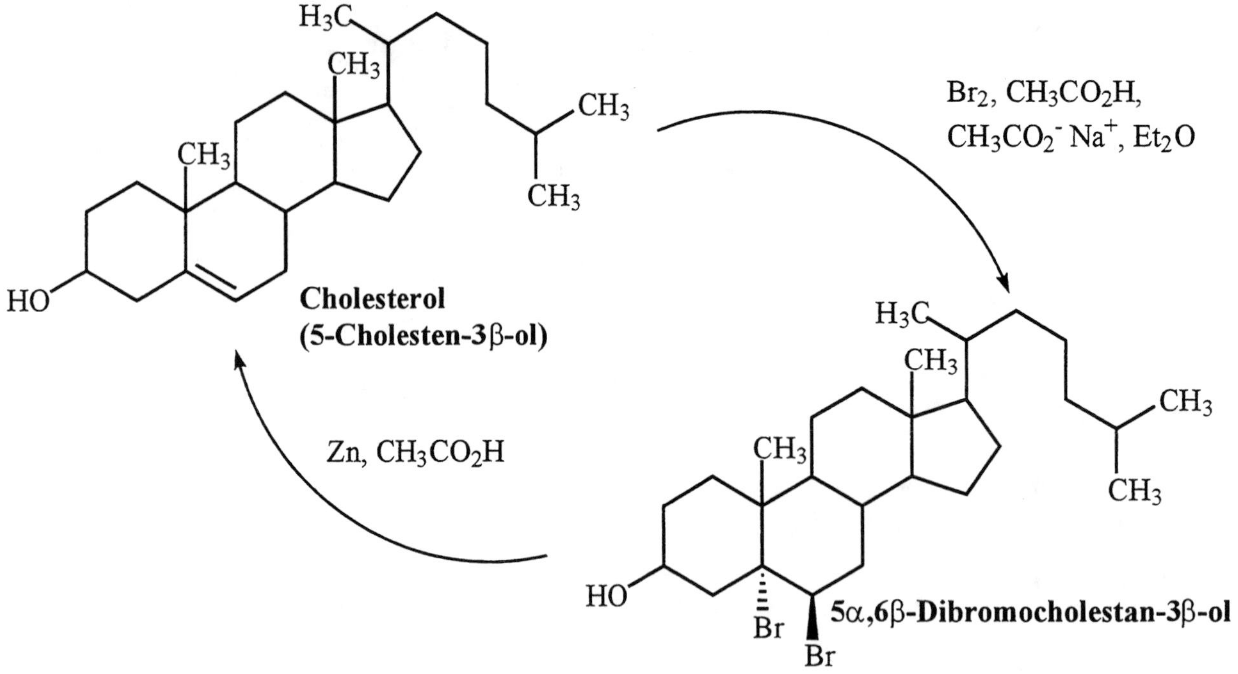

Br$_2$, CH$_3$CO$_2$H,
CH$_3$CO$_2^-$ Na$^+$, Et$_2$O

Cholesterol
(5-Cholesten-3β-ol)

Zn, CH$_3$CO$_2$H

5α,6β-Dibromocholestan-3β-ol

Discussion

In this lab we will conduct the purification of an organic compound, Cholesterol, via derivitization. The specific reaction is shown above. Cholesterol isolated from natural sources is always contaminated by compounds that are structurally very similar to cholesterol itself (**Figure 1**). Because of the structural similarity of these natural products, purification via crystallization or chromatography is not effective in producing material that is pure.

Since standard purification techniques are not suitable for separating cholesterol from these other naturally occurring compounds, chemical means must be employed. It turns out that cholesterol can be selectively brominated (**Figure 2**) in the presence of the other structural analogs. The dibromocholesterol derivative of cholesterol is structurally distinct from the other cholesterol analogs and can be cleanly crystallized away from the impurities. Once separated, the dibromocholesterol can then be chemically transformed back into cholesterol by reduction with zinc metal.

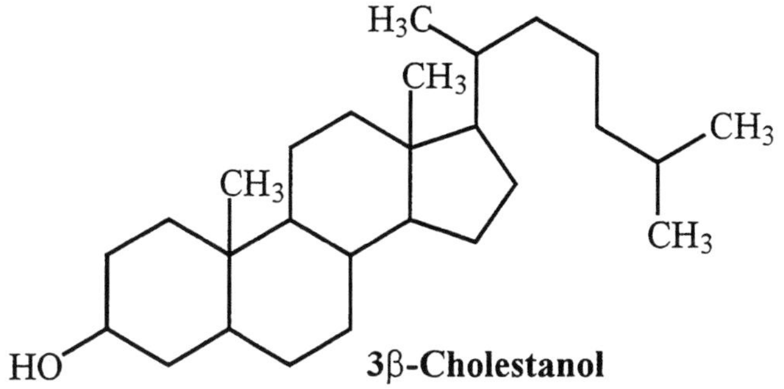

3β-Cholestanol

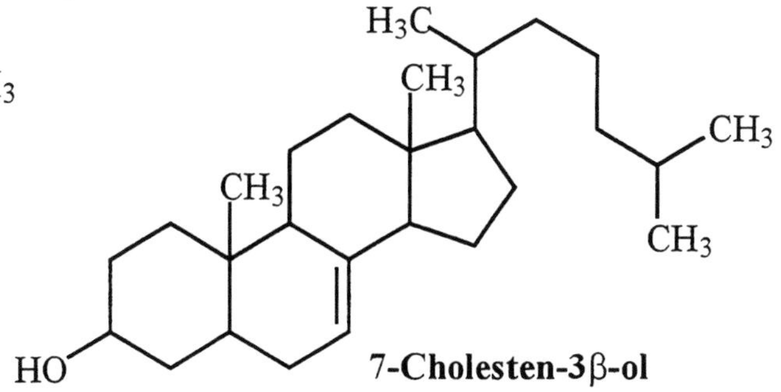

7-Cholesten-3β-ol

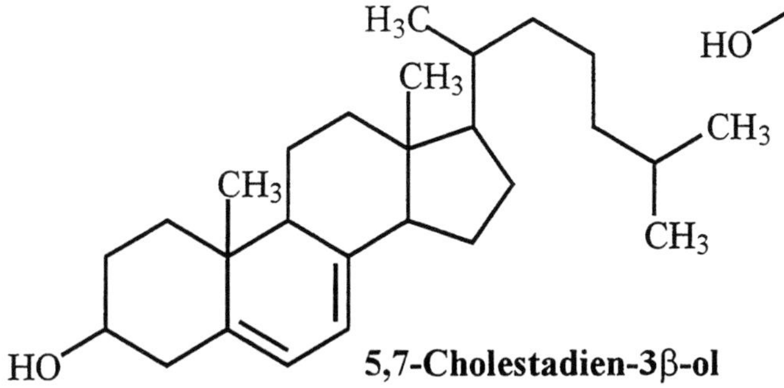

5,7-Cholestadien-3β-ol

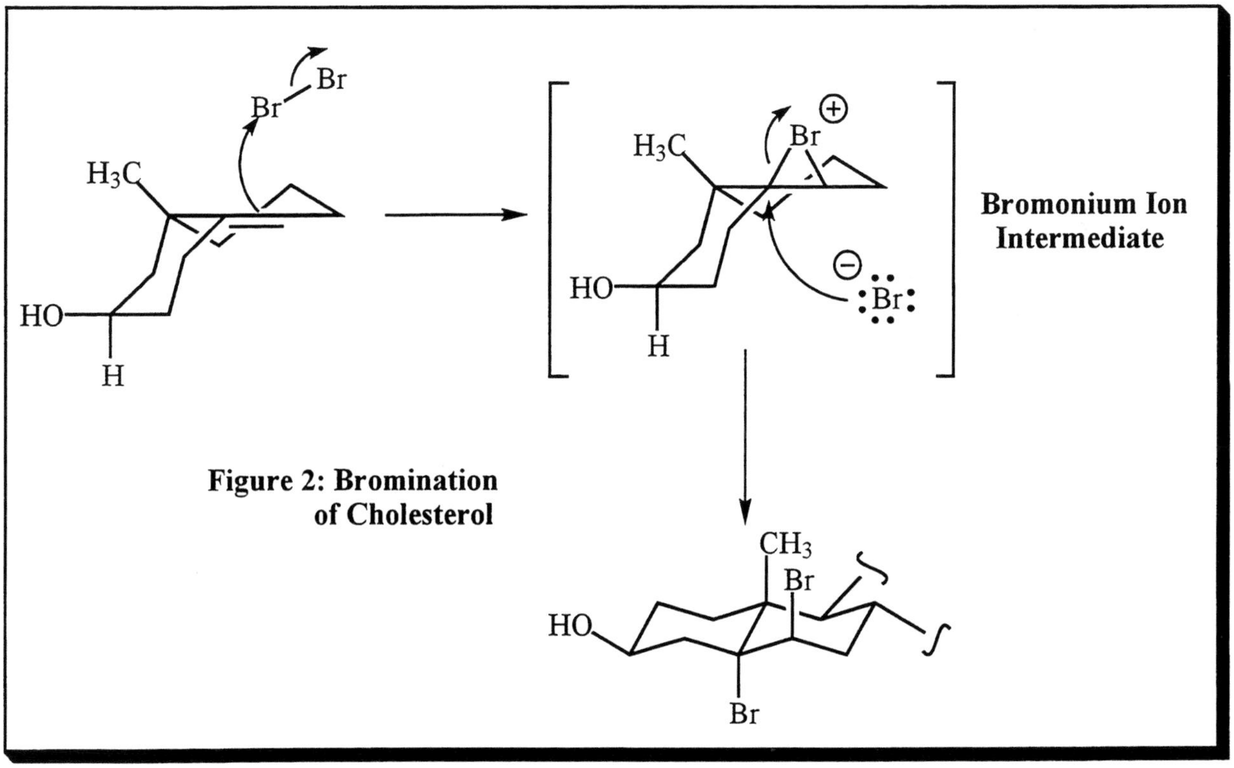

Figure 2: Bromination of Cholesterol

Bromonium Ion Intermediate

Procedure

In a 25 mL Erlenmeyer flask dissolve 1 g of commercial cholesterol in 10 mL of ether by gentle warming. Once dissolved, add 5 mL of the bromine and sodium acetate in acetic acid solution with a syringe. The cholesterol dibromide will begin to crystallize in approximately 2 minutes. Cool the solution in an ice bath and stir the crystalline paste with a stirring rod for 10 minutes. While stirring, cool a mixture of 3 mL of ether and 7 mL

49

of acetic acid in an ice bath. Collect the dibromocholesterol crystals using the small Büchner funnel and wash with the cold solution of ether and acetic acid. Perform a final wash with 10 mL of cold methanol. Take the crystalline product and transfer it to a clean 50 mL Erlenmeyer flask.

To the flask containing the dibromocholesterol add 20 mL of ether, 5 mL of acetic acid, 0.2 g of zinc dust and a magnetic stir bar. Place the flask on a magnetic stirrer and stir for 10 minutes. A white precipitate, zinc acetate, will begin to form during this time. While continuing to stir, add water dropwise (about 0.5 mL) and continue stirring until the zinc acetate (white precipitate) dissolves (Note: not all of the zinc metal will react). Discontinue stirring and decant the solution from the residue zinc metal into a separatory funnel. Wash the ethereal solution twice with water and then once with a 10% sodium hydroxide solution. Wash the ethereal layer one more time using a saturated sodium chloride (brine) solution, then transfer the ether layer to a clean, dry 125 mL Erlenmeyer flask, dry with anhydrous sodium sulfate, and decant into a 50 mL beaker. Add 10 mL of methanol and boiling chips to the ethereal solution and then heat the solution gently until the cholesterol begins to crystallize. Remove the solution from the heat source and let crystallize at room temperature and then in an ice bath. Collect the crystals by vacuum filtration and wash with small portions of cold methanol. Once dry, weigh the crystals, obtain a melting point, and calculate your percent yield.

Questions

1) In the bromination mechanism, why doesn't the acetate ion attack the bromonium ion intermediate instead of the bromide ion?

2) What important peaks would be absent from the infrared spectra of the dibromocholesterol that could distinguish it from the infrared spectra of cholesterol.

¹³C & DEPT NMR Spectroscopy

Discussion

With the advent of Fourier transform (FT) NMR spectrometers, ¹³C NMR spectroscopy is now available as a simple and routine tool for the structure determination of organic molecules (See **Figure 1**, ¹³C Spectrum of Isophorone). Since ¹³C is of low natural abundance (1.1%), addition of many spectra is required in order to obtain acceptable signal-to-noise levels. With modern spectrometers ¹³C spectra can often be acquired simply by issuing software commands to the spectrometer. (It should be recognized that the magnetogyric ratio (γ) for the ¹³C nuclei is approximately 25% that of the ¹H nuclei. Therefore, a 200 MHz NMR spectrometer used for ¹H nuclei must be reset to 50 MHz for the ¹³C nucleus.)

Generally, ¹³C NMR spectra are acquired while the entire ¹H frequency range is irradiated by a second radio frequency coil inside the spectrometer. These spectra are referred to as broadband-decoupled ¹³C spectra and they do not show the effect of spin-spin coupling to the ¹H nuclei. Such decoupling is done because the ¹H-¹³C coupling constants can be quite large (a few hundred Hz) relative to the chemical shift differences, which leads to multiplets split over a large portion of the spectrum. This often leads to complex and difficult to interpret spectra (See **Figure 3**, ¹³C Spectrum of Isophorone without broadband decoupling). The spin-spin coupling between two ¹³C nuclei is typically not observed because of the unlikelihood that two ¹³C nuclei will be adjacent to one another because of their low natural abundance. Broadband decoupling of the ¹H is used routinely in ¹³C NMR spectroscopy. It therefore would seem necessary to employ broadband decoupling of the ¹³C nuclei when acquiring a ¹H NMR spectrum. This is not required however, because of the low natural abundance of the ¹³C nuclei. Occasionally, the peaks from the ¹H-¹³C coupling can be seem with very intense singlets in the ¹H spectrum. Small peaks will appear around the singlet spaced equidistant in each direction. These peaks are known as the ¹³C satellites. Their intensity is 1.1% the intensity of the singlet itself.

The ¹³C NMR chemical shifts follow the same rough trends as seen with ¹H NMR chemical shifts. A brief listing of approximate ¹³C chemical shifts is provided in **Table 1**. As with ¹H NMR, Tetramethylsilane [$Si(CH_3)_4$] is used as an internal reference and the chemical shift of the methyl carbons is assigned to zero. In the example ¹³C NMR spectra shown, the TMS peak is not used because a second reference peak, the carbon of $CDCl_3$, is used instead. In order to be analyzed by either ¹H or ¹³C NMR, an organic molecule is typically dissolved in a solvent such as deuterated chloroform ($CDCl_3$). The solvent must be deuterated so that it does not contain any protons that would interfere with the ¹H NMR of the sample itself. In the example shown in **Figure 1**, the CDCl₃ carbon shows up as a triplet at 77 ppm. (The reason that the peak occurs as a triplet is that deuterium has a spin quantum number $I=1$.)

Table 1: Approximate ¹³C NMR Chemical Shifts

Functional Group	Carbon	Chemical Shift δ (ppm)
Alkyl Carbon Atoms	1° R-CH₃	~5 - 30
	2° R-CH₂-R'	~15 - 35
	3° R-CHR'R"	~20 - 40
	4° RCR'R"R'"	~25 - 45
Alkenyl Carbon Atoms	H₂C=C	~100 - 125
	HRC=C	~125 - 145
	RR'C=C	~130 - 150
Aromatic Carbon Atoms		~120 - 160
Alkynyl Carbon Atoms		~65 - 90
Nitrile Carbon Atoms	R-CN	~115 - 125
Amines	C-N	~30 - 55
Alcohols & Ethers	C-OH(R)	~50 - 75
	C-O (epoxides)	~35 - 55
Alkyl Halides	C-X	~25 - 75
Ketones & Aldehydes	RCOR', RCHO	~195 - 220
Carboxylic Acids & Esters	RCO₂H, RCO₂R'	~165 - 180
Amides & Anhydrides	RCON, RCO₂OCR'	~160 - 175

Typical ¹³C NMR spectroscopy provides an NMR spectrum that is not amenable to integration due to factors such a nOe and insufficient relaxation delays. An nOe or nuclear Overhauser effect is a product of the broadband decoupling. By decoupling the ¹H nuclei from the ¹³C nuclei, extra energy is transferred from the ¹H nuclei to the ¹³C nuclei they are attached to. This therefore leads to signal enhancement of the carbons that have more hydrogens on them over the carbons that have fewer or none. The insufficient relaxation delays deal with the slow rate of return of the excited carbon nuclei back to the ground state. Many successive ¹³C NMR spectra must be acquired and added in order to produce the final spectrum. If certain ¹³C nuclei have not fully relaxed back to the ground state prior to the next acquisition sequence, their intensity will not be truly represented relative to other ^{13}C nuclei that have fully relaxed.

One method that has been devised in order to address the integration problem discussed above is known as the DEPT (Distortionless Enhancement by Polarization Transfer) experiment. DEPT ^{13}C NMR spectroscopy provides a rapid way of determining the number of hydrogen atoms attached to a given carbon atom. In DEPT spectra, all peaks are singlets and quaternary carbons (without attached hydrogen atoms) are not seen. The CH and CH$_3$ carbon peaks appear as singlets of positive intensity and the CH$_2$ carbons appear as singlets with negative intensity (See **Figure 2**, DEPT spectrum of Isophorone.) In combination with a routine ^{13}C NMR spectrum, DEPT spectra allow unambiguous assignment of the number of hydrogens attached to each carbon. In practice, such spectral editing techniques are not perfect, and one often sees small residual peaks where, in principle, there should be none; these are usually small enough to be readily distinguished from the "real" peaks.

Procedure

You will be working in groups assigned by your instructor. All of the ^{13}C and DEPT spectra are contained in **Appendix I**. Your task will be to analyze the assigned spectra for your group and determine which of the compounds on page 55 matches your unknown.

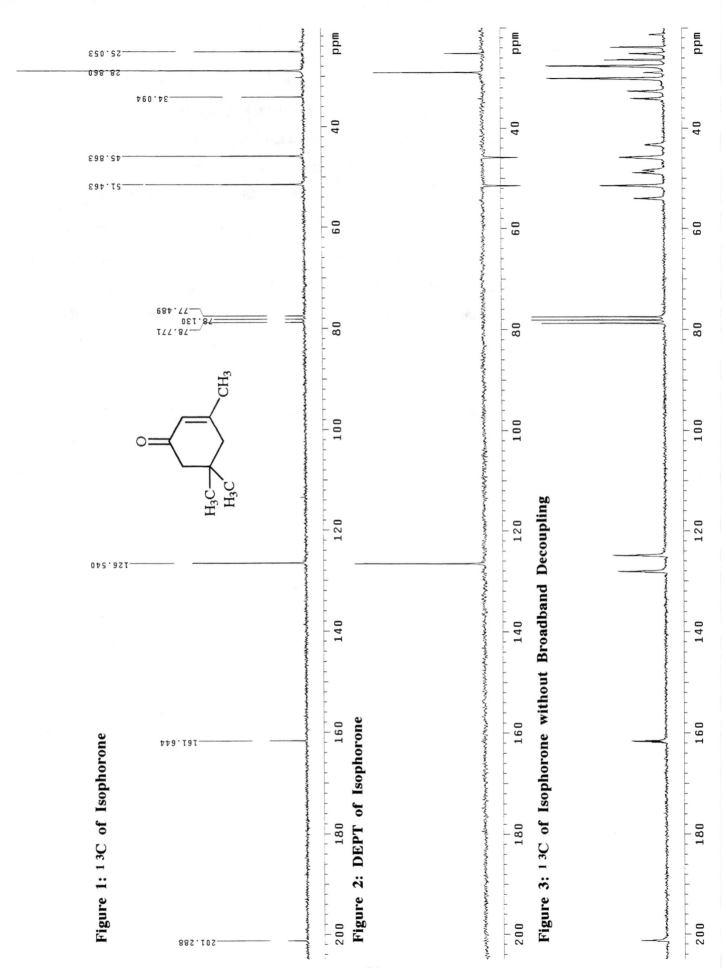

Figure 1: 13C of Isophorone

Figure 2: DEPT of Isophorone

Figure 3: 13C of Isophorone without Broadband Decoupling

54

C-13 & DEPT Laboratory Structures

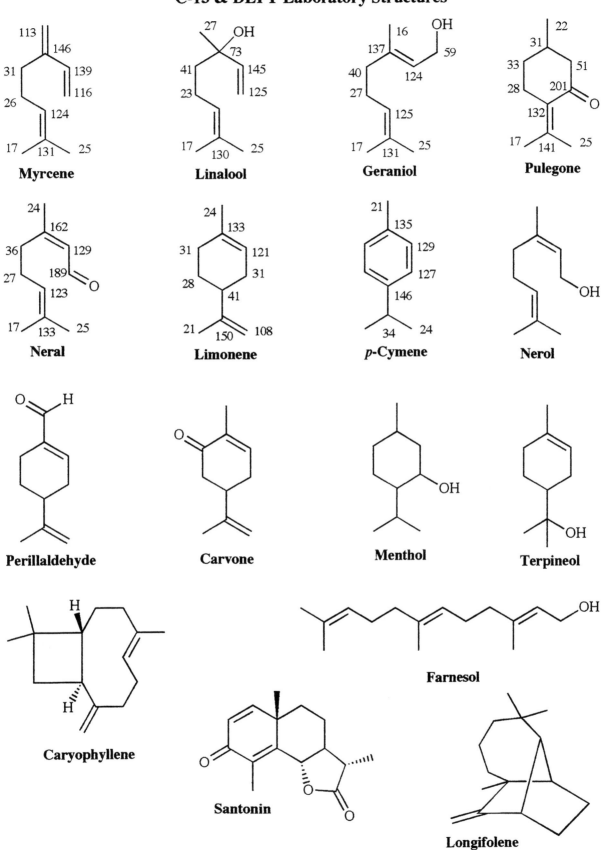

Myrcene

Linalool

Geraniol

Pulegone

Neral

Limonene

p-**Cymene**

Nerol

Perillaldehyde

Carvone

Menthol

Terpineol

Caryophyllene

Farnesol

Santonin

Longifolene

Proton NMR: Coupling Constants (J_{ab})

Discussion

We have discussed the chemical shift of proton NMR signals and the information one can get from these shifts in lecture. We have also used integral information from each proton NMR signal to determine how many how many protons of that particular type there are in a given compound. As you may recall, the third and most useful type of information available from a NMR spectrum is the "spin-spin splitting" information which is interpreted by using the (N+1) Rule. That is, a ^1H NMR signal is split into (N+1) peaks when the protons causing that signal have N identical nearest neighbor protons on an adjacent carbon.

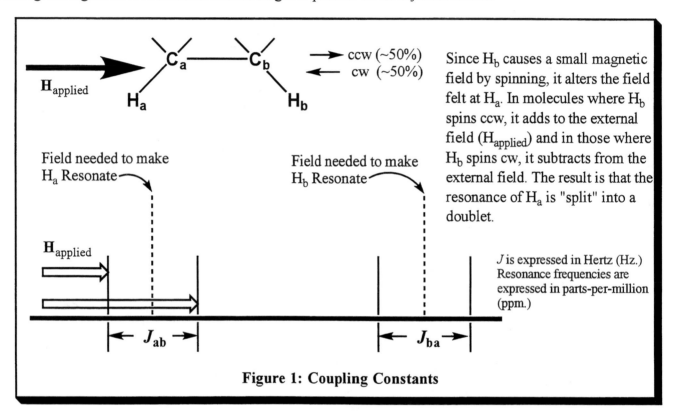

Since H_b causes a small magnetic field by spinning, it alters the field felt at H_a. In molecules where H_b spins ccw, it adds to the external field ($H_{applied}$) and in those where H_b spins cw, it subtracts from the external field. The result is that the resonance of H_a is "split" into a doublet.

J is expressed in Hertz (Hz.) Resonance frequencies are expressed in parts-per-million (ppm.)

Figure 1: Coupling Constants

Figure 1 shows that the "splitting" of the H_a signal by the magnetic field of H_b is a direct measure of the influence of H_b on H_a. Since H_b's magnetic field causes the disturbance of H_a by traveling through the bonding electrons connecting H_b to H_a, the size of the coupling constant J_{ab} depends on the number of bonds between H_a and H_b. In general, the greater the distance between H_a and H_b, the smaller the coupling constant J_{ab} is. Since the size of J_{ab} is measured by the distances between the sub-peaks of the signal on the X-axis, J_{ab} will have the same units as the X-axis (or chemical shift axis in NMR). That means that coupling constants are generally measured in units of Hertz, abbreviated Hz.

Recall that the X-axis scale in NMR is generally divided into units of δ (delta, measured in parts per million) of the frequency at which the proton signal for Tetramethylsilane [TMS, $(CH_3)_4Si$] appears. This, in turn depends on the strength of the magnetic field used by the particular NMR instrument. The first generation of commercial NMR instruments used a magnetic field of 14,076 Gauss. In this field, the upper spin state of TMS protons is 60,000,000 Hz (60 Megahertz, 60 MHz) higher in energy than the lower spin state, consequently the radio oscillators used in these instruments were pre-tuned to 60 MHz. The six identical protons of an ethane (CH_3CH_3) molecule are less heavily surrounded by electrons as compared to the twelve equivalent TMS protons and have a slightly greater energy gap between upper and lower spin states. This requires a slightly higher radio frequency to cause a spin-flip or resonance to occur. The frequency is 60,000,060 Hz, or just 60 Hz higher than the frequency needed for TMS. The ratio of 60 Hz to 60,000,000 Hz is just one part per million, or one delta (δ). The second generation of NMR instruments had more powerful magnets which caused a larger energy gap between the upper and lower spin states of the TMS protons, and thus required higher frequency radio oscillators to bring the TMS and ethane protons into resonance: 100,000,000 Hz and 100,000,100 Hz, respectively. The ratio of the increase needed for ethane (100 Hz) to the basic frequency of TMS (100,000,000 Hz) is still 1:1,000,000 or 1 δ. Our instrument is a fourth generation NMR which uses a 200,000,000 Hz radio oscillator for TMS protons; ethane protons show up at 200,000,200 Hz, but note that is still one part per million above the TMS frequency. The chemical shift position of a signal expressed in Hz depends on the strength of the magnetic field employed in the particular instrument, but chemical shift expressed in δ units (parts per million of the TMS frequency) is the same in all instruments.

Coupling constants measured in Hz, on the other hand, are identical regardless of the magnetic field strength of the instrument used to take the spectrum. Two protons which split each other by 12 Hz in a 60 MHz instrument split each other by 12 Hz in a 200 MHz instrument. This is important, since whether or not their signals follow the (N+1) rule depends on the ratio of the chemical shift difference (Δ c.s.) between the two signals to the coupling constant, J_{ab}. If Δ c.s. $\geq$ 10 x (J_{ab}) then the (N+1) rule is obeyed. Suppose you have a compound with two different kinds of protons H_a and H_b as in **Figure 1**; Proton H_a shows up at 7 δ and H_b at 6 δ. Suppose further that they are coupled to each other by 12 Hz, i.e., J_{ab} = 12 Hz. If you take the spectrum using a 60 MHz instrument, Δ c.s. = 1 δ = 60 Hz. Jab = 12 Hz. Since Δ c.s. is only 5 x J_{ab}, the spectrum would not obey the (N+1) rule and would be difficult to interpret. On the other hand, if the same spectrum is taken by a 200 MHz instrument, Δ c.s. = 1 δ = 200 Hz; since 200 Hz is more than ten times as big as the 12 Hz J_{ab}, the spectrum obeys the (N+1) rule and is straightforward to interpret. This is one advantage of taking spectra on instruments which work at higher fields.

The angle between two coupled protons H_a and H_b is also an important factor in determining the size of J_{ab}. **Figure 2** shows the angular dependence of J_{ab} on the H-C-H angle for geminal protons, that is, two protons which are attached to a single carbon atom. As you can see, J_{ab} can be quite large if the angle between the two coupled hydrogen atoms is less than 106°. Surprisingly, *J* for geminal hydrogens can also be quite small if the H-C-H angle is about 120°. This is a surprise because geminal are always quite close to each other, and so would be expected to couple strongly with each other all other things being equal. This means that geminal methylene protons like the vinyl protons of 2-chloropropene will split each other with a very small coupling constant, usually less than 2 Hz. Sketch out the 2-chloropropene molecule on scratch paper taking care to render the H-C-H angle on C-1 accurately in order to understand this point.

The geminal H-C-H coupling is called the "two bond coupling", since the magnetic field of H_a travels through two bonds in order to split H_b. The H-C-C-H dihedral coupling is called the "three bond coupling", since the path between the two coupled hydrogens is three bonds long in that case. (**Figure 3**)

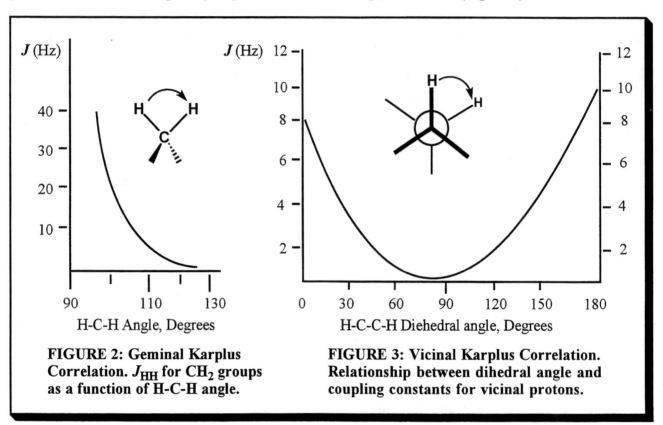

FIGURE 2: Geminal Karplus Correlation. J_{HH} for CH_2 groups as a function of H-C-H angle.

FIGURE 3: Vicinal Karplus Correlation. Relationship between dihedral angle and coupling constants for vicinal protons.

A special kind of 3 bond coupling arises when a terminal vinyl group is involved. In **Figure 4**, H_a, H_b, and H_c are all inequivalent, therefore they will all split each other with an appropriate *J*-constant. Each of the proton signals will be split into what is known as a doublet of doublets instead of the (N+1) rule triplet. More about the doublet of doublets will be said in pre-lab.

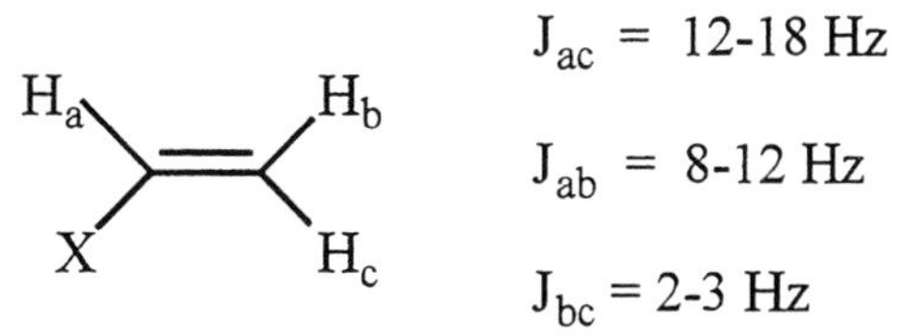

Figure 4. A compound containing a terminal vinyl group.

$J_{ac} = 12\text{-}18$ Hz

$J_{ab} = 8\text{-}12$ Hz

$J_{bc} = 2\text{-}3$ Hz

Note that the trans hydrogens H_a and H_c have a larger coupling constant than the cis hydrogens (H_a and H_b) even though the cis hydrogens are closer together. This fact can be used to determine whether a disubstituted double bond is cis- or trans- in compounds containing an alkene of unknown stereochemistry.

Hydrogens separated by four bonds do not noticeably split each other in normal circumstances unless special factors are present. This is because they are too far apart for the magnetic field of one of them to be felt at the other nucleus. However, four bond coupling between hydrogens does happen if one or more of the connecting bonds is specially strong or short. This is most common in aromatic, allylic, or propargylic positions. (See **Figure 5**.)

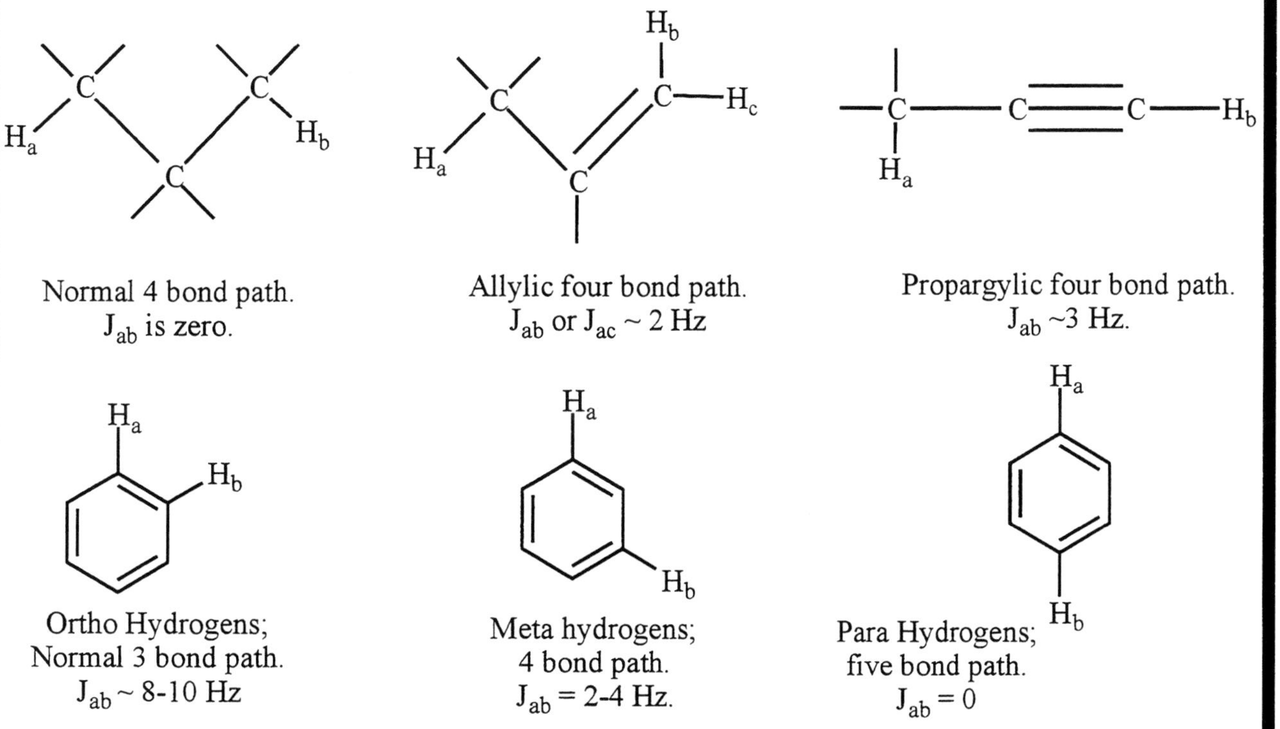

Normal 4 bond path.
J_{ab} is zero.

Allylic four bond path.
J_{ab} or $J_{ac} \sim 2$ Hz

Propargylic four bond path.
$J_{ab} \sim 3$ Hz.

Ortho Hydrogens;
Normal 3 bond path.
$J_{ab} \sim 8\text{-}10$ Hz

Meta hydrogens;
4 bond path.
$J_{ab} = 2\text{-}4$ Hz.

Para Hydrogens;
five bond path.
$J_{ab} = 0$

FIGURE 5

Normally, a four bond path is too far for H_a to influence H_b, so that the observed $J=0$ Hz. This case is shown at the top left. However, if one of the four bonds is a double bond, the H_a is allylic and will couple with the vinyl protons. In general $J_{ab} > J_{ac}$. If one of the four bonds is a triple bond, H_a is propargylic, and again there is noticeable H_a/H_b coupling. In aromatic rings, meta hydrogens couple with each other, even though it is a four bond path; para hydrogens are too far apart to show measurable coupling except in a few rare instances.

Your assignment in this lab is to complete the analysis of one proton NMR spectrum, assigning each peak to a particular proton and working out all of the coupling constants which are available from a "first order" analysis of the spectrum. Your report is to be between three and four double-spaced typewritten pages, including a half page interaction diagram illustrating the splitting patterns for all coupled protons. The spectrum for each compound is contained in **Appendix II**.

Structures of Compounds for J_{ab} Lab

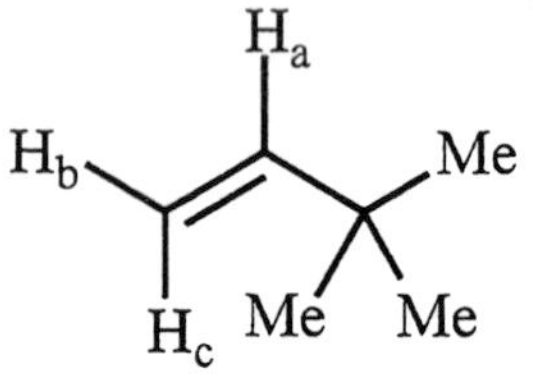

3,3-Dimethyl-1-butene

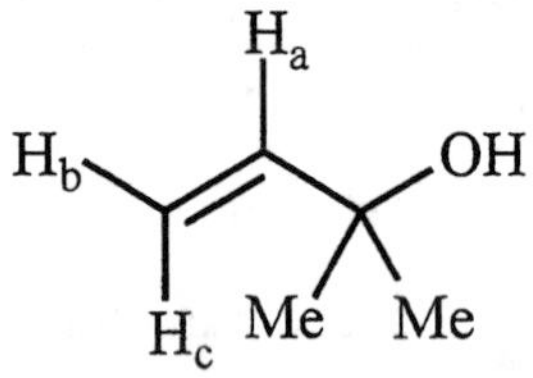

2-Methyl-3-buten-2-ol

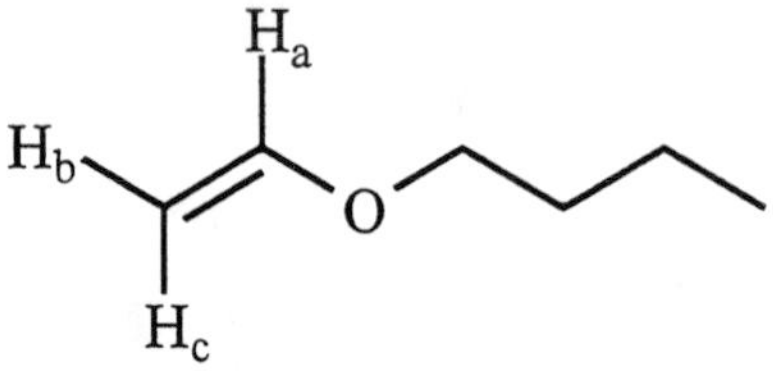

n-Butylvinyl Ether

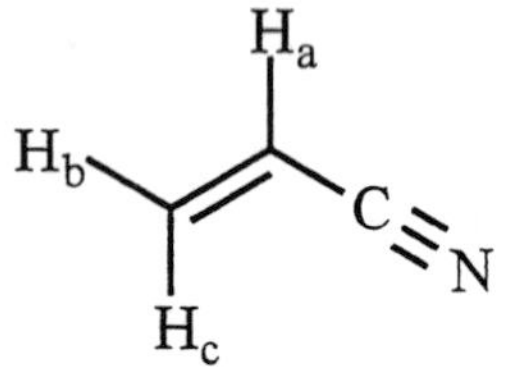

Acrylonitrile

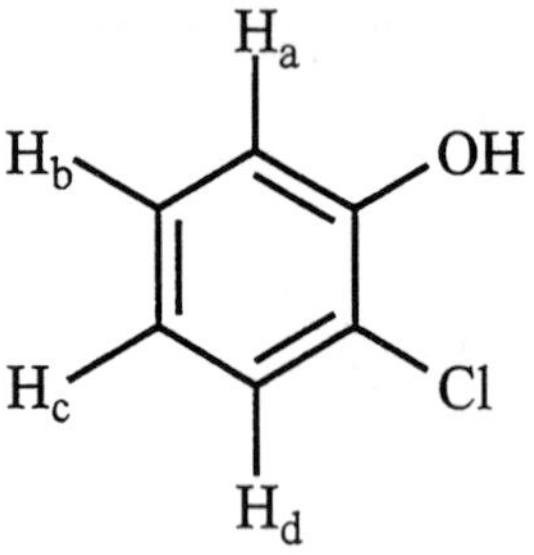

ortho-Chlorophenol

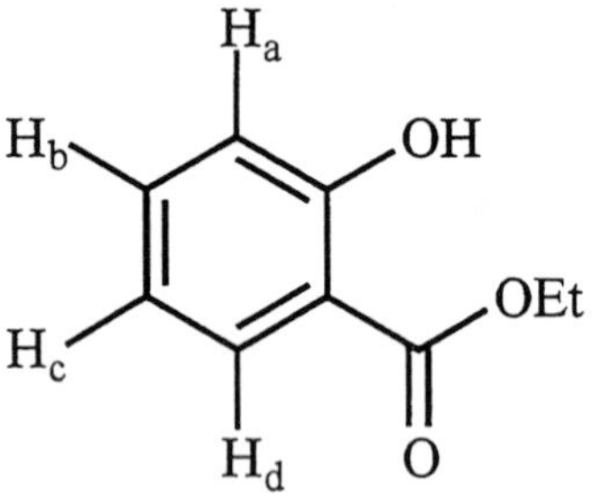

Ethylsalicylate

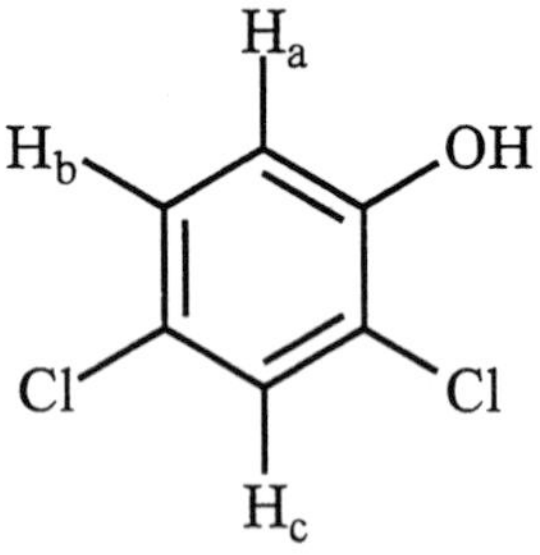

2,4-Dichlorophenol

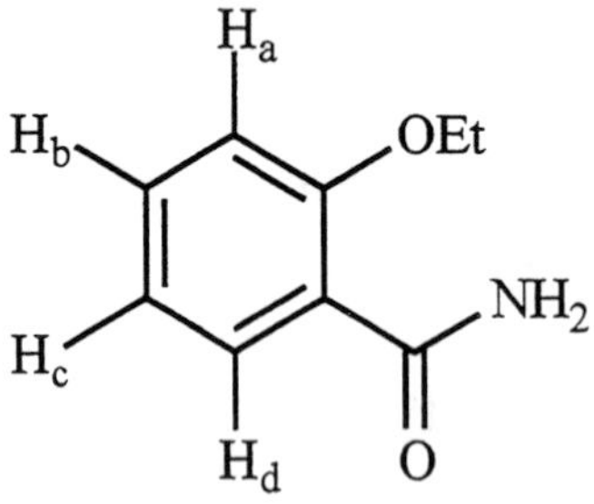

2-Ethoxybenzamide

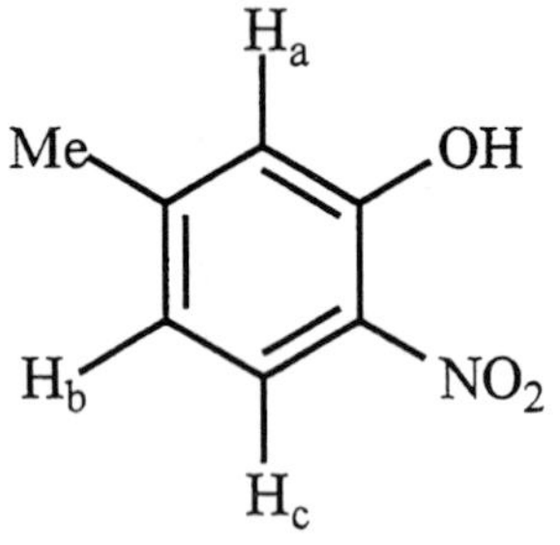

2-Nitro-5-methylphenol

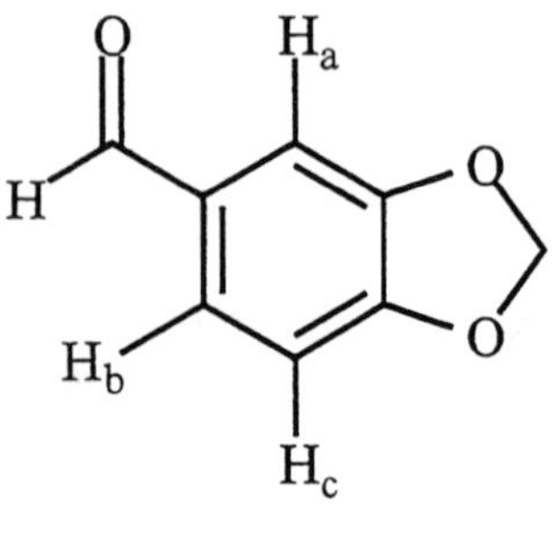

3,4-Methylenedioxybenzaldehyde

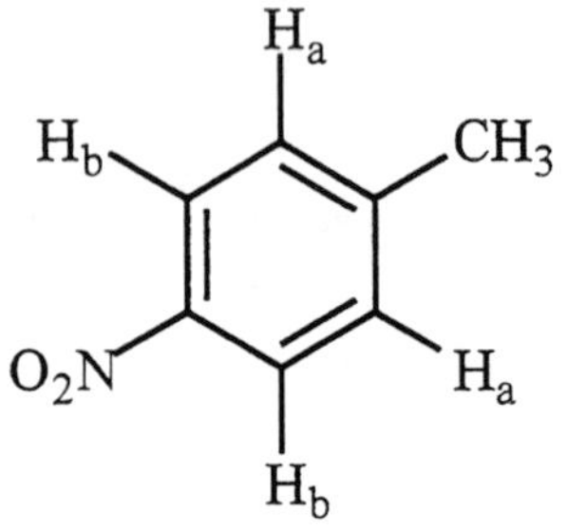

para-Nitrotoluene

Bromination of *trans*-Cinnamic Acid

Reaction

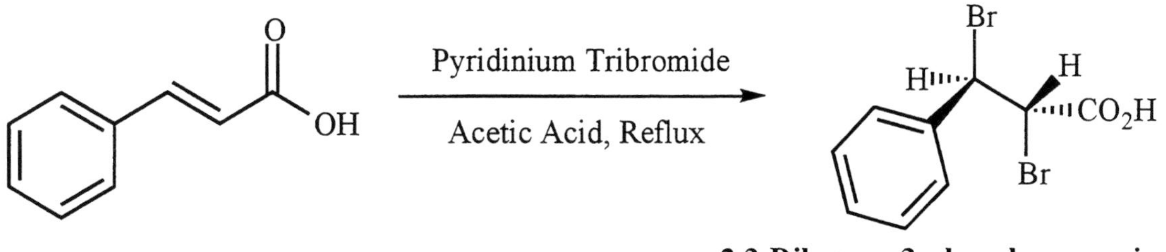

trans-Cinnamic Acid
MW 148.16
mp 133° - 134° C

2,3-Dibromo-3-phenylpropanoic Acid
MW 306.09
mp 202° - 204° C (Erythro)
mp 93° - 95° C (Threo)

Discussion

In this lab we will conduct an example of the addition reaction between bromine (Br_2) and an alkene (*trans*-Cinnamic Acid). The specific reaction is shown above. The organic starting material for this lab is the pure trans-diastereomer of cinnamic acid (IUPAC = trans-3-phenylpropenoic acid). Although there are no chiral centers in this compound, the product contains two chiral centers at C-2 and C-3. We know from our earlier study of stereochemistry (Solomons, section 5.11 pp. 205-211 and section 8.6 pp. 339-344) that a molecule with two chiral centers has a maximum of four stereoisomers: a (d,l) pair of erythro or "matched" structures, and a (d,l) pair of threo or "mismatched" structures (See **Figure 1**). [In this case we consider the bromines and hydrogens at C-2 and C-3 to be two pairs of similar substituents; although the CO_2H at C-2 is not very similar to the phenyl ring at C-3, we will consider them to be the third pair of "similars". (See **Figure 2**.)] The object of this lab is to: (1) Determine whether the product of bromine addition to *trans*-cinnamic acid is the erythro or the threo diastereomer or a mixture of both and (2) determine what the result of (1) indicates about the syn- or anti- nature of bromine addition to alkenes.

How will you determine whether your product is erythro, threo, or a mixture of both? Fortunately that is rather easy to do! The erythro and threo products are diastereomers, they have different physical properties. We will use the melting points of the two in order to distinguish them. Erythro 2,3-dibromopropanoic acid has a m.p.= 202° - 204° C, while the threo isomer has a m.p.= 93° - 95° C. This is because the erythro molecules fits into an orderly lattice arrangement that has high intermolecular attractive forces and hence, a higher melting point. When your product is clean and dry (free from solvent), simply take its melting point to determine whether you have erythro, threo, or a mixture (broad range).

This lab employs a brominating agent known as pyridinium tribromide. Pyridinium tribromide is a corrosive reagent and a lachrymator. For these reasons, handle the reagent only in your hooded lab desk and open your hood baffles at the beginning of lab. Furthermore, goggles must be worn at all times! A sodium thiosulfate solution is on hand which can be used to clean up any spilled material. As you know, sodium thiosulfate reduces bromine to harmless bromide ion, and thus can be used to prevent burns to the skin if applied quickly. The best method of avoiding burns, however, is to handle the solution carefully enough so that it doesn't spill to begin with.

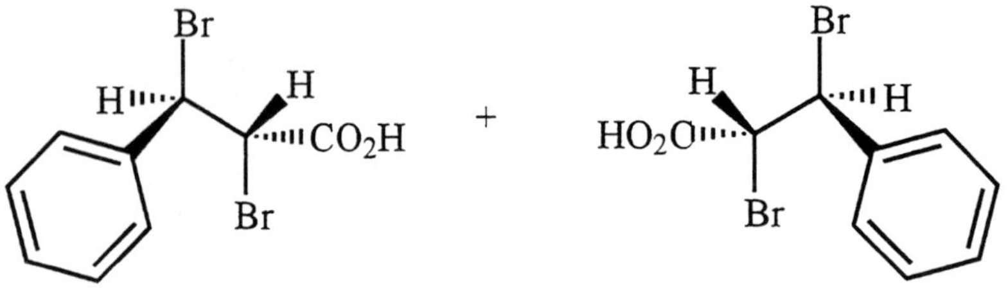

Erythro Pair of Enantiomers from *trans*- addition of Bromine

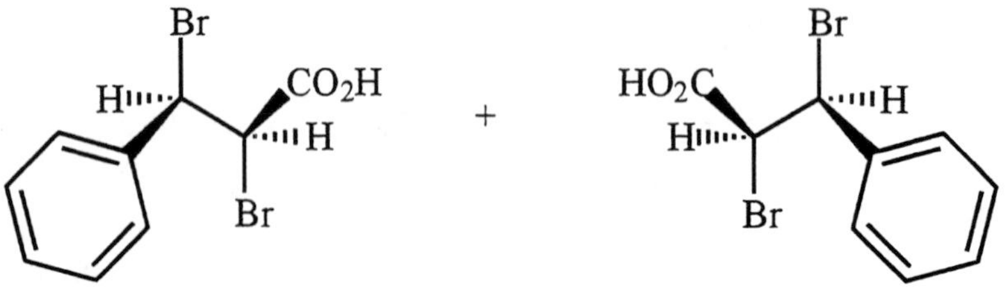

Threo Pair of Enantiomers from *cis*- addition of Bromine

Figure 1

Procedure

Weigh and place 500 mg (3.37 mmol) of *trans*-cinnamic acid in a 50 mL round-bottom flask containing a magnetic stir bar. In a fume hood, weigh 1.2 g (3.37 mmol) of pyridinium tribromide and place it in the same flask. (Pyridinium tribromide is a corrosive reagent and a lachrymator. For these reasons, handle the reagent only in your hooded lab desk and open your hood baffles at the beginning of lab. Furthermore, goggles must be worn at all times! A sodium thiosulfate solution is on hand which can be used to clean up any spilled material. As you know, sodium thiosulfate reduces bromine to harmless bromide ion, and thus can be used to prevent burns to the skin if applied quickly. The best method of avoiding burns, however, is to handle the solution carefully enough so that it doesn't spill to begin with.) After the both solid material has been added to the flask, add 15 mL of glacial acetic acid via the dispensing pipette. Attach the flask to a water-cooled reflux condenser and place a heating mantle under the flask. Begin stirring using the magnetic stirrer and turn on your Variac to 65 volts. Heat the mixture at reflux for 45 minutes.

When the reflux is finished, cool the orange solution to room temperature. With a Pasteur pipet, transfer, in small portions, the solution to a 50 mL Erlenmeyer flask. Cool the solution in an ice bath for 10 minutes, and then slowly add 15 mL of cold water in three 5 mL portions. Swirl the contents of the flask between additions. A pale yellow precipitate should form. Collect the crude product by vacuum filtration using a Hirsch funnel. Was the filter cake with three 2 mL portions of cold water.

Allow the material to air dry until your next laboratory period. Obtain a melting point of your product and determine whether you have the Erythro or Threo set of enantiomers. Arrange to visit the NMR in order to obtain a proton-NMR of your product.

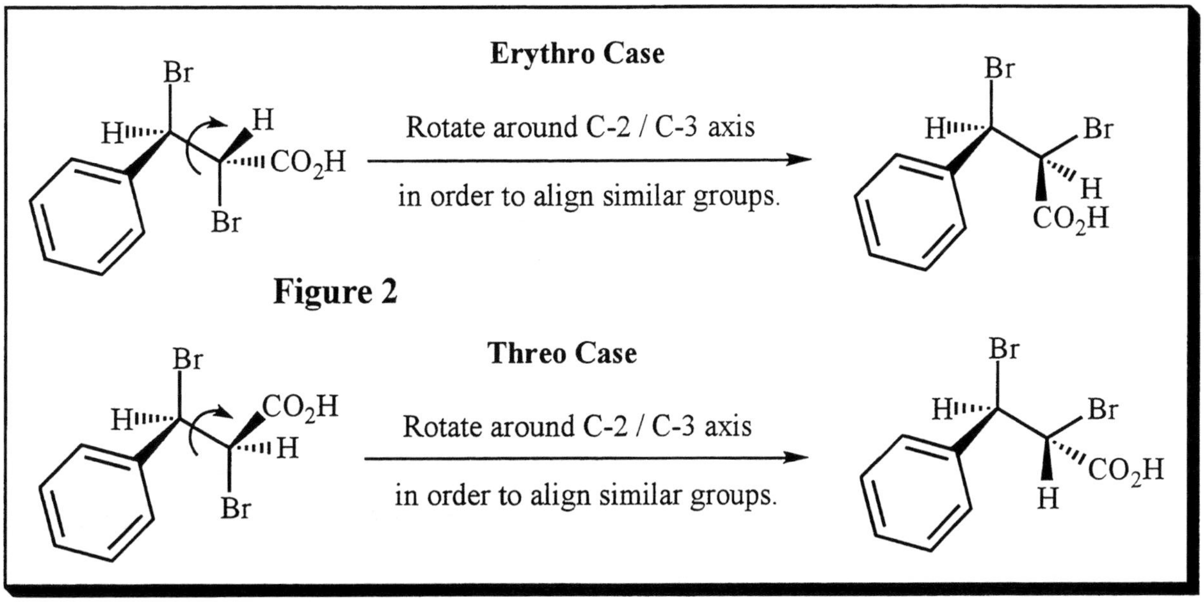

Figure 2

Questions

1) Write a mechanism that explains the formation of both enantiomers of the erythro dibromo product.

2) If *trans*-stilbene (*trans*-diphenylethene) were used in the reaction instead of the *trans*-cinnamic acid, would the reaction produce a pair of enantiomers?

Synthesis of a Secondary Alcohol via Reduction of a Ketone

Norborneol from Norcamphor

Reaction

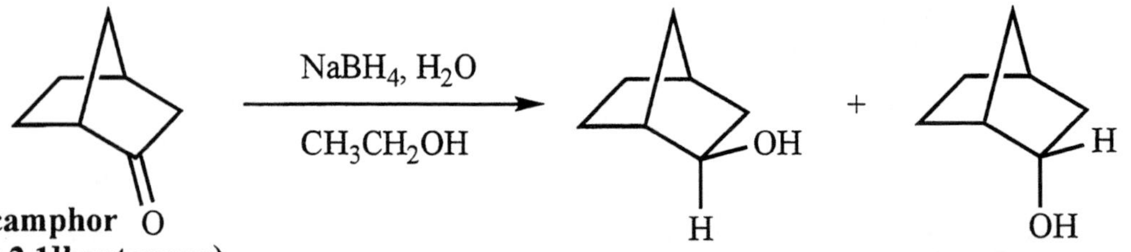

Norcamphor
(Bicyclo[2.2.1]heptanone)

exo-Bicyclo[2.2.1]
heptanol
MW 112.07
mp 124° - 126° C

endo-Bicyclo[2.2.1]
heptanol
MW 112.07
mp 149° - 150° C

Discussion

One method of alcohol synthesis is via the reduction of an aldehyde or ketone by hydride (**Figure 1.**) If the reactant is an aldehyde, the final product will have one alkyl group and two hydrogens on the carbinol carbon and will be the conjugate base (alkoxide ion) of a primary alcohol. If a ketone is reduced by hydride nucleophilic attack, the carbinol carbon will carry two alkyl groups and one hydrogen- this is the conjugate base of a secondary alcohol. Either of these alkoxide ions quickly accepts an H+ from water affording the parent alcohol.

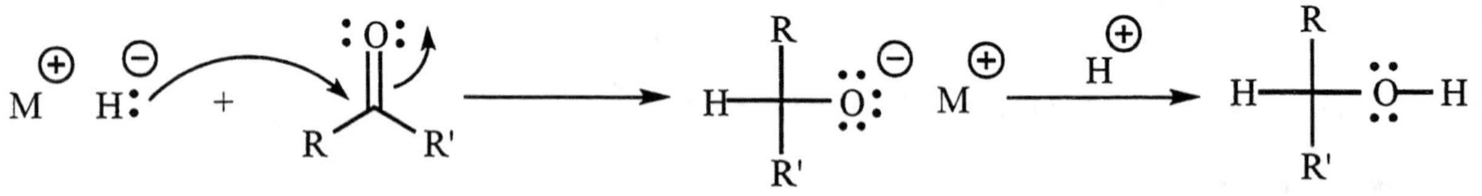

Figure 1: Hydride Attack on a Carbonyl

Hydride ion itself is not the preferred reducing agent for this reaction. Hydride is a very strong base, and liberates hydrogen gas in a strongly exothermic reaction when traces of water are present. Generally speaking, this leads to explosions. This awkward tendency of the hydride ion can be controlled by using a form of hydride ion which has been "tamed" by being covalently bonded to another atom, but can still be donated to a carbonyl. Two common hydride ions are available: $[AlH4]^-$, the aluminum hydride ion, and $[BH4]^-$, the borohydride ion. The aluminum hydride ion is much the stronger of the two, and still presents the hazard of explosion in the presence of traces of water, so we will not be using it in lab. The borohydride ion, while strong enough to reduce ketones and aldehydes, is suitable for use by inexperienced personnel. While it does react with water to produce hydrogen gas, the decomposition is slow and easily controlled.

The ketone we will reduce in this procedure is a bicyclic one related to the natural product camphor.

Camphor is shown on the left of **Figure 2**. Note that it has methyl substituents on carbons 1 and 7 (you should be able to apply the isoprene rule to natural camphor.) Norcamphor, the molecule you will reduce, is identical with camphor except for the methyls which it lacks. (Nor- is an old nonsystematic prefix which means a molecule lacking one or more methyl groups found in a precursor molecule; epinephrine and norepinephrine for instance.)

When borohydride ion reduces the ketone, a hydrogen will be added to C-2. However, the hydride could be added from the bottom of the structure which would force the final -OH group to be in the upward position called exo- or the hydride could be added from the top of C-2 which would force the -OH in the final structure downward, endo-. The two alcohol's are cis-trans isomers, since the exo- carries the -OH cis to C-7 and the endo carries the -OH trans to C-7. Thus, they are diastereomers and have different physical properties. The endo-melts at 149° - 150° C, while the exo melts 124° - 126° C.

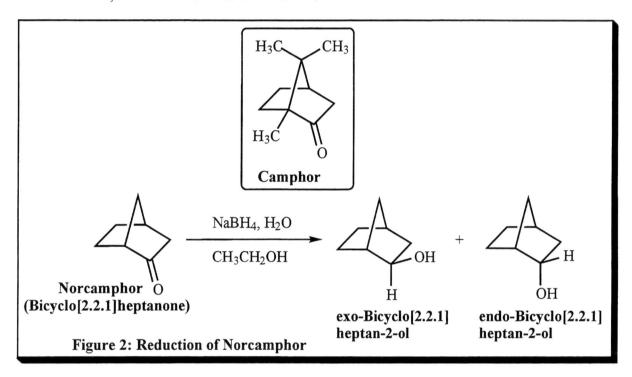

Figure 2: Reduction of Norcamphor

The product of this reaction is conveniently purified by sublimation. Some solids do not melt when heated, but instead pass directly from the solid to the vapor state without ever liquefying. In such cases sublimation is an efficient way to remove impurities, since these generally will remain behind as a melt or as unmelted solids. Care must be taken to exclude solvents or water from the crude sublimation sample. Liquids which boil lower than the sublimation temperature will reflux in the sublimation vessel, redissolving the pure sublimed crystals and returning them to the crude material endlessly. **Figure 3** illustrates the sublimation apparatus that you will be using to purify your alcohol product from the reduction of the ketone.

Procedure

Weigh out 10 mmoles (1.0×10^{-2} moles) of norcamphor to the nearest 0.1 g on a weighing paper. Add the norcamphor and 5.0 mL of ethanol (95%) to a 50 mL Erlenmeyer flask, then chill this solution in an ice bath. Next weigh out 10 mmoles of $NaBH_4$, place it in a standard test tube, and add 50 drops of ice-cold deionized water to dissolve; keep the solution cold. [You may use a stirring rod to speed the dissolution, but do not loiter! You will note gas bubbles forming, this is formation of hydrogen and it indicates that some of the borohydride is being destroyed prior to ketone reduction.] As soon as the salt has dissolved, add the borohydride solution to the norcamphor-ethanol solution and stir well. Allow the mixed solution to stand on the desk top at room temperature for ten minutes, then add 5 mL of water and warm on the hot plate for five minutes. [Do not allow the solution to boil!] Cool the solution in the ice bath and then transfer your material to a separatory funnel. Extract with 20 mL of pentane, then 10 mL of pentane in the second extraction; combine the pentane extracts and dry over $MgSO_4$. Allow five minutes for drying.

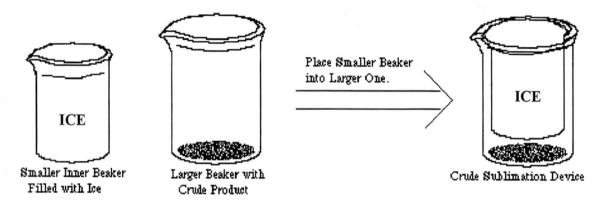

Figure 3: Crude Sublimation Device

Filter the dry pentane solution into the clean 150 mL outside beaker of the "sublimation set", add two boiling chips, and with your hot plate turned to 2.0 boil off the pentane. [Hood baffles open.] Make sure that the last pentane vapors are gone and that only a solid deposit of crude white norborneol remains in the beaker, but do not heat until the beaker "smokes." [Why?] Remove the outer beaker from the hot plate, half fill the inner beaker with ice, taking care not to get ice or water into the crude norborneol, and position the inner beaker inside the outer so that about 1 cm. separates the dry, lower bottom of the inner from the top of the crude norborneol deposit. Turn the hot plate to 3.0 and place the sublimation apparatus on it; continue sublimation until no more norborneol is adhering to the bottom of the inner beaker. At that point remove the apparatus from the hot plate, allow it to cool for two minutes, and take out the inner beaker. Scrape the clean, sublimed crystals onto a weighing paper without spilling water or ice among them. If any of the sublimed crystals fall into the bottom of the outer (crude norborneol) beaker, you may avoid loss of material by reassembling the apparatus and subliming them back up onto the inner beaker.

Determine the melting range of your sample and use this to establish whether you have produced exo-, endo-, or a mixture of both. Weigh the sample, calculate the percent yield, and turn in the product in a small sample vial. Which side of the bicyclic ketone did the BH_4^- attack, exo or endo?

Synthesis of a Homobarrelene Derivative by Valence Tautomer Trapping: Anti-Tricyclo[3.2.2.0²,⁴]non-6-en-endo-8-endo-9-dicarboxylic Anhydride (1)

Reaction

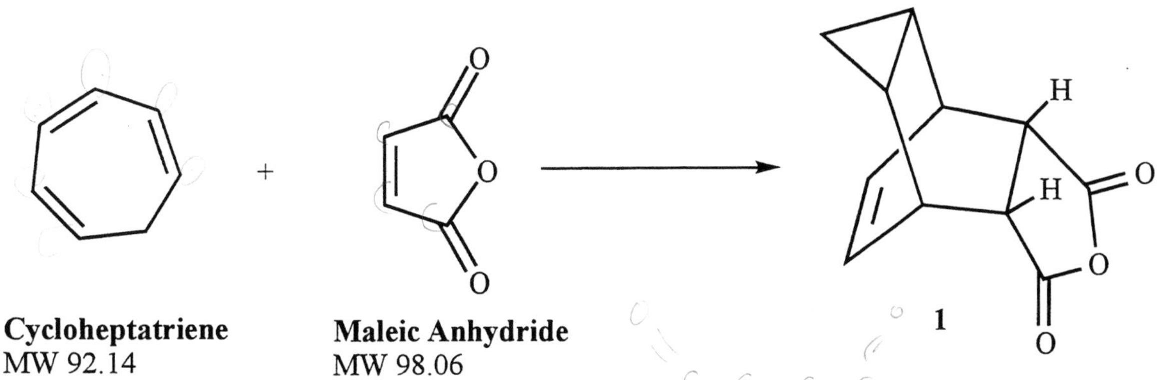

Cycloheptatriene
MW 92.14
bp 116° - 117° C
density 0.888

Maleic Anhydride
MW 98.06
mp 54° - 56° C

1

Discussion

1,3-Cyclopentadiene and 1,3-Cyclohexadiene undergo Diels-Alder reactions with a variety of dienophiles roughly one million times as fast as acyclic dienes. The reason for this is that the molecules are constrained into the S-cis conformation instead of being allowed to adopt the lower energy S-trans conformation. Because the Diels-Alder adducts of monocyclic dienes are bicyclic systems, which are difficult to obtain in other ways, Diels-Alder reactions of cyclic dienes and even trienes have been studied closely. One of the most interesting of these reactions is that of cycloheptatriene (**2**) with maleic anhydride (**3**), the product of which is the title compound (**1**).

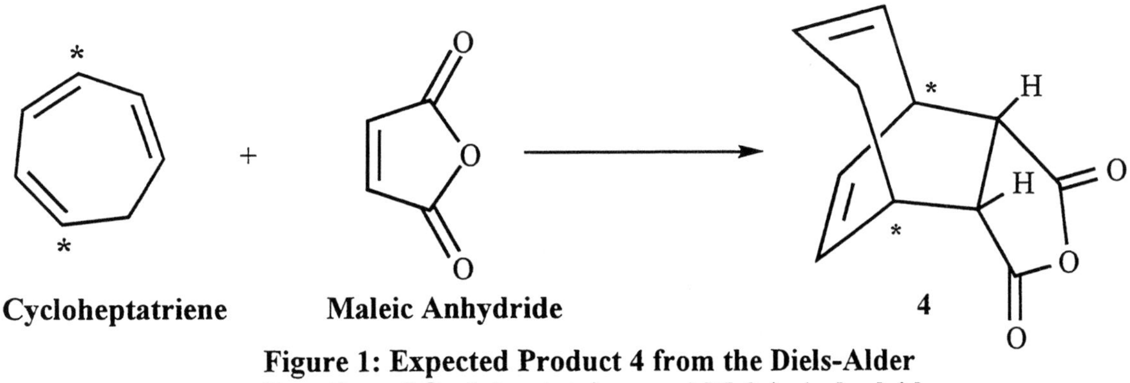

Cycloheptatriene   **Maleic Anhydride**   **4**

Figure 1: Expected Product 4 from the Diels-Alder
Reaction of Cycloheptatriene and Maleic Anhydride.

This reaction was first studied by Kohler and co-workers in 1939,[1] a decade after Diels and Alder published the first article on their reaction. Kohler and his colleagues were smart enough to realize that the adduct they obtained from the reaction was not the expected structure (**4**), but rather an isomer of it (**Figure 1**). Although Kohler and his co-workers were working before the availability of infrared and NMR spectrometry, they suggested that (**1**) was the most likely structure of the adduct. Structure was confirmed by chemical degradation more than a decade later,[2] although its formation from reactants **2** and **3** was still unexplained.

This unusual reaction was studied once again in 1971 (after NMR was available) and the assignment of structure **1** as the major product was confirmed.[3] The research group also detected about 10% of the exo,exo isomer of **1** and less than 1% of the expected adduct **4**. In this lab you will prepare and recrystallize compound **1** and study the reaction that produces it.

References:

1. Kohler, E.P.; Tishler, M.; Potter, H.; Thompson, H.T. J. Am. Chem. Soc., **1939**, *61*, 1057
2. Alder, K.; Jacobs, G. Chem. Ber., **1953**, *86*, 1528.
3. Ishitobi, H.; Tanida, H.; Tori, K.; Tsuji, T. Bull. Chem. Soc. Japan, **1971**, *44*, 2993.

Procedure

Cycloheptatriene (15.0 mmole, 1.38 g, 1.55 mL) and finely powdered maleic anhydride (15.0 mmole, 1.47 g) were refluxed in 10 mL of mixed xylenes in a 50 mL round bottom flask for two hours. After 2 hours, the condenser was reset for distillation and 5-7 mL of the solvent was distilled off. The pot mixture was then poured into a small beaker, the flask rinsed with 3 mL of ethyl acetate, and the rinses were added to the beaker. Hexane (10-12 mL) was then added to the solution which was then chilled in an ice bath for 15 minutes. Large needles of product were then isolated on a Hirsch funnel to afford cream colored crystals (m.p.= 98.5° - 99.5° C).

Questions

1. Cycloheptatriene does not add to maleic anhydride in a normal Diels-Alder fashion. From your knowledge of how a Diels-Alder reaction works, use the structure of the actual adduct **1** to deduce the structure of the diene which actually added to the maleic anhydride. This is, work backward from the adduct **1** to the structure of the actual diene reactant by detaching the skeleton of maleic anhydride.

2. The actual diene reactant whose structure you have deduced is called Norcaradiene. Write its structure next to the that of cycloheptatriene. Next, use mechanistic arrows to suggest how cycloheptatriene might isomerize to form norcaradiene.

3. Isomerizations such as the one hinted at in Question 2 are called Valence Tautomerizations. Two structures related like cycloheptatriene and norcaradiene are referred to as valence tautomers. It is not necessary to shift hydrogens to turn one valence tautomer into another. However, valence tautomers are not resonance forms

of the same molecule either, since bond lengths and angles are different between the two. Write an equation which shows the interconversion of cycloheptatriene and norcaradiene as an equilibrium.

4. The equation you wrote for Question 3 expresses the fact that a bottle of cycloheptatriene always contains some of the norcaradiene tautomer. However, norcaradiene is much less stable than cycloheptatriene and comprises less than 1% of the equilibrium mixture. For every molecule of norcaradiene present, there are 99 or more molecules of cycloheptatriene. Proving the existence of an unstable molecule by causing it to react selectively with some other compound is called trapping. In this lab we used maleic anhydride as a trap to react with norcaradiene. Try to suggest a reason that the norcaradiene, rather then cycloheptatriene is trapped by maleic anhydride.

Nitration of Methyl Benzoate

Reaction

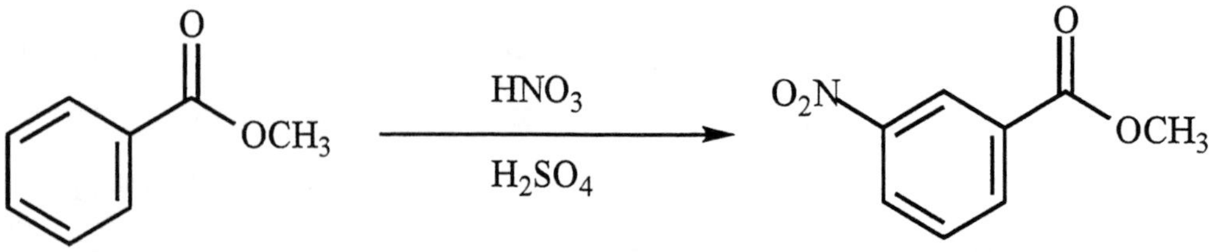

Methyl Benzoate
MW 136.16
mp -12° C
density 1.094

Methyl 3-nitrobenzoate
MW 181.15
mp 78° - 80° C

Discussion

In this lab you will be performing an electrophilic aromatic substitution reaction on a mono-substituted benzene ring. Since the benzene ring is stabilized by aromaticity, the pi-system is less reactive as compared to the pi-system of an alkene. For this reason, a very strong electrophile will be needed in order to cause a reaction to occur. The electrophile used in this experiment is the nitronium ion (**1**) which is formed from the reaction of nitric acid and sulfuric acid (**Figure 1**).

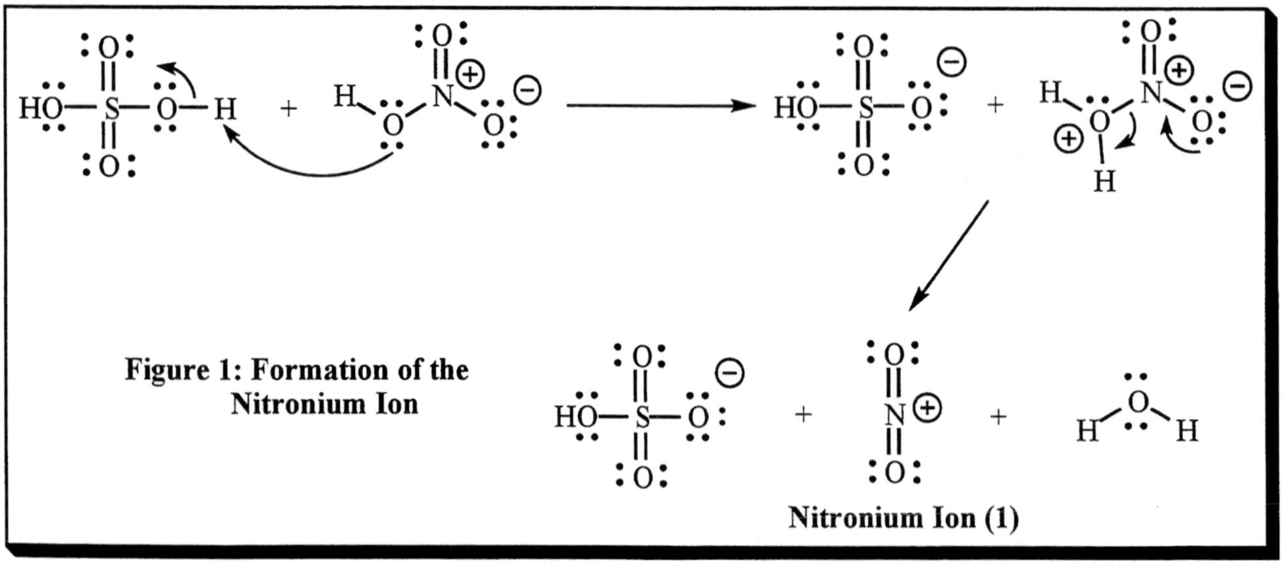

Figure 1: Formation of the Nitronium Ion

Nitronium Ion (1)

Once the electrophilic nitronium ion is formed, the aromatic ring will nucleophilically attack **1** to form the arenium ion (**2**) (**Figure 2**). Resonance forms of the arenium ion are shown in **Figure 3**. Since the benzene ring was substituted with an ester group, the position at which the nitro group will add to becomes important. An ester substituent is referred to as a **Deactivating Group**. Deactivating groups direct an incoming electrophile to the *meta-* position relative to itself. Deprotonation of the arenium ion then restores the aromatic character of the ring.

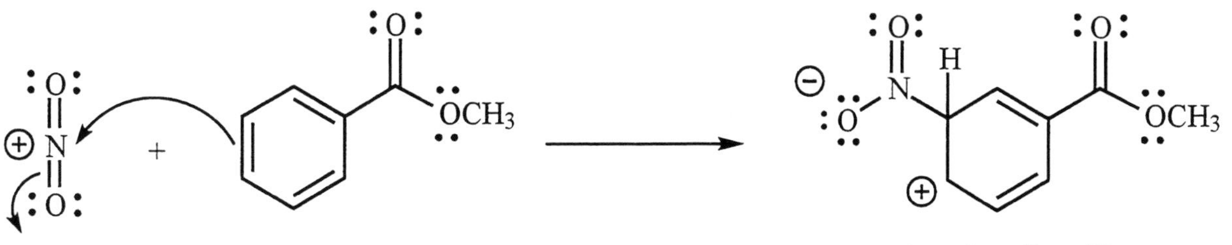

Figure 2: Mechanism of Electrophilic Aromatic Nitration

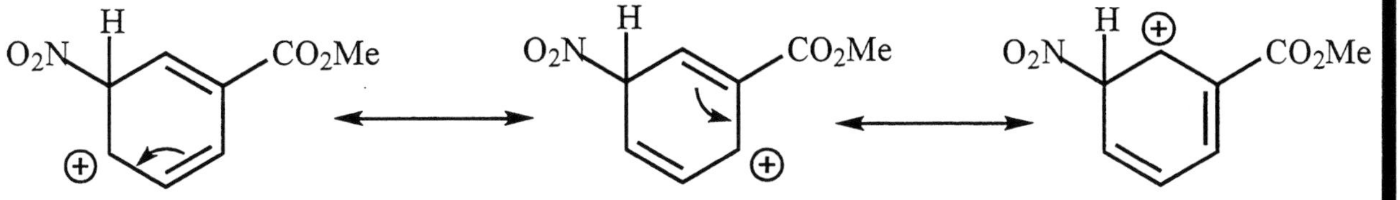

Figure 3: Resonance Forms of the Arenium Ion

Procedure

Warning! You will be using concentrated Nitric Acid and concentrated Sulfuric Acid. Please reread your safety guidelines about handling concentrated acids. Make sure that your glassware is completely dry before adding either of the two acids in order to prevent a vigorous, exothermic reaction which could cause acid splashing and serious burns.

In a 125 mL Erlenmeyer flask equipped with a magnetic stir-bar, cool 12 mL of concentrated sulfuric acid to 0° C and then and 6.1 g of methyl benzoate. Again cool the mixture to 0° C and begin stirring. Now add dropwise, using a Pasteur pipette, a cooled mixture of 4 mL of concentrated sulfuric acid and 4 mL of concentrated nitric acid. During the addition of the acids, stir the mixture and maintain the temperature between 5° C - 15° C.

When all of the nitric acid has been added, warm the mixture to room temperature. After 15 minutes at room temperature, pour the mixture slowly on to 50 g of cracked ice in a 250 mL beaker. Isolate the solid product by suction filtration using a small Büchner funnel and wash well with water, then with two 10 mL portions of ice-cold methanol. A small sample is saved for melting point determination. The remainder is weighed and

71

crystallized from an equal weight of methanol.

Questions

1) Draw the arenium ion that would result if the nitronium ion would have added to the *para-* position instead of the *meta-* position.

2) Draw all resonance structures of the arenium ion that you wrote in Question 1.

3) Compare the resonance structures from Question 2 to those in **Figure 3**. Why would the reaction prefer the pathway to the *meta-* product versus the pathway leading to the *para-* product?

4) Why does only one nitro group add to the methyl benzoate?

Friedel-Crafts Alkylation of Dimethoxybenzene

Reaction

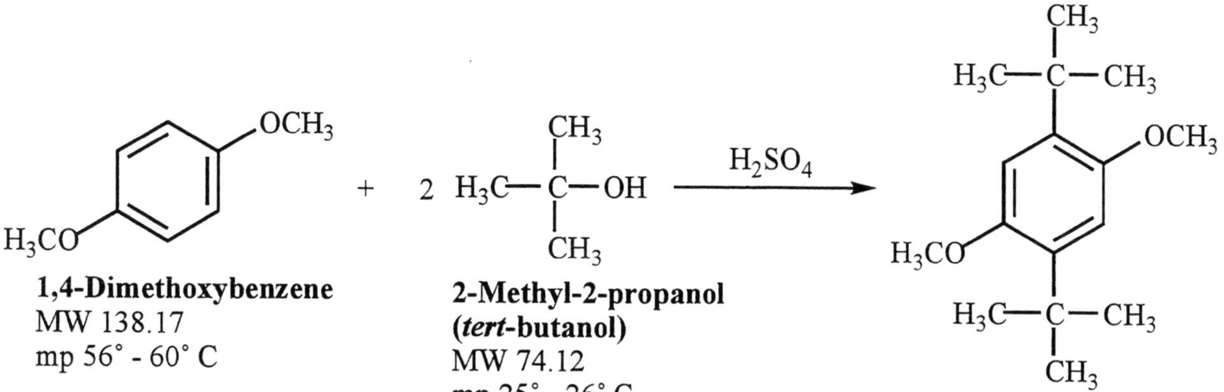

1,4-Dimethoxybenzene
MW 138.17
mp 56° - 60° C

2-Methyl-2-propanol
(***tert*-butanol**)
MW 74.12
mp 25° - 26° C
bp 83° C
d 0.775

1,4-Di-*tert*-butyl-2,5-dimethoxybenzene
MW 248.17
mp 102° - 104° C

Discussion

In this lab you will be performing an electrophilic aromatic substitution reaction on a di-substituted benzene ring. Since the benzene ring is stabilized by aromaticity the pi-system is less reactive as compared to the pi-system of an alkene. For this reason, a very strong electrophile will be needed in order to cause a reaction to occur. The electrophile used in this experiment is 3° carbocation (**1**) which is formed from the reaction of *t*-butyl alcohol and sulfuric acid (**Figure 1**).

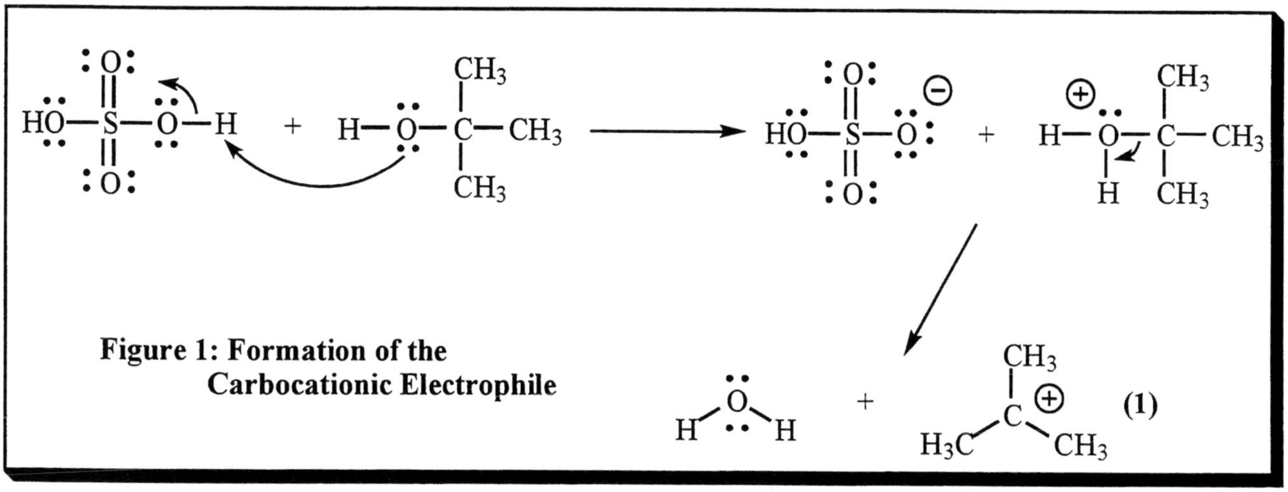

Figure 1: Formation of the Carbocationic Electrophile

Once the electrophilic carbocation is formed, the aromatic ring will nucleophilically attack **1** to form the arenium ion (**2**) (**Figure 2**). Resonance forms of the arenium ion are shown in **Figure 3**. Since the benzene ring was substituted with an two ether moieties, the position at which the *t*-butyl group will add to becomes important. An ether substituent is referred to as an **Activating Group**. Activating groups direct an incoming electrophile to the *ortho-* or *-para* positions relative to itself. Deprotonation of the arenium ion then restores the aromatic character of the ring. The entire reaction would then have to repeat itself in order for the second *t*-butyl group to be added.

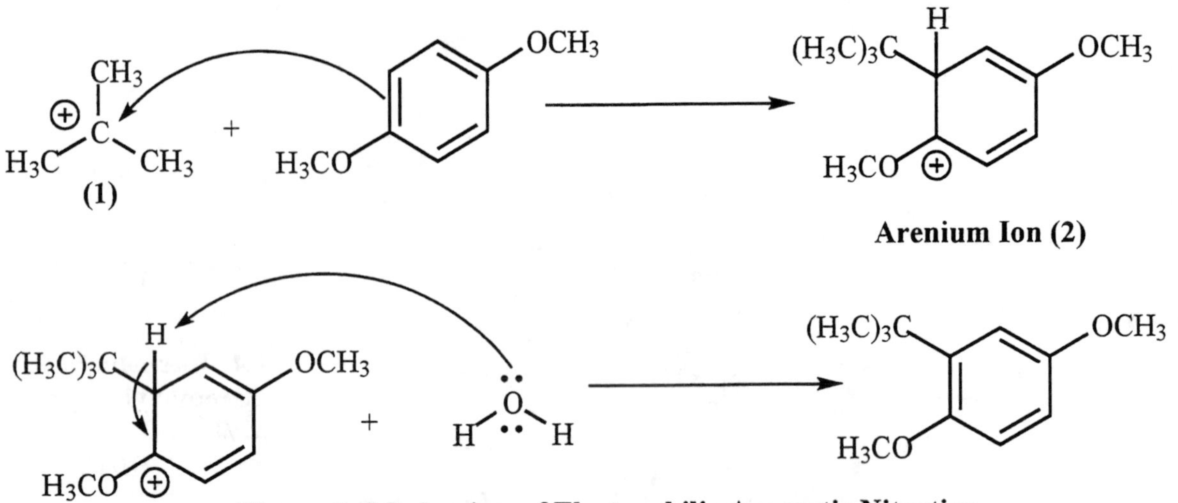

Figure 2: Mechanism of Electrophilic Aromatic Nitration

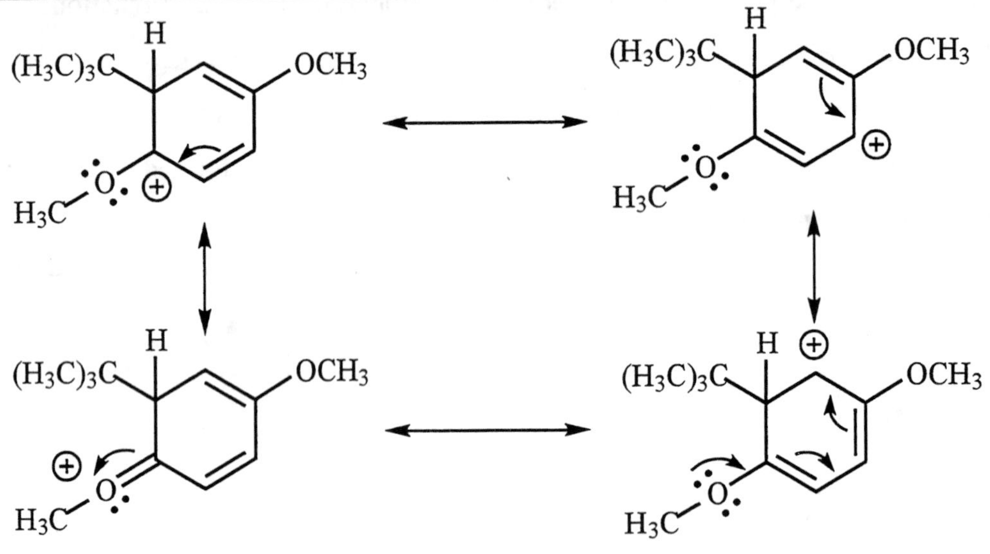

Figure 3: Resonance Forms of the Arenium Ion

Procedure

Warning! You will be using concentrated concentrated Sulfuric Acid. Please reread your safety guidelines about handling concentrated acids. Make sure that your glassware is completely dry before adding the acid in order to prevent a vigorous, exothermic reaction which could cause acid splashing and serious burns.

Clamp a 125 mL Erlenmeyer flask, equipped with a stir bar, in an ice bath on top of the magnetic stirrer.

To the 125 mL Erlenmeyer flask, add 6 g of 1,4-dimethoxybenzene (hydroquinone dimethyl ether), 10 mL of *t*-butyl alcohol and 20 mL of acetic acid. Cool the mixture, with stirring, to the 3° C - 5° C range. **Do not use your thermometer as a stirring rod and do not leave your thermometer in the solution unsupported.**

While you are waiting for the solution in the 125 mL Erlenmeyer to cool, measure 30 mL of concentrated sulfuric acid into a 50 mL Erlenmeyer flask. **Make sure that your glassware is completely dry before adding the acid in order to prevent a vigorous, exothermic reaction which could cause acid splashing and serious burns.** Clamp the 50 mL Erlenmeyer containing the acid into an ice bath and cool to the 3° C - 5° C range. Clamp an iron ring above the 125 mL Erlenmeyer and place a separatory funnel in the iron ring so that the tip of the funnel extends into the 125 mL Erlenmeyer. Add the cold concentrated sulfuric acid to the separatory funnel. **Make sure that your separatory funnel is closed before you add your acid.**

Slowly add the cold concentrated sulfuric acid to the solution in the 125 mL Erlenmeyer flask. Adjust the drop rate so that the addition of all of the acid takes about 10 minutes. Solid product may begin to form during your addition. If the stirrer becomes stuck, unclamp the 125 mL Erlenmeyer and swirl gently in the ice bath to mix the material. Check the temperature periodically, the temperature should not exceed 20° C - 25° C. Once the addition is complete, stir (or swirl) the mixture for an additional 5 minutes and then cool the material in the ice bath.

Add 20 g of ice to the 125 mL Erlenmeyer in order to dilute the acidic solution, and then add water to bring the level of the solution to the 125 mL mark on the flask. Cool the solution for an additional 10 minutes and then collect the product through vacuum filtration using your large Büchner funnel. **(Note: Use two pieces of filter paper because the strongly acidic solution may cause the paper to tear.)** Wash the filter cake with a three 30 mL portions of cold methanol.

Place the moist material in a 125 mL Erlenmeyer flask and add 15 mL of dichloromethane. Once the material is dissolved, add anhydrous sodium sulfate (a full scupula's worth) to the solution and swirl for 5 minutes. Carefully decant the solution into another 125 mL Erlenmeyer flask followed by 30 mL of methanol. Heat the solution on your hot plate until the level is approximately at the 30 mL mark. Allow the solution to cool to room temperature. Product crystals should begin to precipitate out of solution. Cool the mixture in an ice bath for 15 minutes before collecting the product by vacuum filtration.

Questions

1) Why did the two *t*-butyl groups substitute 1,4 from each other? Why didn't they substitute 1,2 or 1,3 from each other on the aromatic ring?

2) Could 2-methylpropene be used in the reaction instead of *t*-butyl alcohol?

3) Could *t-butyl* chloride and aluminum trichloride be used in the reaction instead of *t*-butyl alcohol.

Dibenzylacetone via the Aldol Condensation

Reaction

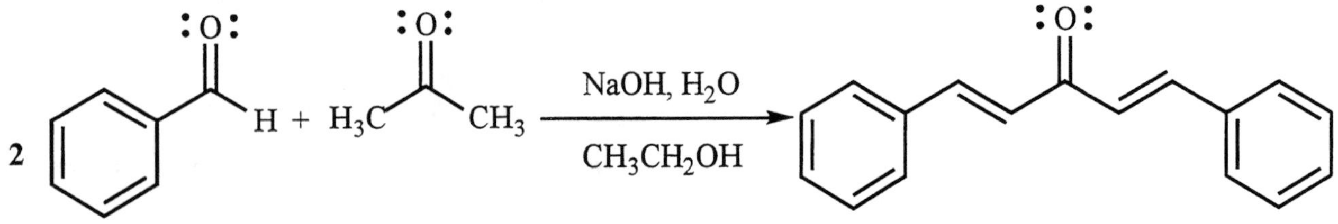

Benzaldehyde
MW = 106.13
bp 178° C
Density = 1.04

Acetone
MW = 58.08
bp 56° C
Density = 0.79

Dibenzylacetone
MW = 234.30
mp 110° C - 111° C

Discussion

The reaction that will be performed in this lab involves a mixed aldol condensation (also known as the Claisen-Schmidt reaction.) Only one of the two reagents that contain a carbonyl can be enolized. Acetone contains α-hydrogens that can be deprotonated by an appropriate base, while benzaldehyde contains no α-hydrogens. There is the possibility that acetone could undergo a self-condensation (self-aldol), but it turns out that most aldehydes are more reactive than ketones, therefore allowing the reaction to occur with reasonable efficiency. The mechanism of the reaction is shown in **Figure 1**.

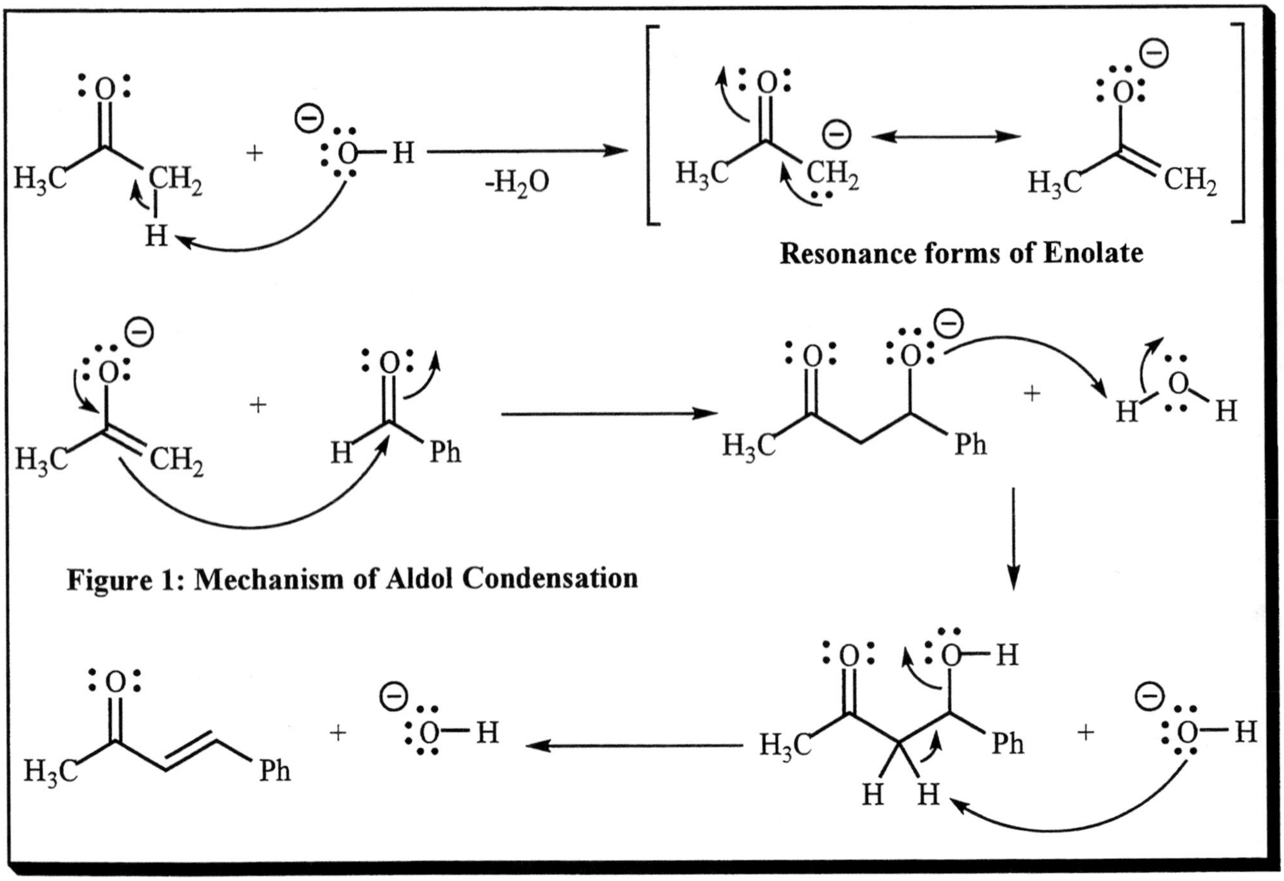

Figure 1: Mechanism of Aldol Condensation

Procedure

Mix 0.05 moles of benzaldehyde with the theoretical quantity of acetone in a 50 mL beaker. Add of this mixture to a 500 mL Erlenmeyer flask that contains 5 g of sodium hydroxide, 40 mL of ethanol, and 50 mL of water. Stir the mixture for 15 minutes and then add the remaining half of of the aldehyde/ketone mixture. Rinse the container with 10 mL of ethanol to complete the transfer. Stir the mixture for 30 minutes.

Collect the product by vacuum filtration with your large Büchner funnel. Once all of the liquid has been suctioned through the funnel, carefully break the vacuum at your filter flask (**Break the vacuum first, then turn it off**) and add 50 mL of water on top of your product. Reapply the vacuum to remove the water. Repeat this procedure four more times. Finally, press the product as dry as possible on the filter (with vacuum) by first applying a piece of filter paper on top and then pressing down with a cork. Recrystallize your material from ethanol using 10 mL of ethanol for each 4 g of product.

Questions

1) Draw the product that would result if acetone had condensed with itself instead of benzaldehyde.

2) The product is shown to have the trans- / trans- stereochemistry around the double bonds. Draw all of the stereoisomers of the product. Are any of these isomers expected to be thermodynamically more stable? Explain.

3) How would you change the reaction conditions if you only wanted benzylacetone as your product?

Identification of an Unknown Aldehyde

Reaction

2,4-Dinitrophenylhydrazine
MW 198.14

2,4-Dinitrophenylhydrazone

Discussion

Identification and characterization of the structures of unknown substances are an important part of organic chemistry. It is sometimes possible to establish the structure of a compound on the basis of spectra alone (IR, UV, MassSpec, NMR), but these spectra must usually be supplemented with other information about the unknown: physical state, elementary analysis, solubility, and confirmatory tests for functional groups. This lab will provide the IR and ^{1}H NMR spectra for unknown aldehyde. In addition to evaluating the supplied spectra, you will also need to perform a chemical test on the unknown to aid in your structure determination. The test will involve the formation of a hydrazone derivative. The hydrazone derivative will have a distinctive melting point that can be cross referenced on the supplied table of melting points of hydrazone derivatives. Specifically, you will be converting your aldehyde into the 2,4-dinitrophenylhydrazone (**Scheme 1**).

Procedure

You will be assigned a partner and an unknown. Be sure to write down the number of the unknown in your notebook. The spectra corresponding to your unknown aldehyde can be found in **Appendix III**. To 10 mL of the stock solution of 2,4-dinitrophenylhydrazine in phosphoric acid add about 0.1 g of the compound to be tested. Ten milliliters of the 0.1 M 2,4-dinitrophenylhydrazine solution contains 1 millimole (mmol) of the reagent. If the compound to be tested has a molecular weight of 100 then 0.1 g is 1 mmol. Warm the reaction mixture for a 10 minutes in a water bath and then let crystallization proceed. Collect the product by suction filtration on your large Büchner funnel, wash the crystals with a large amount of water to remove the phosphoric acid, press a piece of moist litmus paper on to the crystals, and if they are acidic wash them with more water. Press the product as dry as possible between sheets of filter paper and recrystallize from ethanol. Occasionally a high-molecular weight derivative won't dissolve in a reasonable quantity (20 mL) of ethanol. In that case cool the hot suspension and isolate the crystals by suction filtration. The boiling ethanol treatment removes impurities so that an accurate melting point can be obtained on the isolated material.

Scheme 1: Mechanism of Hydrazone Formation

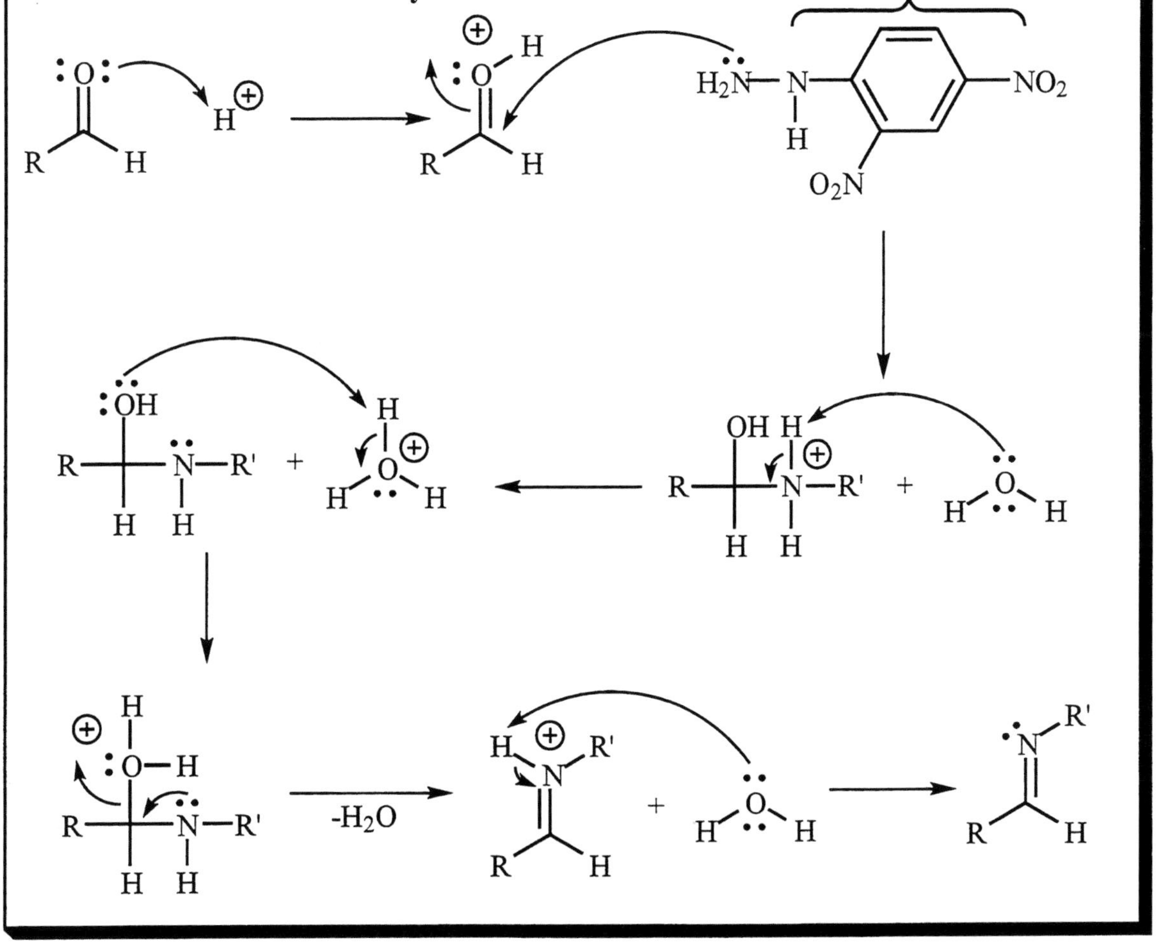

Identification of an Unknown Organic Compound

Discussion

Identification and characterization of the structures of unknown substances are an important part of organic chemistry. It is sometimes possible to establish the structure of a compound on the basis of spectra alone (IR, UV, MassSpec, NMR), but these spectra must usually be supplemented with other information about the unknown: physical state, elementary analysis, solubility, and confirmatory tests for functional groups. This lab will provide the IR, ^{13}C NMR and ^1H NMR spectra for unknown organic compound. In addition to evaluating the supplied spectra, you will also need to perform several chemical tests on the unknown to aid in your structure determination. During the next couple of weeks your laboratory work will be an independent experience in solving organic "unknowns". You will be given about 1.0 g of each compound you are to identify; your compounds will be selected to be different from those of any other student in your section. You may think that we will have a difficult time finding that many different organic compounds; however it is not hard to find them as there are over five million different organic compounds known at this time. At least 120,000 of them are rather common. In principle, your unknown could be any of these more common organic compounds. In practice however, most of the unknowns we hand out are purchased from a couple of chemical manufacturers whose combined output is a mere 15,000 or so compounds. How does a lab worker go about narrowing down a search from 15,000 possibilities to just one choice?

This is precisely the kind of problem a physician faces when he begins to diagnose a patient's condition. A task so complex requires a plan which classifies the unknown into one of a reasonable number of categories. One such set of categories we have for organic compounds is functional groups. If we can figure out what functional group our unknown contains, we can then make use of the physical properties of the compound such as its melting point or boiling point and refractive index. For instance, it does little good to know that an unknown boils at 200° C (hundreds of organic compounds have the same boiling point), but if you know that it is a ketone which boils at 200±2° C the choices are narrowed down to less than ten compounds, and a second physical constant may very well point to a single possibility. So we want to test our unknowns with reagents that will give positive tests for specific functional groups.

It will not be necessary to perform a chemical test for all possible functional groups however. You will begin the identification process by first determining the acid/base and solubility behavior of your unknown. By this process, you will be able to narrow your search down to a few possible functional groups. The solubility testing protocols are outlined in and elaborated on in your text. After you have classified your unknown by its solubility and acid/base characteristics, you will then choose the appropriate functional group tests (also described in your text) in order to confirm your suspicions. A selection of known organic compounds will be available so you can check to see if you have done the functional group test correctly. In conjunction with the solubility tests, you should also be evaluating your spectral data in order to arrive at the correct conclusions. Once you have determined the identity of your unknown, neatly fill in the data sheet and turn it in to your instructor.

By this time in the course, you have acquired all of the skills and tools necessary to perform this lab independently. The instructor will not indicate whether you have done something correctly or not. The instructor will be available for general consultation only.

Procedure:

An unknown will be assigned to each group. Be sure to write down the number of your unknown in your notebook. The spectra corresponding to your unknown are contained in **Appendix IV**. You should perform the solubility tests outlined in **Appendix V** in order to narrow your search. If your compound is a solid, obtain its melting point. If your compound is an oil, obtain its refractive index. Once you have narrowed your search and you may begin to do chemical tests for functional groups. The chemical tests for each type of functional group are given in **Appendix V**. Check with your instructor before performing any of the chemical tests.

Once you have identified the unknown compound, fill in the data sheet and turn it in to your instructor.

The Perkin Reaction: Synthesis of α-Phenylcinnamic Acid

Reaction

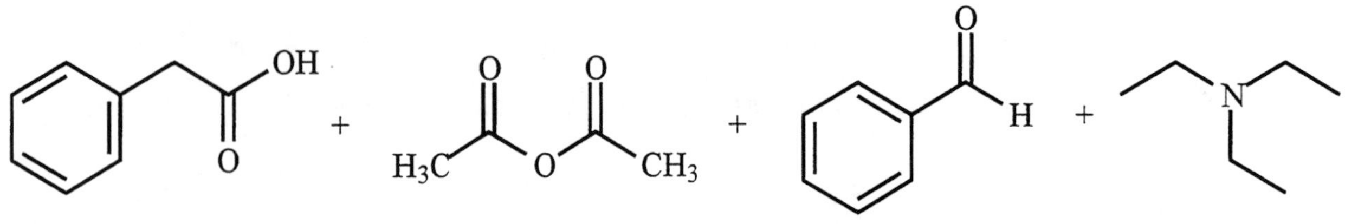

Phenylacetic Acid
MW 136.14
mp 77° C
bp 265° C

Acetic Anhydride
MW 102.09
bp 138° - 140° C

Benzaldehyde
MW 106.12
density 1.046
bp 179° C

Triethylamine
MW 101.19
density 0.729
bp 89.5° C

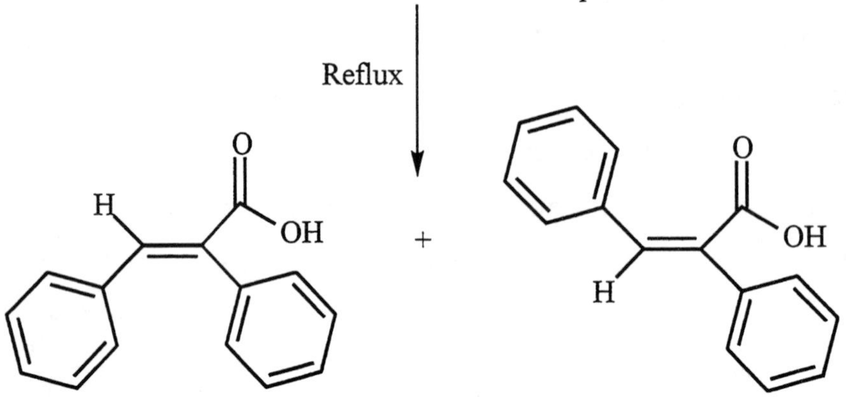

Reflux

E-α-Phenylcinnamic Acid
MW 224.25
mp 174° C
pK$_a$ 6.1

Z-α-Phenylcinnamic Acid
MW 224.25
mp 138° C
pK$_a$ 4.8

Discussion

The reaction of phenylacetic acid (**1**) with benzaldehyde (**2**) to produce a mixture of α-carboxylic derivatives of Z- and E-stilbene, a form of aldol condensation known as the Perkin reaction, is effected by heating a mixture of the components with acetic anhydride (**3**) and triethylamine (**4**). In the course of the reaction the phenylacetic acid is probably resent in both as anion and as the mixed anhydride resulting from equilibration with acetic anhydride (**Scheme 1**). The mixed anhydride (**5**) then undergoes an Aldol condensation / Dehydration sequence with benzaldehyde to yield the α-phenylcinnamic acid products (**Scheme 2**). E-Stilbene (**6**) is a by-product of the condensation, but experiment has shown that neither the E- nor Z-acid undergoes decarboxylation under the conditions of the experiment (**Scheme 3**).

At the end of the reaction the α-phenylcinnamic acids are present in part as the neutral mixed anhydrides, but these can be hydrolyzed by addition of excess hydrochloric acid. The organic material is then taken up in ether and the acids extracted with alkali. Neutralization with acetic acid (pK$_a$ = 4.76) then causes precipitation of only the less acidic E-acid. The Z-acid separates on addition of hydrochloric acid.

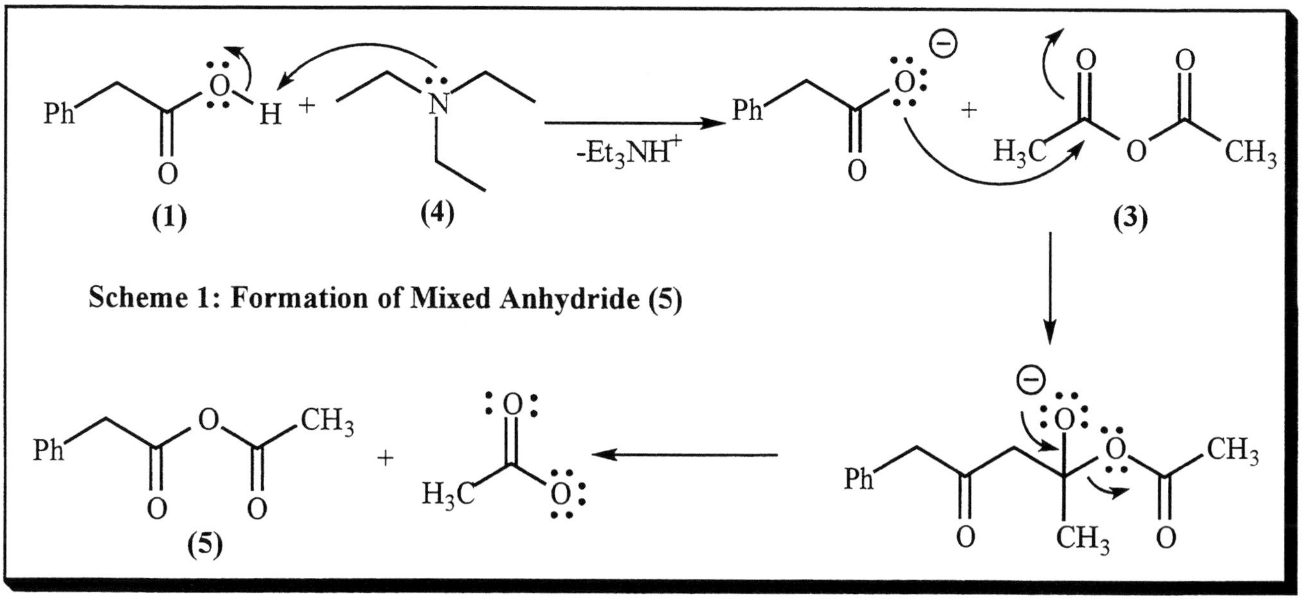

Scheme 1: Formation of Mixed Anhydride (5)

Whereas Z-stilbene is less stable and lower melting than E-stilbene, the reverse is true of the α-carboxylic acids, and in this preparation the more stable, higher melting E-acid is the predominant product. Evidently the steric interference between the carboxyl and phenyl groups in the Z-acid is greater than that between the two phenyl groups in the E-acid. Steric hindrances also evident from the fact that the Z-acid is not subject to Fischer esterification (ethanol and an acid catalyst) whereas the E-acid is.

Procedure

Warning! You will be using concentrated Hydrochloric Acid. Please reread your safety guidelines about handling concentrated acids. Measure into a 25 mL round bottomed flask 2.5 g of phenylacetic acid, 3 mL of benzaldehyde, 2 mL of triethylamine, and 2 mL of acetic anhydride. Add a water cooled condenser and a boiling chip and reflux the mixture for 35 minutes. Cool the yellow melt, add 4 mL of concentrated hydrochloric acid, and swirl, whereupon the mixture sets to a stiff paste. Add ether, warm to dissolve the bulk of the solid using hot (not boiling) water, and transfer to a separatory funnel with the use of more ether. Wash the ethereal solution twice with water and then extract it with a mixture of 25 mL of water and 5 mL of 10% sodium hydroxide solution. Acidify the combined, colorless, alkaline extract to pH 6 by adding 5 mL of acetic acid and collect the E-acid that precipitates. You may wash the crystals with cold water. **Be sure to save the filtrate.** Crystallize the E-acid by dissolving it in 8 mL of ether, adding 8 mL of low boiling petroleum ether, heating briefly to the boiling point, and then letting the solution stand.

Addition of 5 mL of concentrated HCl to the aqueous filtrate from the previous step produces a cloudy emulsion, which, on standing for about one-half hour, coagulates into crystals of the Z-acid.

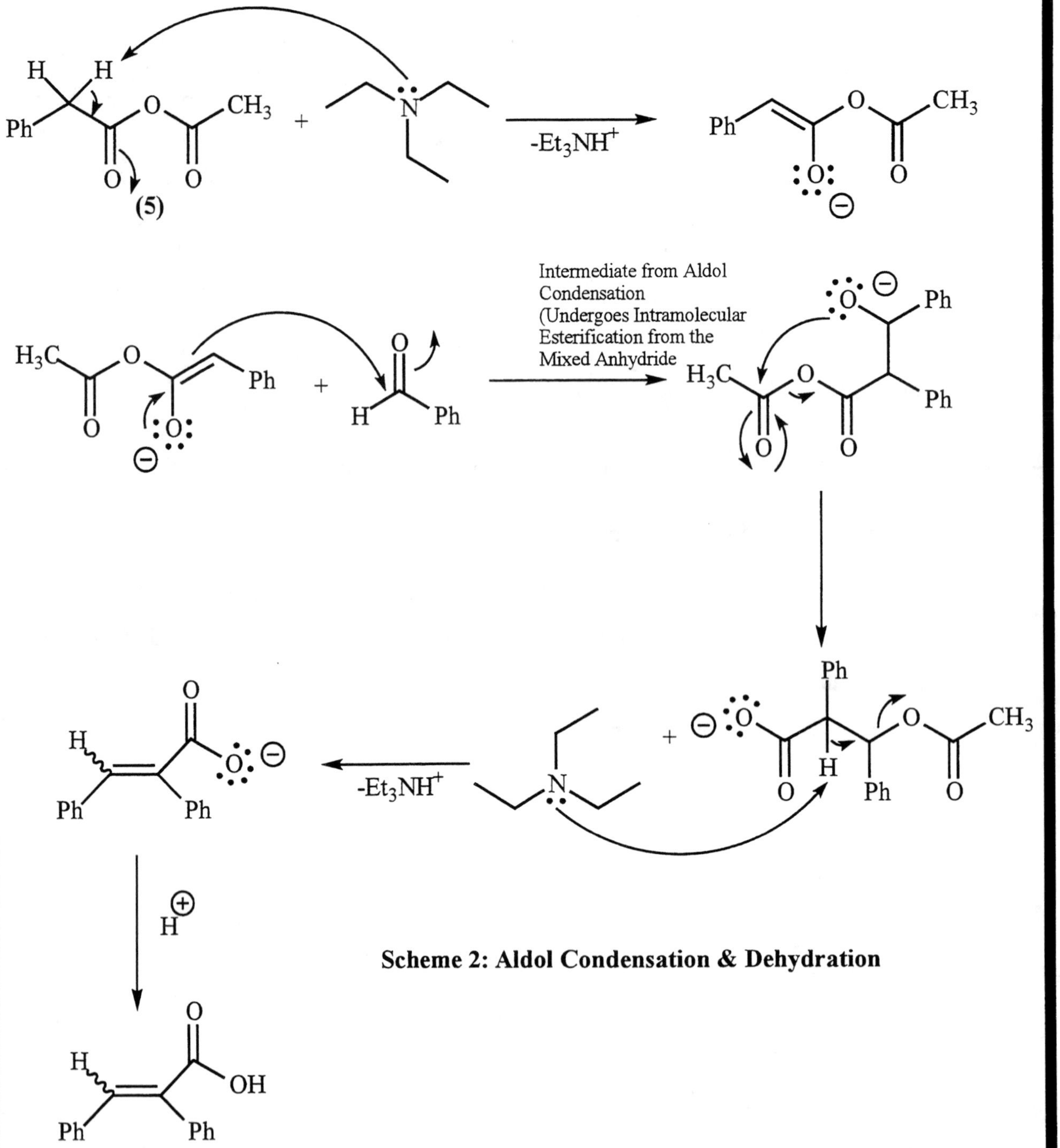

(5)
-Et3NH+
Intermediate from Aldol
Condensation
(Undergoes Intramolecular
Esterification from the
Mixed Anhydride
-Et3NH+

Scheme 2: Aldol Condensation & Dehydration

Scheme 3: Formation of E-Stilbene (6) via Decarboxylation

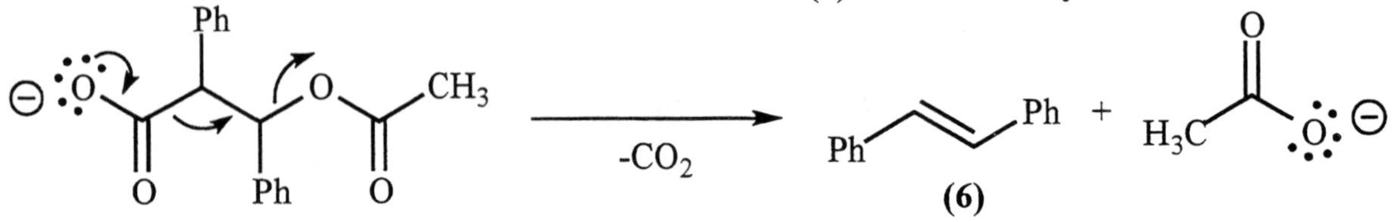

-CO2
(6)

Synthesis of Lidocaine

Reaction

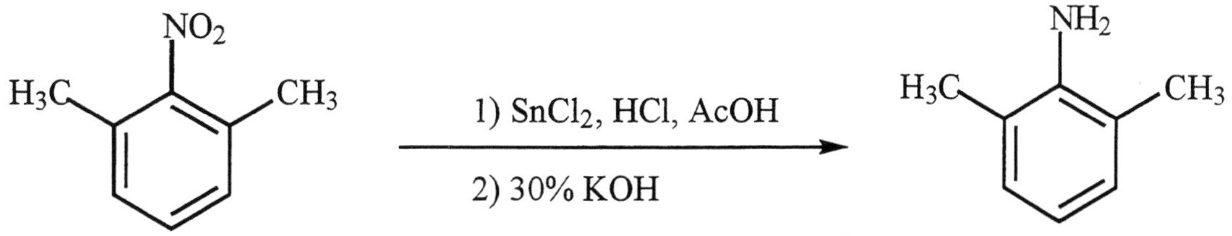

1,3-Dimethyl-2-nitrobenzene
(2-Nitro-*m*-xylene)
MW 151.17
mp 14° - 16° C
d 1.112

2,6-Dimethylaniline
(2,6-xylidine)
MW 121.18
mp 12° - 12° C
d 0.984

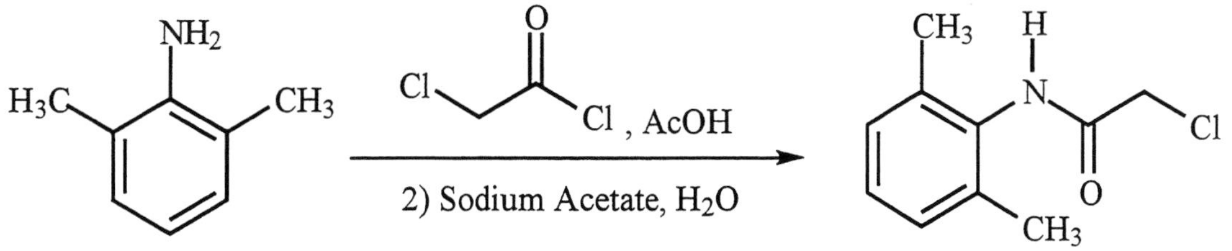

α—Chloro-2,6-dimethylacetanilide

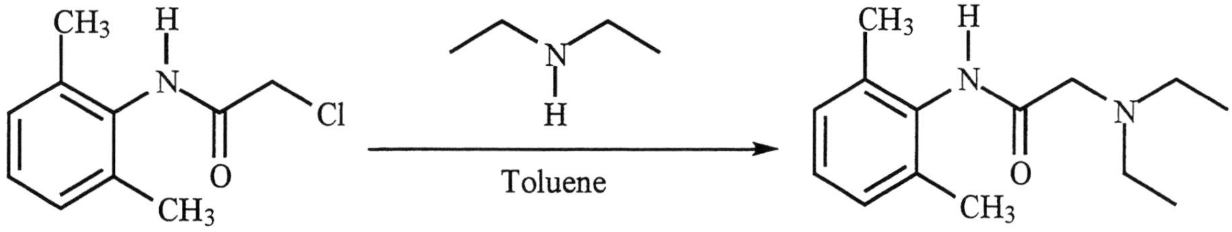

Lidocaine
2-(Diethylamino)-N-
(2,6-dimethylphenyl)-acetamide
MW 234.34
mp 66° - 69° C

Discussion

Lidocaine, probably the most commonly used local anesthetic in the world, is a member of the "-caine family" of local anesthetics, all of which are modeled on the single natural member of the family, cocaine. The development of the series of local anesthetics from their natural progenitor, cocaine, is in many ways typical of the stages of drug discovery and development. Cocaine was used by the native peoples of the Andes for millennia as a painkiller and CNS stimulant. It is interesting that Andean people usually smear the coca leaf with lime before chewing it; this results in extraction of the cocaine as a free base, releasing it quickly for extraction into saliva. In the nineteenth century European observers deduced the presence of an alkaloid in coca leaf and successfully isolated cocaine, a drug that was later to gain currency and popularity in the works of Sigmund Freud, Arthur Conan Doyle, and the Coca-Cola company.

After the addictive nature of cocaine was discovered, physicians and chemists attempted to prepare analogs which retained its analgesic and CNS stimulative properties without the addictive effects. The basic postulate for this effort was the theory that each action of the drug is caused by some particular structural feature of the molecule. If this idea is true, then one could conceivably create a compound which retained the beneficial parts of the molecular structure, but not the negative features. This idea, that the several actions of a drug molecule derive from different features of the molecular structure, is only occasionally true, but it has proved to be largely true in the series of -caine analgesics and anesthetics.

As you can see in **Figure 1**, the structure of lidocaine written in conventional form (to the right of the cocaine structure) does not resemble the bicyclic form of cocaine at all. However, if the lidocaine structure is redrawn so as to emphasize the steric features around the 3° amine and the distance from the amine group to the aromatic moiety, a resemblance to cocaine emerges. Over the years the efforts of many chemists and drug companies have identified a wide variety of molecules with analgesic and CNS stimulating agents of which novocain (procaine), tetracaine, and benzocaine are a few examples (**Figure 2**). Some members of this series have other side effects- including toxicity and stimulation of cardiac activity. The main variable features of this family of drugs are the spacing between the 3° amine unit and the polarity of the carbonyl group proximate to the benzene ring. It is postulated that all these drugs fit into a single type of physiological "active site" or receptor located somewhere in the CNS system. The exact manner of their fit to the site is thought to dictate the nature of the response- that is, whether that particular agent is a strong or weak cardiac stimulant, or a possesses a long or short analgesic effect at a particular concentration.

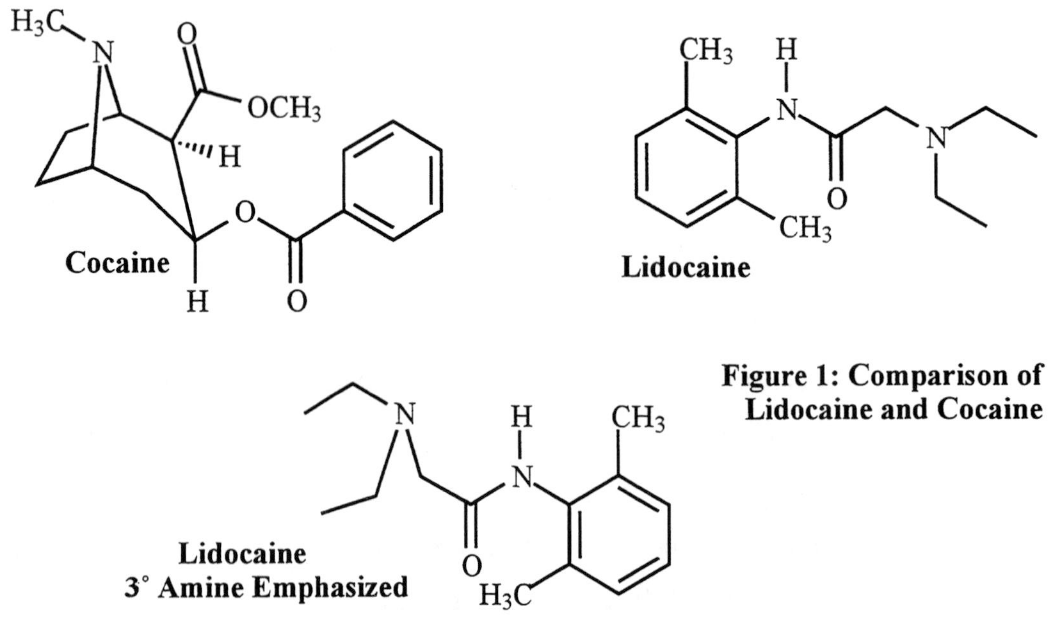

Figure 1: Comparison of Lidocaine and Cocaine

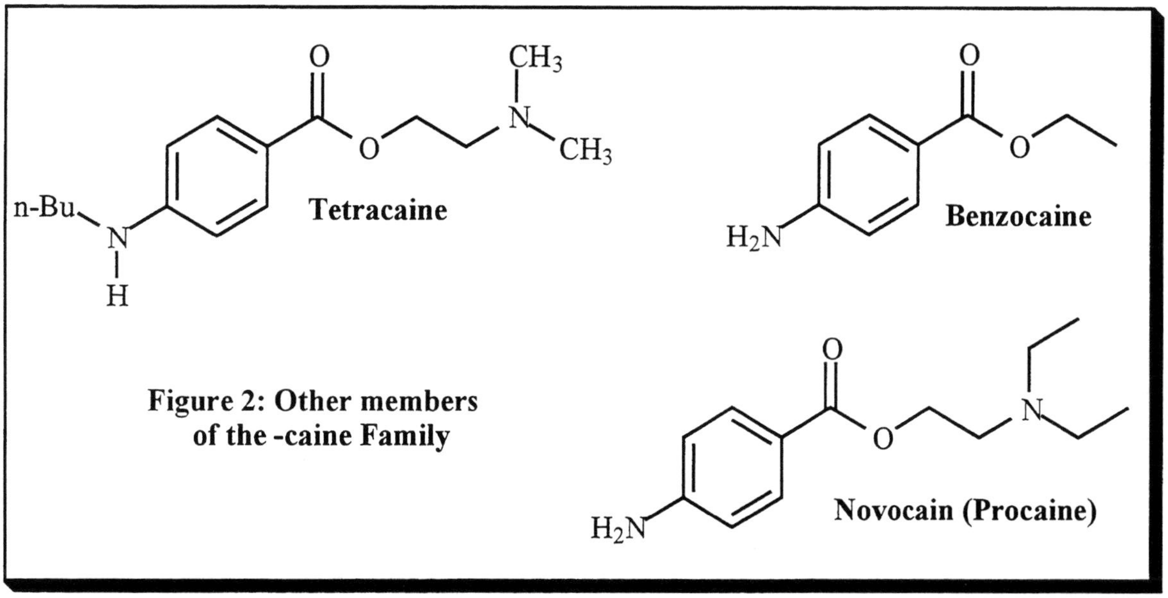

Figure 2: Other members of the -caine Family

During the Lidocaine synthesis itself, you will carry out three separate transformation. Since the product from each of the first two reactions will be used as the starting material for the next reaction in the sequence, care should be taken in order to maximize the yield at each step. The first reaction involves the reduction of the nitro group to the amine. In this step, Sn(II) will be used as the reducing agent becoming oxidized to Sn(IV) in the process. The most important thing to realize in this step is that the reaction product is actually the ammonium salt. In order to isolate the amine, also known as the free base, it is necessary to treat the salt with base (**Figure 3**). It is also important to realize that the ammonium salt, being polar, will be soluble in aqueous solvent. Once deprotonated however, the free base, being less polar, will become soluble in organic solvents such as ether. The second step involves the formation of the amide from the amine (**Figure 4**.) Amides are not nearly as basic as amines, so we will not have to worry about the materials aqueous solubility as a function of pH as we did in the first step. The last step is a simple S_N2 type of substitution of the chloride by the 2° amine (**Figure 5**.) Since the product is an amine, we will again have to be aware of the pH of the solution containing the product.

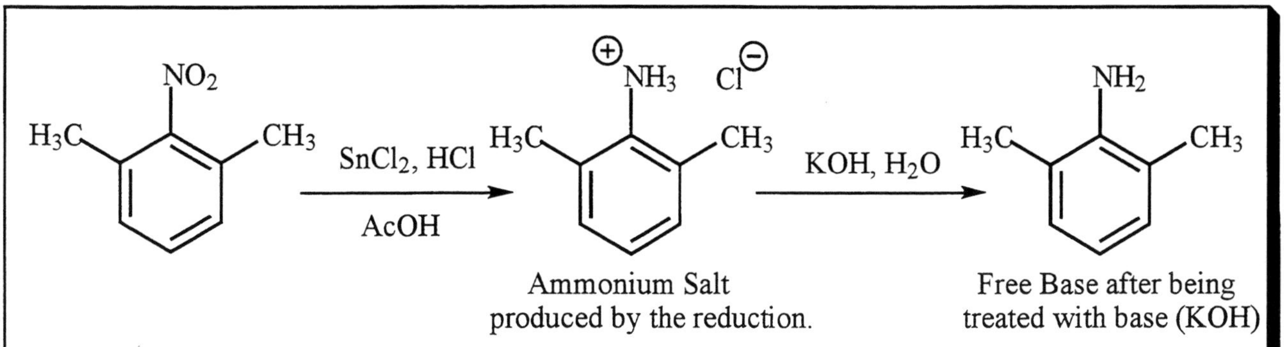

Figure 3: Reduction of Nitro Group to Amine

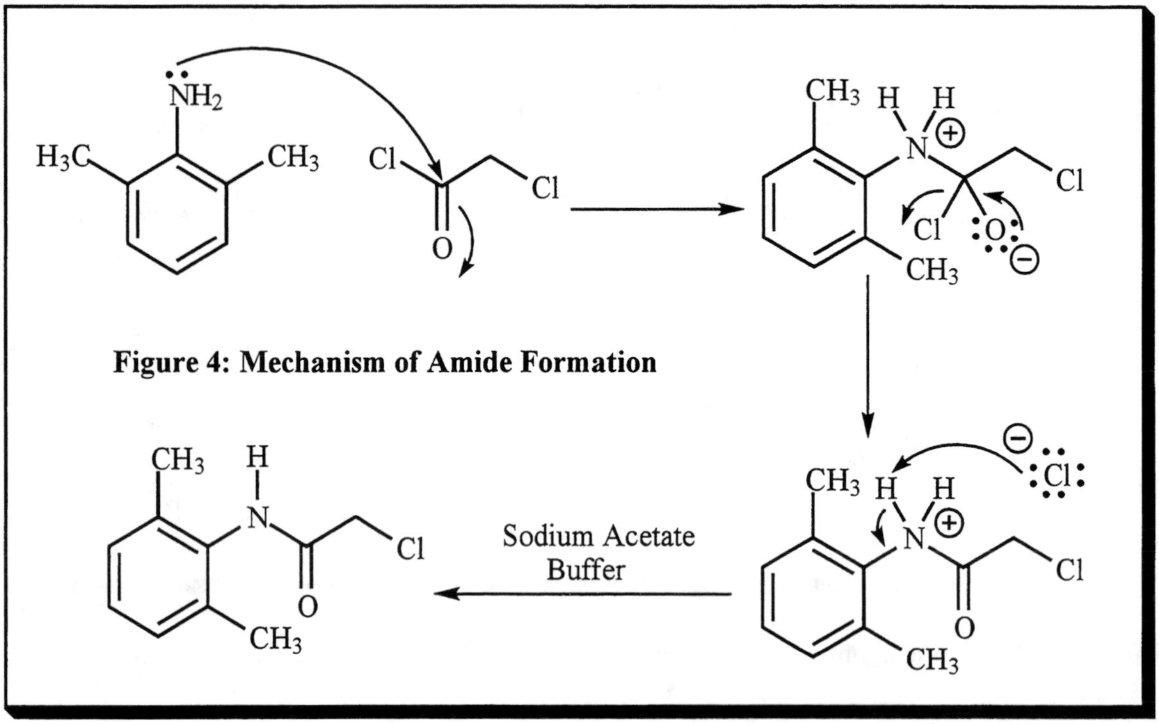

Figure 4: Mechanism of Amide Formation

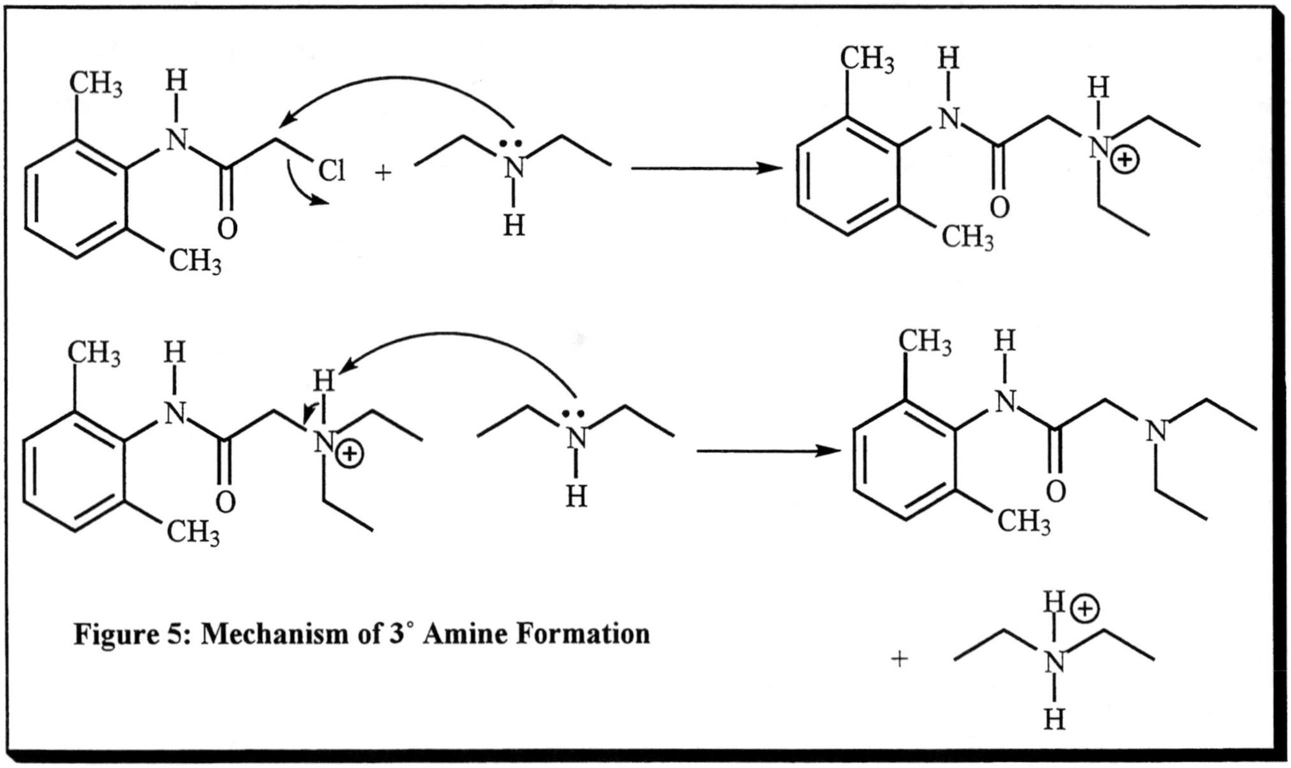

Figure 5: Mechanism of 3° Amine Formation

Procedure

A) Nitro reduction

2,6-Dimethylnitrobenzene (5.00 g, 33.1 mmols) are dissolved in 50 mL of glacial acetic acid in a 250 mL Erlenmeyer and set aside. Tin[II] chloride dihydrate (23.0 g, 100.0 mmols) is completely dissolved in 40 mL of concentrated HCl in a separate beaker or flask, then added in one portion to the nitroxylidene. The combined solution is stirred briefly then allowed to stand for fifteen minutes. After the reaction time has elapsed, cool the mixture to ice bath temperature (use a thermometer to check) and collect the mixture of solid tin salts and solid 2,6-dimethylanilinium hydrochloride on a large Büchner filter. The tin salts are removed by replacing the moist crystalline mass in the Erlenmeyer flask, adding 20 mL of water, and then adding 30% KOH solution with stirring until the mixture is thoroughly basic to litmus; about 45 mL will be required. Use the ice bath to cool the two phase mixture to 10° C, transfer the mixture to your separatory funnel, and extract with three 20 mL portions of diethyl ether, combining the ether extracts. Dry the combined extracts over anhydrous potassium carbonate, then decant into a dry, tared 250 mL beaker containing two boiling chips, and remove the ether cautiously using your steam bath. Weigh the beaker after evaporation and determine the rough weight of 2,6-dimethyl aniline produced.

B) Amine to α-chloro amide.

Dilute the crude 2,6-dimethylaniline in the beaker with 25 mL of glacial acetic acid; then add chloroacetyl chloride (3.7 g, 2.70 mL, 32.7 mmols) to the solution. **Caution! Chloroacetyl chloride is a potent lachrymator; obtain it from the hood and use immediately! Do not sniff the material!** Warm the solution on the hotplate to 50° C, then remove from heat and add a solution of 5.0 g of sodium acetate dissolved in 100 mL of water to buffer and precipitate the amide. Cool in the ice bath to 5° - 10° C, then filter the abundant, off white precipitate of α-chloro-2,6-dimethylacetanilide on a Büchner funnel, air dry, and leave until next period.

C) α-Chloro amide to Lidocaine.

Caution! You have invested one period already in this material, and the acid/base transfers involved in this procedure make it likely that a careless operator who does not understand amine acid-base chemistry will discard his or her product. Before doing this part of the procedure, be sure you understand whether amines are soluble in aqueous solutions in their conjugate acid or conjugate base forms. Weigh the α-chloro-2,6-dimethylacetanilide produced last period to two decimal places and calculate how many moles of it you have obtained. After removing a melting point sample of it, place the dry product in your 100 mL round bottom flask (powder funnel.) Measure three moles of diethylamine (density d= 0.71g/mL) for every one mole of alpha chloro-2,6-dimethylacetanilide you produced, and add it to the flask; also add 35 mL of dry toluene and a boiling chip. Put a reflux condenser in place and boil the mixture for 90 minutes.

After 90 minutes of actual boiling, cool the mixture to room temperature and filter through a dry Büchner funnel in order to remove any crystals of diethylammonium chloride that have formed. Now use a separatory funnel to extract the filtrate with three 20 mL portions of 3M HCl (the dilute hydrochloric acid on the desk top is 6M.) (Where is the organic product? Does it remain in the organic phase?) Combine the aqueous acidic layers in a 250 mL Erlenmeyer and add 30% KOH until the solution is strongly basic to litmus. Clean your separatory funnel so that no traces of acid remain and extract the aqueous suspension with three 20 mL portions of pentane. Obtain good deionized water and check its pH to ensure that it is not acidic. Use this water to extract the combined pentane layers six times with 15 mL portions of water. Dry the pentane layer over anhydrous potassium carbonate, and decant the dried layer from the K_2CO_3 into a dry, tared 100 mL beaker containing two boiling chips. Use a steam bath to carefully distill the pentane off, swirling at the end until all boiling ceases. Cool the oil in an ice bath to crystallize your lidocaine. Weigh, and determine the melting point.

Questions

1) After you had reduced the nitro group with the $SnCl_2$, it was necessary to treat the crude product with 30% KOH in order to isolate the amine. Why was the base necessary?

2) Draw the product from the reaction of Lidocaine and HCl. What solvent would the product be soluble in, ether or water?

Anomeric Glucose Esters: α- & β-Glucopyranose Pentaacetates

Reaction

D-Glucopyranose (α & β isomers)
MW 180.16
mp 112° - 113° C

D-Glucopyranose pentaacetate
(α & β isomers) MW 390.34
mp 130° - 132° C

Discussion

Since monosaccharides are replete with polar functional groups, monosaccharides themselves and their simple derivatives are usually quite soluble in water and not at all soluble in less polar organic solvents. This makes it difficult to design good undergraduate experimental procedures involving sugars, since almost every product one can prepare is too soluble in water to crystallize from an aqueous solution, and too insoluble in less polar solvents to dissolve in and crystallize from them. The following procedure, however, takes advantage of the lower water solubility and higher molecular weight of the hemiacetal monosaccharide pentaacetates in order to prepare and isolate anomeric D-glucose derivatives.

Scheme 1 summarizes the pertinent relationships between the reacting mixture of D-Glucose anomers and the anomeric pentaacetate products. Both alpha and beta D-Glucopyranose react directly with acetic anhydride to produce the alpha and beta-D-Glucose pentaacetates, respectively. Each reaction can be catalyzed by either sodium acetate or zinc chloride. However, the rate of acylation of the α-D-Glucopyranose anomer is much slower than the corresponding reaction of the β-D-Glucopyranose anomer. The reason the alpha anomer reacts more slowly is that acylation of the -OH on the C-1 carbon (the anomeric carbon) is hindered by steric factors. Since the alpha C-1 -OH is axially oriented, it is more sterically hindered and reacts slower than the anomeric C-1 -OH in β-D-Glucopyranose. Thus, when an equilibrium mixture of alpha and beta-D-Glucopyranose react with acetic anhydride, the beta acetate accumulates more rapidly and is the "product of kinetic control." (When the initial rates of formation are controlling the ratio of beta- to alpha- acetate product, beta predominates.)

Since the beta acetate will always form faster than the alpha isomer, how can we ever get a reaction in which the alpha-acetate will be the major product? This can happen only if the alpha pentaacetate is more stable than the beta, that is if the alpha pentaacetate is the "product of thermodynamic control." In fact, that is the case in this example, and it can be proven by reacting the beta pentaacetate with $ZnCl_2$, which catalyses the isomerization to the alpha-isomer (shown in the **Scheme 2**.)

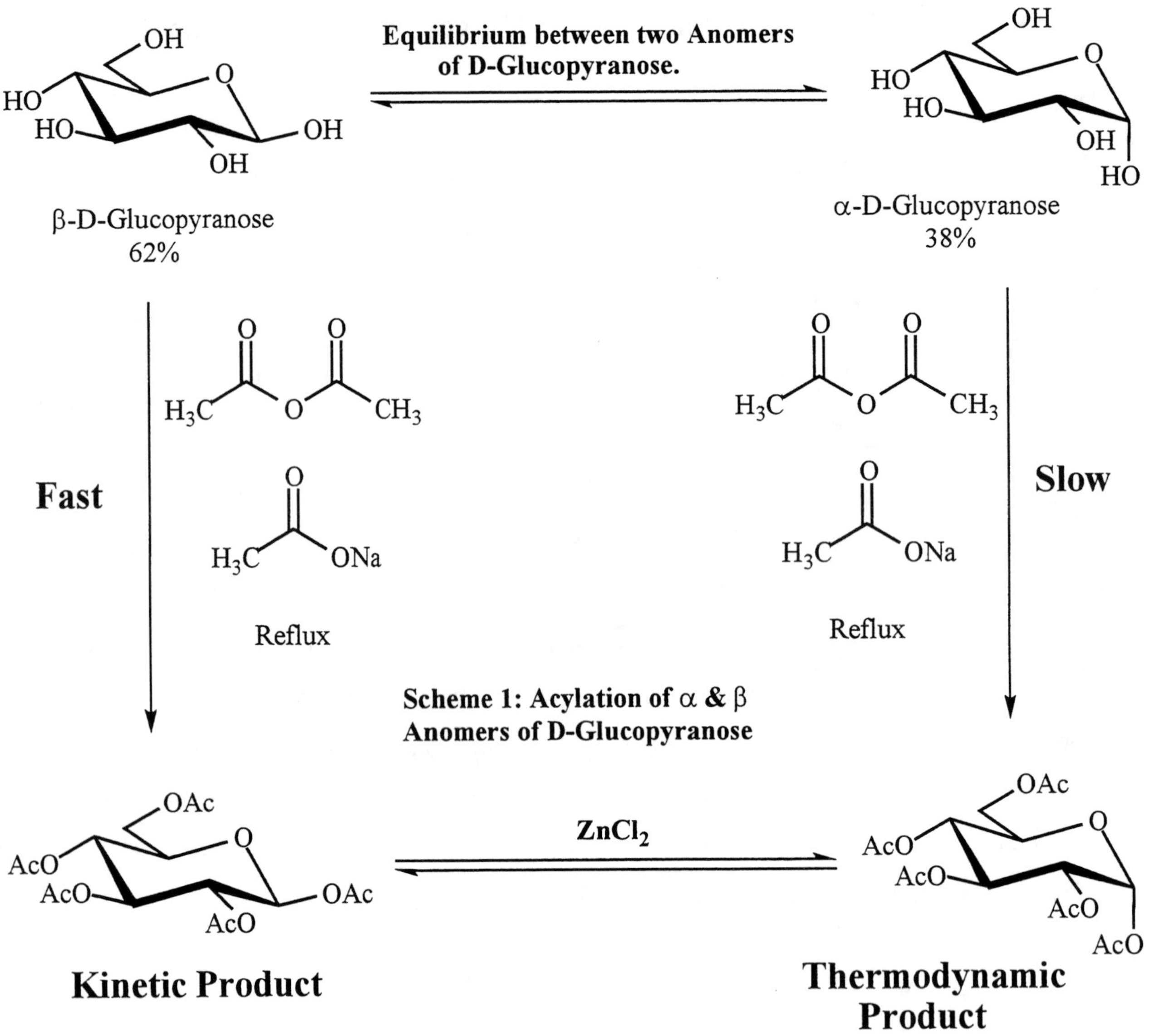

**Equilibrium between two Anomers
of D-Glucopyranose.**

β-D-Glucopyranose
62%

α-D-Glucopyranose
38%

Fast

Slow

Reflux

Reflux

**Scheme 1: Acylation of α & β
Anomers of D-Glucopyranose**

ZnCl$_2$

Kinetic Product

**Thermodynamic
Product**

(Sodium acetate does not catalyze the above isomerization.) Upon extended heating with zinc chloride, the first formed β-pentaacetate is slowly converted to the α-pentaacetate, indicating that α-D-Glucopyranose pentaacetate is the more stable isomer. This is somewhat confusing, since we have learned that β-D-Glucopyranose is more stable than the α-D-Glucopyranose anomer because the anomeric -OH of the beta-isomer is in the equatorial position rather than the axial position. The mutarotation equilibrium mixture of α- and β-Glucopyranose anomers is a 62% β to 38 % α in aqueous solution at room temperature. Although β-D-Glucopyranose is slightly lower in potential energy than its α-isomer, the alpha pentaacetate must be slightly lower in potential energy than the beta-pentaacetate. That is, the stabilities of the acetate anomers are reversed from the stabilities of the anomers of D-Glucose itself! This reversal of stabilities of the α- and β- isomers is due to what is known as the Anomeric Effect. Since the C-1 carbon of the sugar is actually a hemiacetal carbon, factors other than simple axial vs. equatorial positioning come in to play. In many cases, such as this one, it is difficult to predict the preferred isomer.

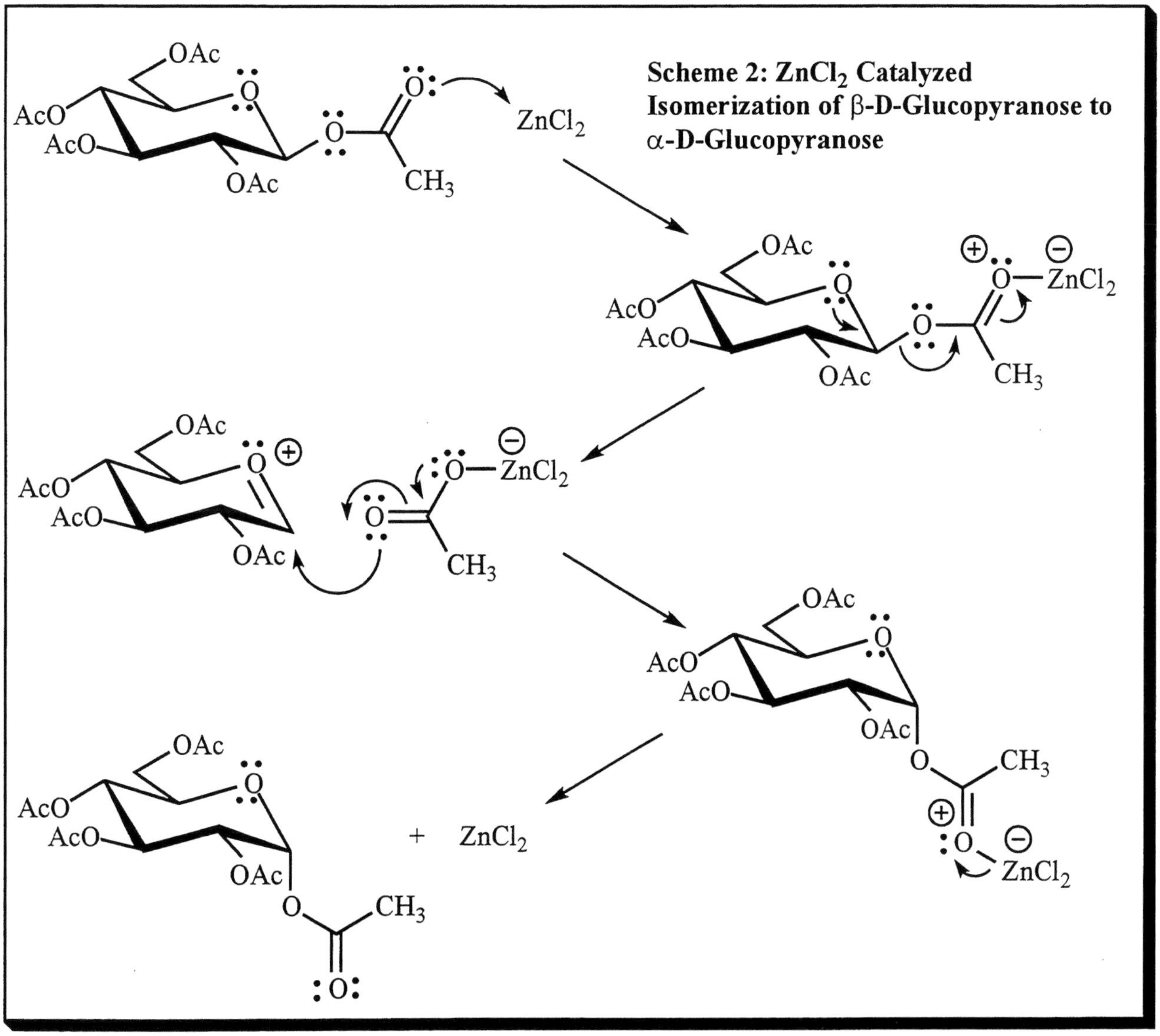

Scheme 2: ZnCl$_2$ Catalyzed Isomerization of β-D-Glucopyranose to α-D-Glucopyranose

Procedure:

α-D-Glucopyranose pentaacetate: Anhydrous D-Glucopyranose (2.0 g, 11.1 mmol) and acetic anhydride (13.0 g, 127 mmol; d= 1.08 g/mL) are placed in a dry 50 mL round bottom flask with a boiling chip and 0.5 g of anhydrous zinc chloride (3.7 mmol; hygroscopic!); the flask is set under a reflux condenser and heated with a heating mantle until boiling commences. (If boiling becomes too vigorous, remove the mantle and cool briefly with a water bath.) Boiling is continued for eight minutes. The hot contents of the flask are then poured slowly into a 400 mL beaker half filled with water and chipped ice. The mixture is stirred until crystallization is complete. The material will actually appear more like a brown paste rather than a crystalline solid. The solid is isolated on the small Büchner funnel and recrystallized from 10 mL of methanol. The melting point of the α-pentaacetate is 112° - 113° C.

β-D-Glucopyranose pentaacetate: Anhydrous D-Glucopyranose (2.0 g, 11.1 mmol) and acetic anhydride

(13.0 g, 127 mmol; d= 1.08 g/mL) are placed in a dry 50 mL round bottom flask with a boiling chip and 1.2 g anhydrous sodium acetate (14.7 mmol.) The reflux is conducted for 10 minutes, and the hot mixture is once more poured into 200 mL of crushed ice and water. Isolation and recrystallization are done as above; the β–pentaacetate m.p. is 130° - 132° C.

Questions

1) Why doesn't the sodium acetate catalyze the isomerization of beta to alpha like the $ZnCl_2$ does?

2) Is it possible that each of the two isomers of D-Glucopyranose pentaacetate is contaminated by the material shown below? If so, how would it be formed?

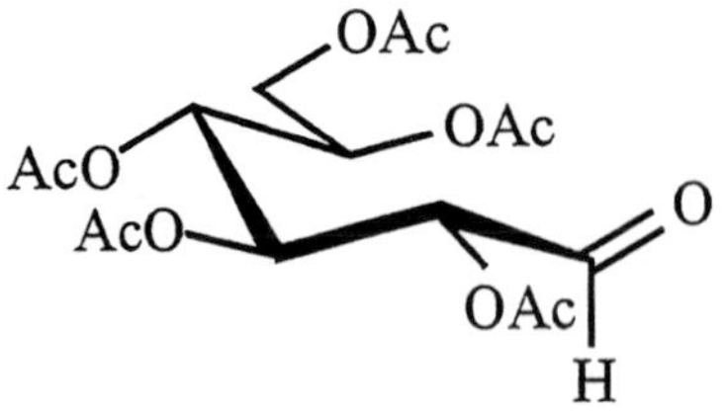

Preparation of an Artificial Flavoring Agent: Coconut Lactone

Reaction

Heptanal
MW 114.19
density 0.818

Malonic Acid
MW 104.06

$(CH_3CH_2)_3N:$
Triethylamine
MW 101.19
density 0.726

85% H_2SO_4

γ-Nonanoic Lactone
MW 156.23
density 0.976

Discussion

The Knoevenagel reaction is an aldol condensation in which the enolate is produced from malonic or acetoacetic acid or their esters. Typically these "condensations" employ very mild organic bases as catalysts, since the corresponding enolates are unusually stable. It is also typical that the aldol condensation is subsequently accompanied by dehydration and decarboxylation under the reaction conditions used. In this lab we will add a two carbon terminal residue on to a seven carbon aldehyde, in effect doing a mixed aldol reaction to create a nine carbon chain headed by a carboxylic acid functional group. The mechanism for the first reaction is shown in **Scheme 1**.

Although the non-conjugated carboxylic acid is the initial product, the reaction conditions are sufficiently vigorous to cause some isomerization to the conjugated carboxylic acid (**Scheme 2**). The second step of the procedure lactonizes the crude acid by forcing its protonation in hot 85% sulfuric acid (**Scheme 3**). The crude mixture of 2- and 3-nonenoic acids is used without purification, since the removal of 3-nonenoic acid by lactonization forces the isomerization of 2-nonenoic acid back to the unconjugated isomer by mass action.

γ–Νοναλαχτονε, the final product of this sequence, has been called "Coconut aldehyde", although it is neither an aldehyde nor found in coconuts. Nonetheless, it is an artificial flavoring agent that has both the flavor and fragrance of coconut in dilute solutions. It is important to note that flavor/fragrance materials can be prepared through organic synthesis [this is presently a business with revenues greater than $30 billion per year in the U.S.], and that the materials which have a given taste or small need not necessarily be identical to the chemicals found in the natural food material itself, although they most frequently are ["Coconut aldehyde" is something of an exception.] It is also important to realize that even when the mixture of organic compounds employed to flavor a given foodstuff is identical to the compounds in the natural substance, the exact flavor will differ from that of the natural food if the concentration of the flavoring agents are lower or higher than in the natural food. The exact "odor" detected by an observer depends not only on the structure of the compounds detected by the nose and taste buds, but also on their concentrations!

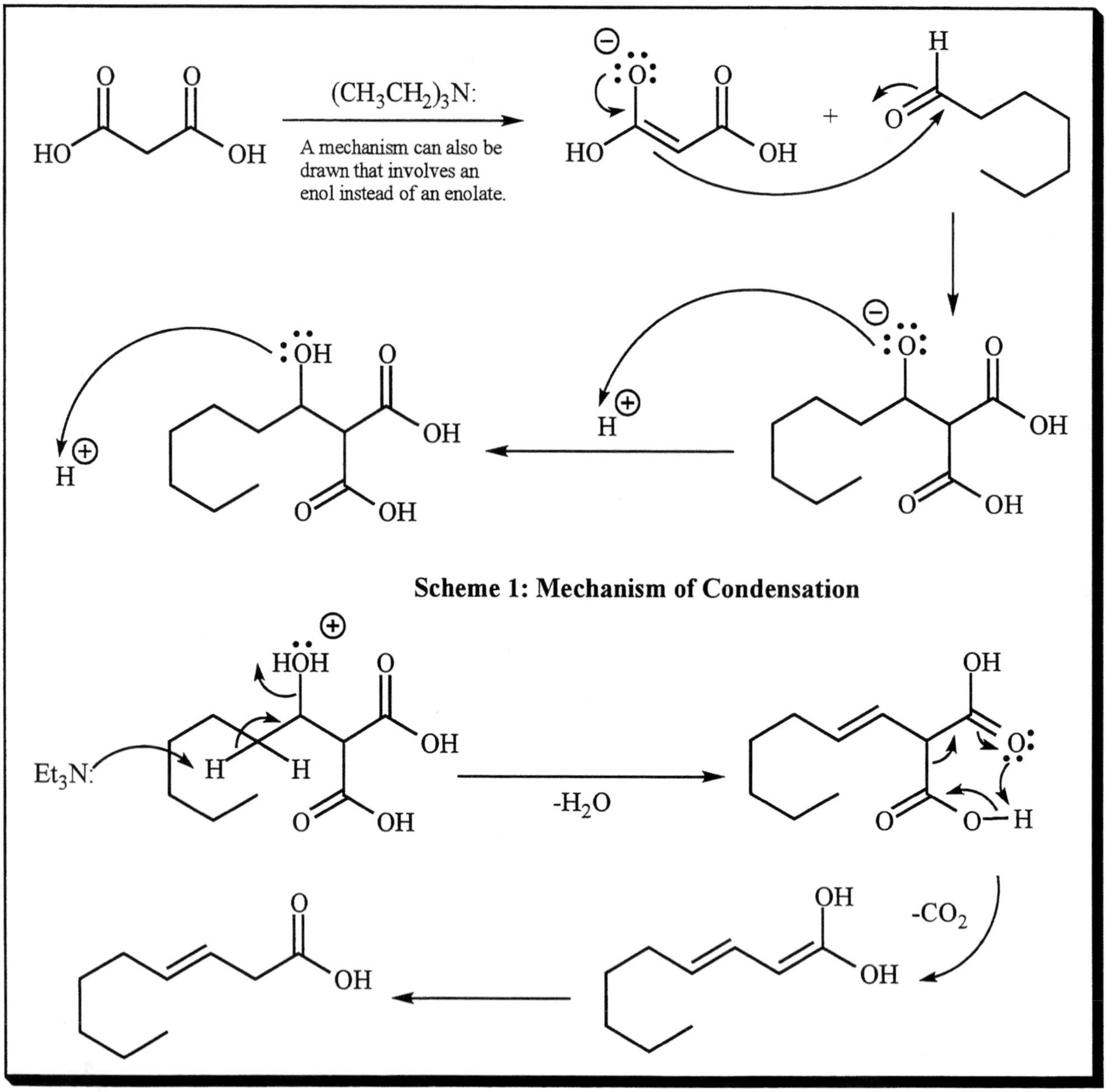

Scheme 1: Mechanism of Condensation

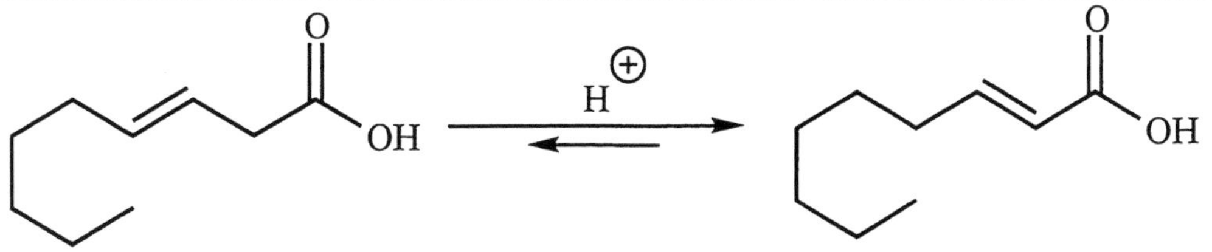

Scheme 2: Isomerization of 3-Nonenoic & 2-Nonenoic Acid

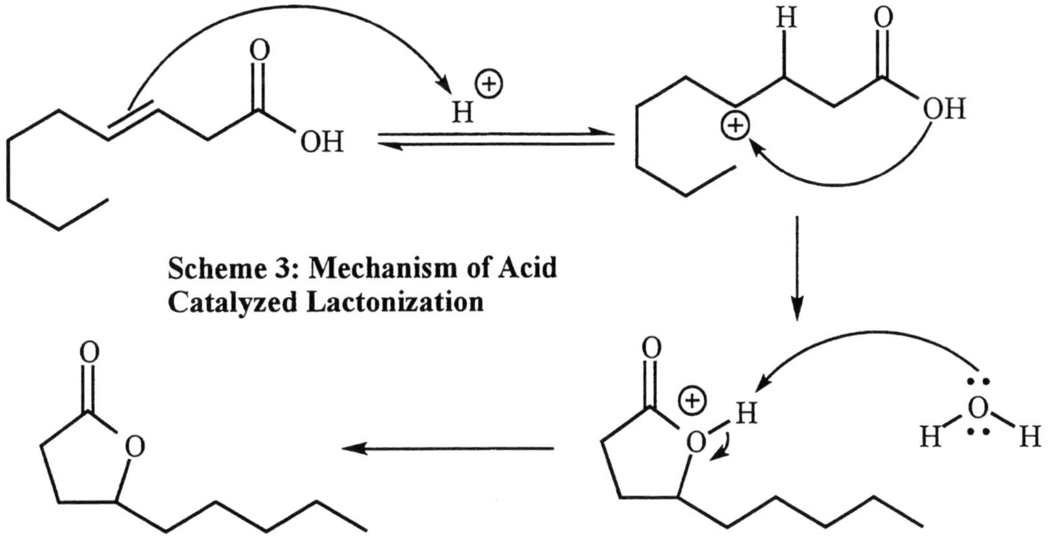

Scheme 3: Mechanism of Acid Catalyzed Lactonization

Procedure

Warning! You will be using concentrated Hydrochloric Acid and 85% Sulfuric Acid. Please reread your safety guidelines about handling concentrated acids. Make sure that your glassware is completely dry before adding either of the two acids in order to prevent a vigorous, exothermic reaction which could cause acid splashing and serious burns. When mixing the acids with water or ice, add the acid to the water slowly.

Step 1. Knoevenagel Reaction.

Malonic acid (50.0 mmol, 5.20 g) and heptanal (50.0 mmol, 5.70 g) are added to triethylamine (72.0 mmol, 7.20 g, 10 mL) in a 125 mL Erlenmeyer flask. Make sure your hood baffles are open! The flask is clamped to a ring stand and immersed in a hot water bath warmed by the hot plate; the temperature is held above 80° C for 45 minutes; if CO_2 evolution is still taking place after 45 minutes continue heating until it ceases. The flask is now cooled in an ice bath while a mixture of 10 mL of concentrated HCl and 25 mL of cracked ice is prepared and added slowly to the flask. After mixing, the flask contents are poured into the separatory funnel and the flask rinsed with 30 mL of diethyl ether, the rinsings added to the separatory funnel also. After shaking the mixture, the water layer is drawn off and the ether layer washed once with 15 mL of cold deionized water. The ether layer is dried with anhydrous $MgSO_4$ and then transferred into a tared 100 mL beaker containing two boiling chips by decantation. The ether is then boiled off using the hot plate (setting 2.5). When active boiling stops the weight of the crude acid is determined and a rough percent yield calculated.

Step 2. Lactonization.

10 mL of 85% Sulfuric acid is added to the mixture of nonenoic acids in the beaker. The beaker is simmered for an hour in a hot water bath on the hot plate, then poured slowly into a magnetically stirred suspension of 25 g of Na_2CO_3 in 100 mL of water in a 400 mL beaker [**Caution! Frothing**.] Half the neutralized mixture is poured into the separatory funnel and extracted with 30 mL of diethyl ether; the water layer is drawn off and the remaining half of the mixture extracted with the same ether layer. After discarding the water layer, the ether layer is washed with 20 mL of deionized water, transferred to a 50 mL Erlenmeyer flask, and dried over anhydrous magnesium sulfate. After thorough drying, the ether layer is filtered through a cotton plug into a tared 100 mL beaker containing two boiling chips, and the ether removed by steam bath. The residual γ-nonalactone is analyzed by gas chromatography.

Questions

1) Draw the mechanism for the interconversion of 3-nonenoic acid to 2-nonenoic acid (**Scheme 2**).

Analysis of Fats & Oils

Discussion

The bulk of plant and animal tissue is composed of three main classes of compounds: carbohydrates, proteins, and lipids. The term lipid includes all substances in living tissues that are soluble in ether, methylene chloride, or similar organic solvents. The most abundant lipids are triesters of glycerol with long-chain "fatty" acids. The triesters, or triglycerides, from animal sources are usually low-melting solids and are called fats, while those from plants are viscous oils that solidify below 0°. The general structures are the same, and the difference in properties arises from the fact that the vegetable oils contain a larger proportion of unsaturated acid groups, with one, two, or three double bonds in the chain. Triglycerides such as beef tallow and other depot fats of animals contain mostly acid chains with one or no double bonds. The degree of unsaturation is important in nutrition, since there is evidence that a high proportion of saturated fats in the diet leads to deposition of cholesterol in blood vessels (atherosclerosis). Fatty acids invariably have chains with an even number of carbon atoms, most commonly 16 or 18 (**Table 1**). A few of the more important fatty acids are listed below; these and several others can occur in any combination in a given triglyceride (**Figure 1**). Butterfat and coconut oil are atypical, since the mixtures of acids in these triglycerides contain a significant number of 8-, 10-, and 12-carbon chains.

Table 1. Typical Fatty Acids

Name	Structure	# of Carbon Atoms
Lauric	$CH_3(CH_2)_{10}CO_2H$	12
Myristic	$CH_3(CH_2)_{12}CO_2H$	14
Palmitic	$CH_3(CH_2)_{14}CO_2H$	16
Stearic	$CH_3(CH_2)_{16}CO_2H$	18
Palmitoleic	$CH_3(CH_2)_5CH=CH(CH_2)_7CO_2H$	16
Oleic	$CH_3(CH_2)_7CH=CH(CH_2)_7CO_2H$	18
Linoleic	$CH_3(CH_2)_3(CH_2CH=CH)_2(CH_2)_7CO_2H$	18
Linolenic	$CH_3(CH_2CH=CH)_3(CH_2)_7CO_2H$	18

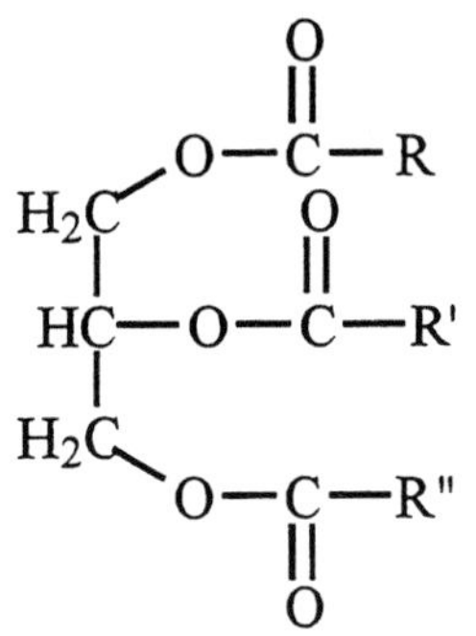

Figure 1. Triglyceride Structure

R, R', R" = Fatty Acid

The classical procedure for obtaining the acids from a fat is saponification with alkali to give the salt (a soap), and then acidification. This hydrolysis is rather slow at room temperature, and at high temperatures, when a glycol is used as solvent, isomerization of the polyunsaturated acids occurs. For analytical purposes, where only a small amount of material is required, this difficulty is avoided by preparing the methyl esters directly from the triglyceride by transesterification. By using a large excess of methanol, the equilibrium is shifted essentially completely to the right. In this experiment, you will be given a sample of a commercially available fat or oil (e.g., a cooking oil) to determine its fatty acid composition by gas chromatography of the methyl esters. From this information you can then identify the oil from among a list of possibilities provided by your instructor.

Procedure

A. Saponification: Combine 0.20 - 0.25 g of an oil to be analyzed with 6 mL of 0.5 M NaOH in methanol in a test tube and boil the tube in a steam jet until the fat globules are no longer visible (they dissolve.) If necessary, a few more mL's of methanol may be added; however it is an advantage if the volume of the saponified solution is much less than 6 mL.

B. Transesterification: Cautiously add 6 mL of 12% BF$_3$-Methanol solution to the sample and boil the mixture in the steam bath for 3 minutes. Pour the sample into a separatory funnel containing 30 mL of hexane or low boiling petroleum ether, add 20 mL of saturated aqueous sodium chloride solution, and extract the fatty acid esters into the hydrocarbon phase. Dry the hydrocarbon layer over anhydrous magnesium sulfate, filter off the drying agent, and concentrate the filtrate in a 50 mL beaker, using a steam bath to boil the hexane down.

C. Analysis: A sample of the hexane concentrate is injected into a gas chromatograph. If using a plain gc a fatty acid methyl ester standard will be required; a gc / ms on the other hand needs no standard. The fatty acid content of oil samples depends strongly on the source of the oil, and if it is an animal oil, on the nutritional state of the animal. In general unsaturated fatty acid esters elute from a gc column before their saturated congeners. That is, of the C18 methyl esters, triple cis methyloctadeca-9,12,15-trienoate (methyl linolenate) should elute first, followed by cis,cis-methyloctadeca-9,12-dienoate (methyl linoleate), then cis-methyloctadeca-9-enoate (methyl oleate), and finally methyloctadecanoate (methyl stearate.) Because of the large spread between the elution of the trienic ester and the saturated ester, one or more of the unsaturates may well elute faster than the C16 saturated ester, methyl palmitoate.

Appendix I
Carbon-13 & DEPT Spectra

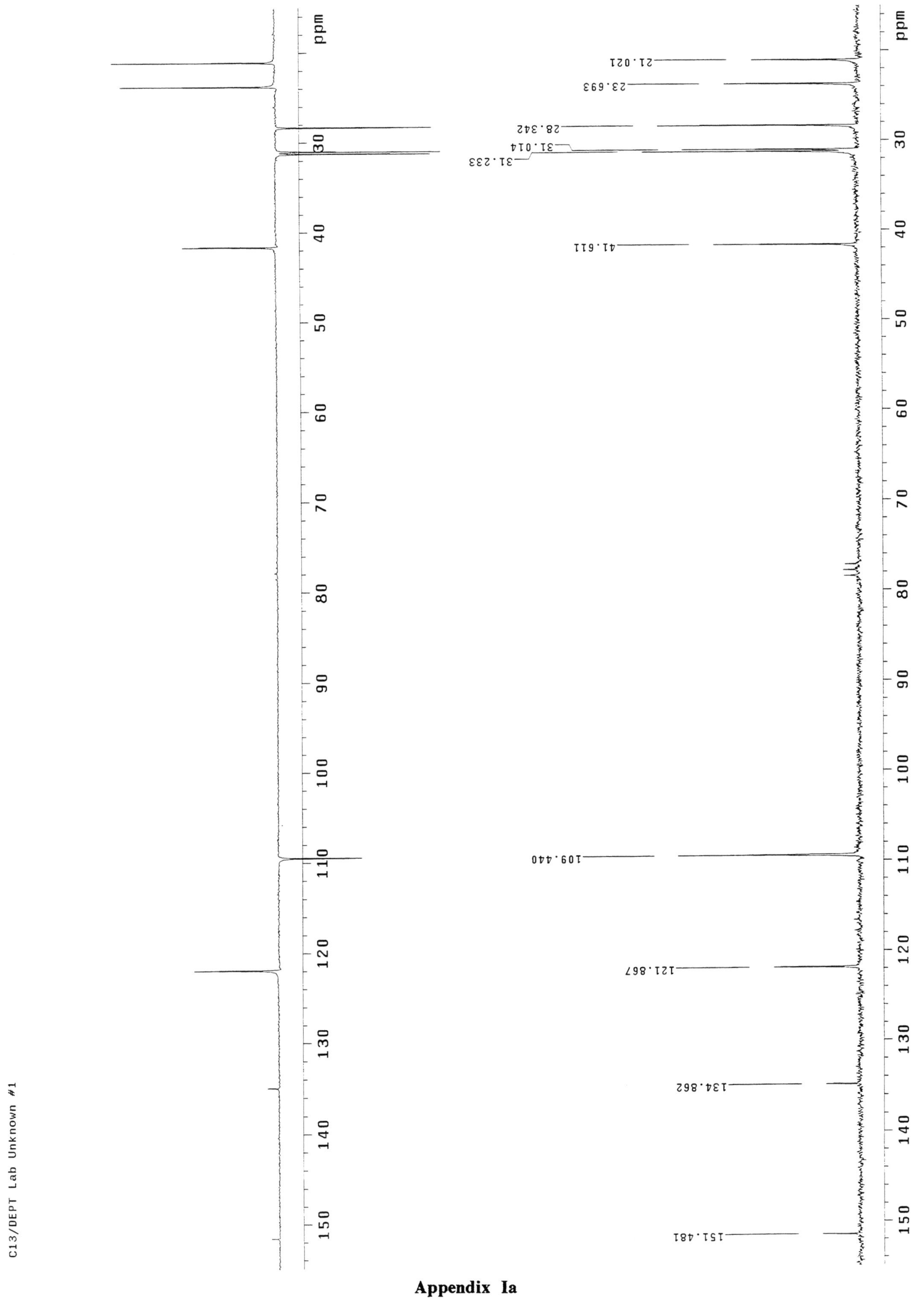

C13/DEPT Lab Unknown #1

ppm

21.021
23.693
28.342
31.014
31.233
41.611
109.440
121.867
134.862
151.481

Appendix Ia

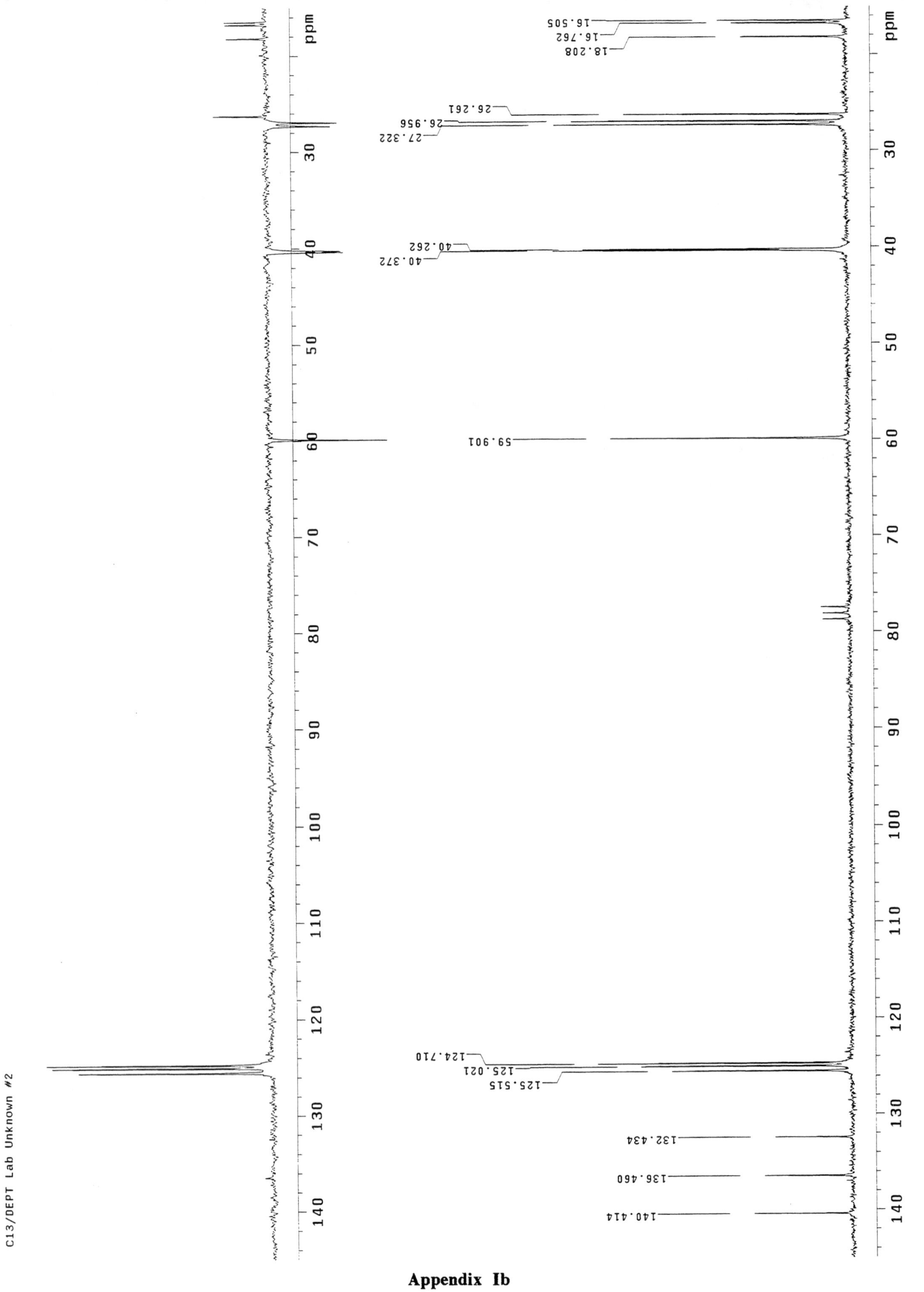

C13/DEPT Lab Unknown #2
ppm
16.505
16.762
18.208
26.261
26.956
27.322
40.262
40.372
59.901
124.710
125.021
125.515
132.434
136.460
140.414
30
40
50
60
70
80
90
100
110
120
130
140

Appendix Ib

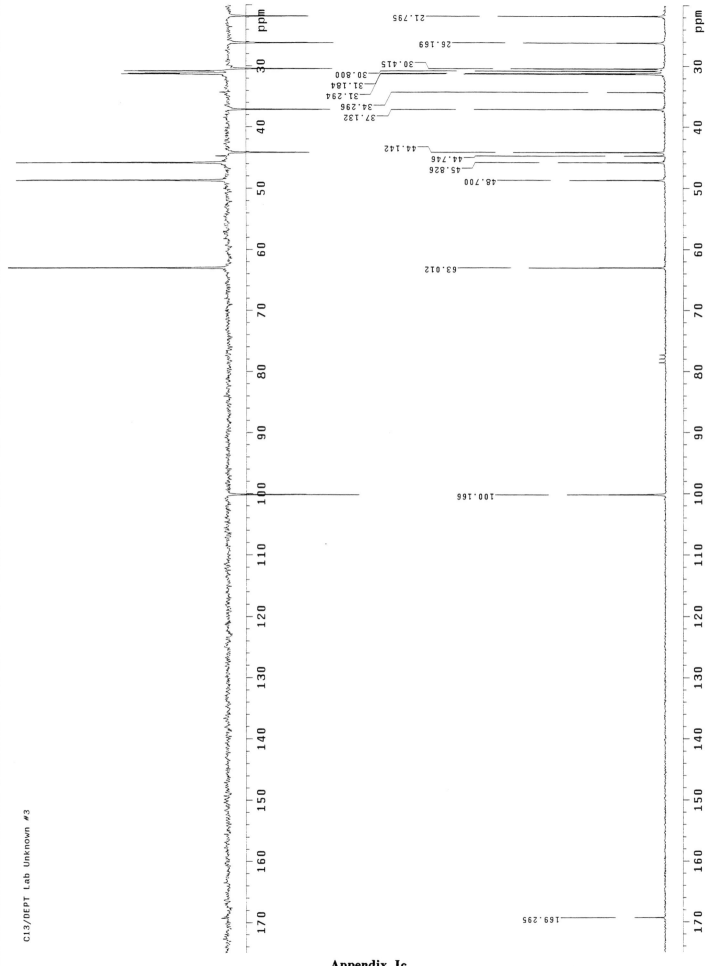

Appendix Ic

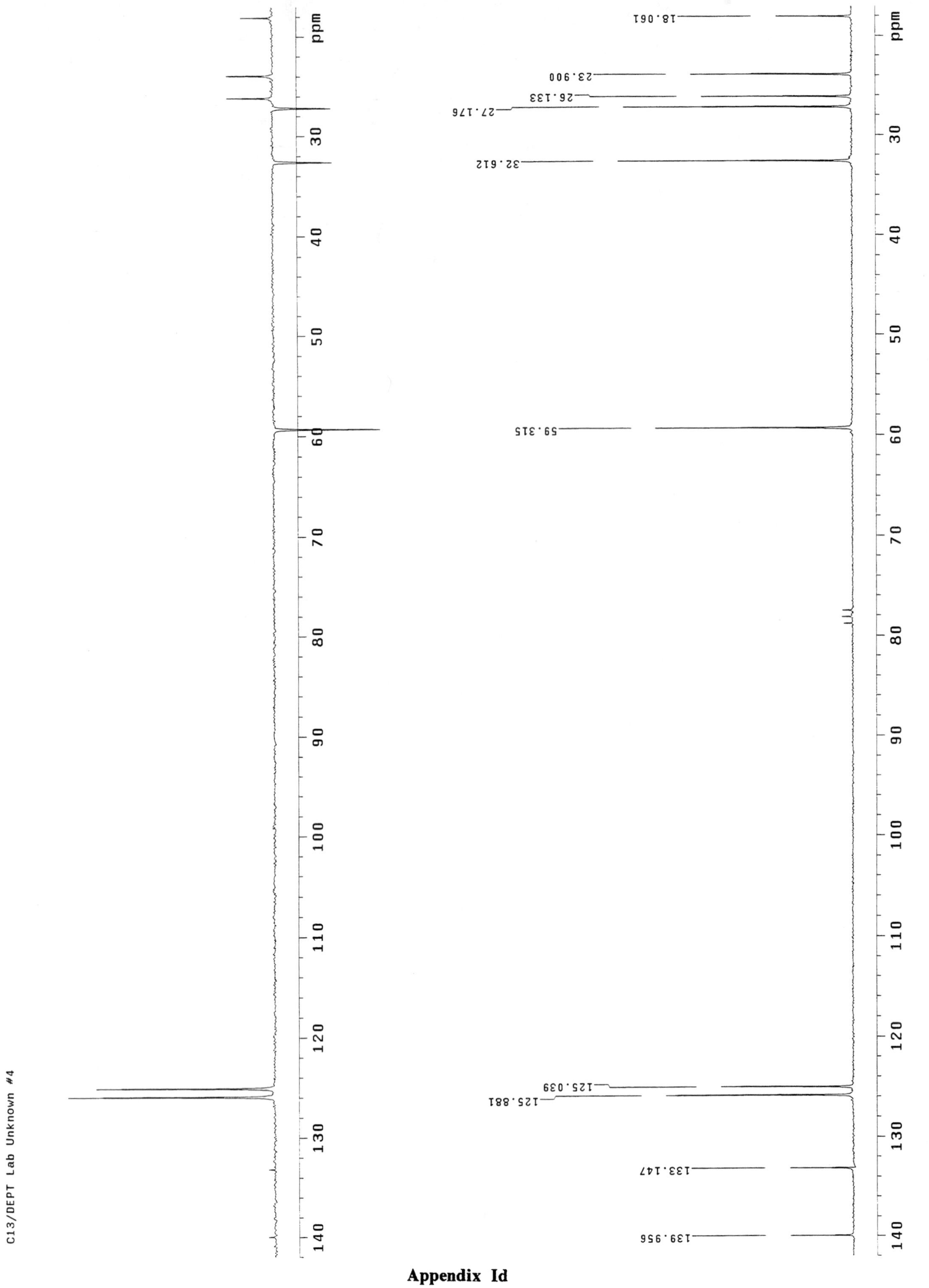

ppm

18.061

23.900
26.133
27.176

32.612

59.315

125.039
125.881

133.147

139.956

ppm

30

40

50

60

70

80

90

100

110

120

130

140

Appendix Id

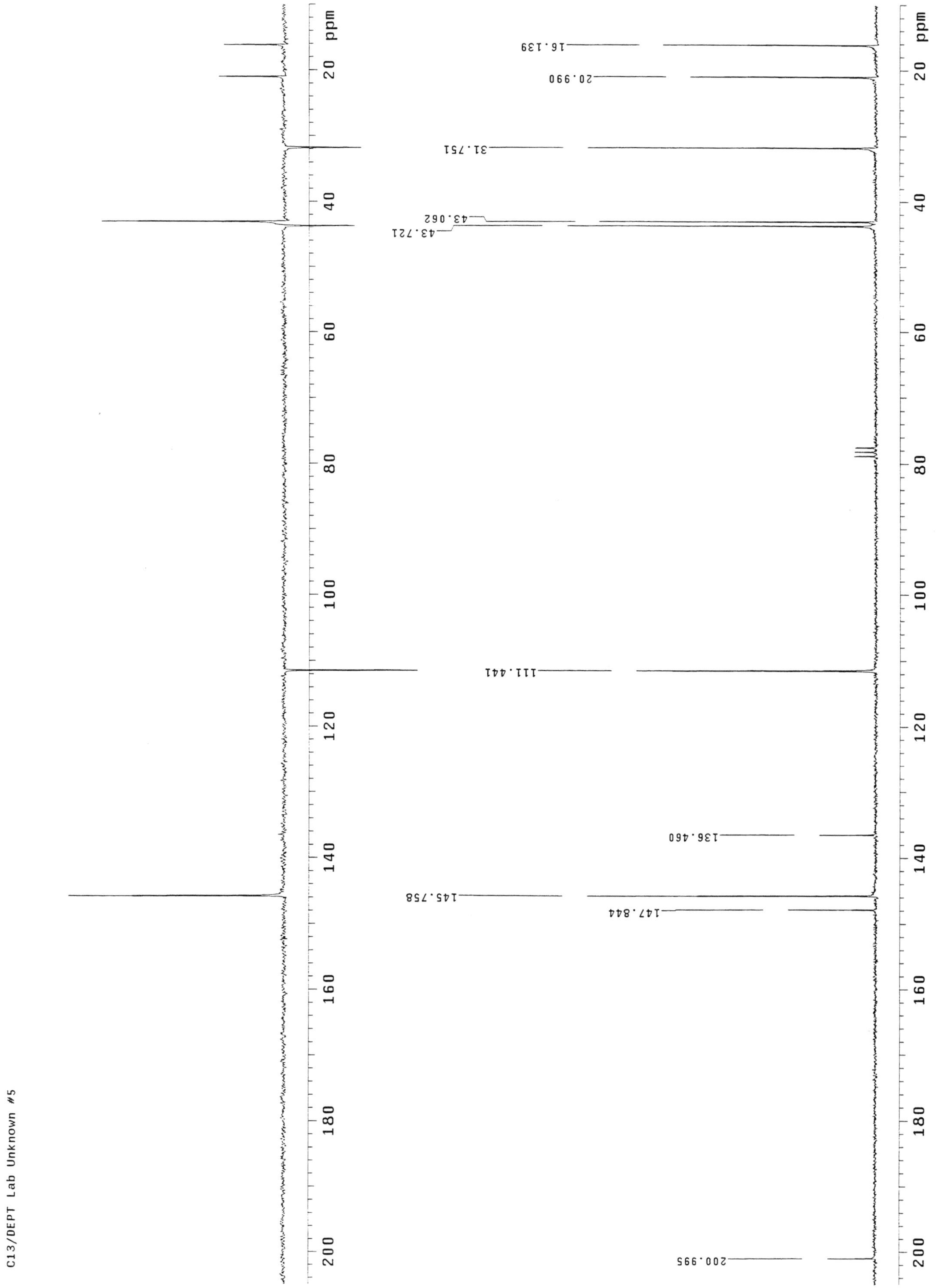

C13/DEPT Lab Unknown #5

16.139
20.990
31.751
43.062
43.721
111.441
136.460
145.758
147.844
200.995

20 ppm
40
60
80
100
120
140
160
180
200

20 ppm
40
60
80
100
120
140
160
180
200

Appendix Ie

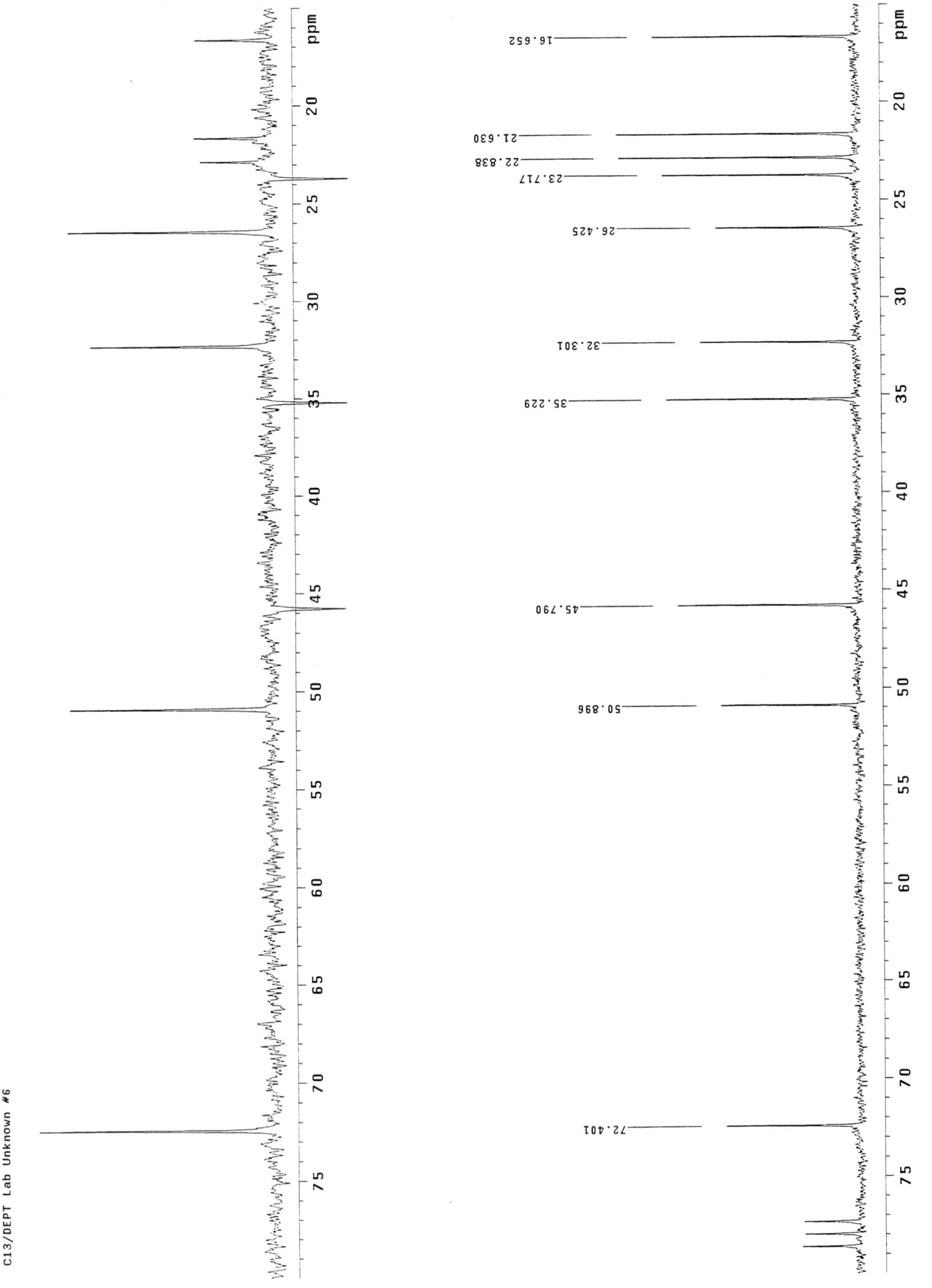

C13/DEPT Lab Unknown #6
ppm
16.652
21.630
22.838
23.717
26.425
32.301
35.229
45.790
50.896
72.401
20
25
30
35
40
45
50
55
60
65
70
75

Appendix If

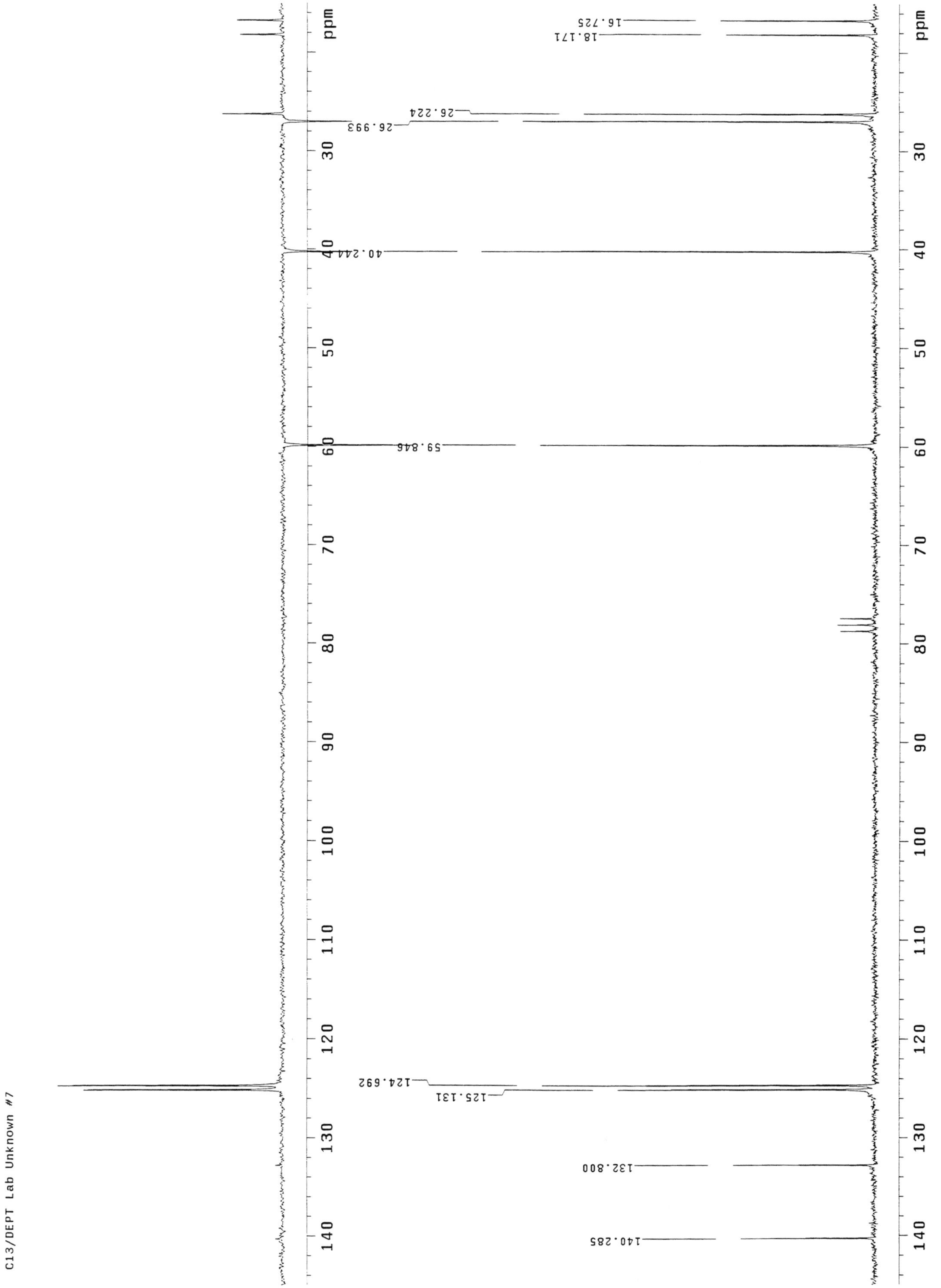

ppm

16.725
18.171

26.224
26.993

30

40.244

40

50

59.846

60

70

80

90

100

110

120

124.692
125.131

130

132.800

140.285

140

ppm

30

40

50

60

70

80

90

100

110

120

130

140

Appendix Ig

C13/DEPT Lab Unknown #8

21.173
22.051
26.865
32.264
41.287
110.526
142.372
149.473
151.798
195.175

ppm

Appendix Ih

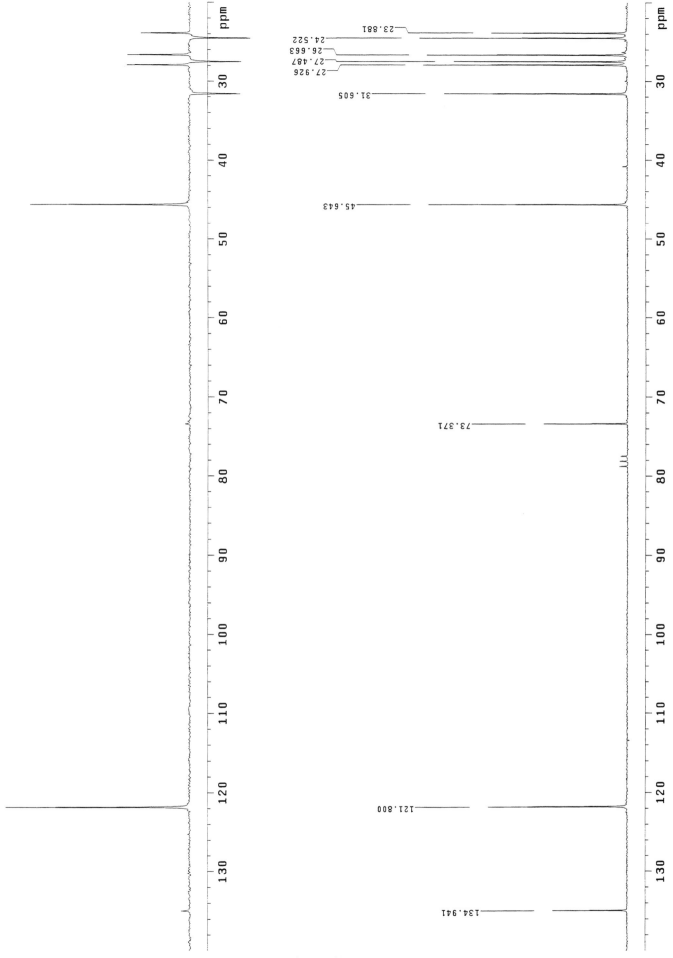

C13/DEPT Lab Unknown #9

Appendix Ii

C13/DEPT Lab Unknown #10

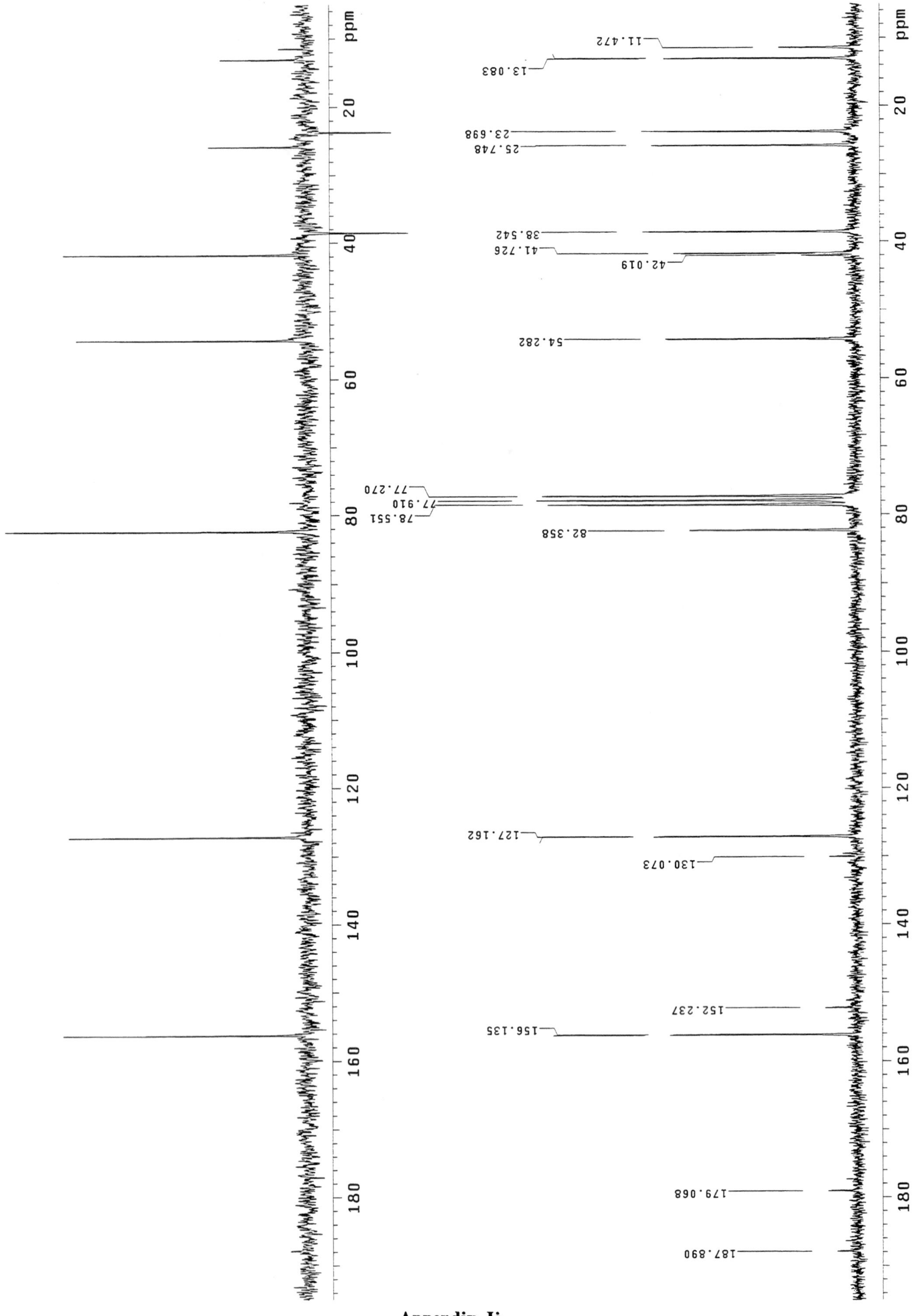

Appendix Ij

11.472
13.083
23.698
25.748
38.542
41.726
42.019
54.282
77.270
77.910
78.551
82.358
127.162
130.073
152.237
156.135
179.068
187.890

ppm
20
40
60
80
100
120
140
160
180

Appendix II

Spectra for Proton NMR &

Coupling Constant Laboratory

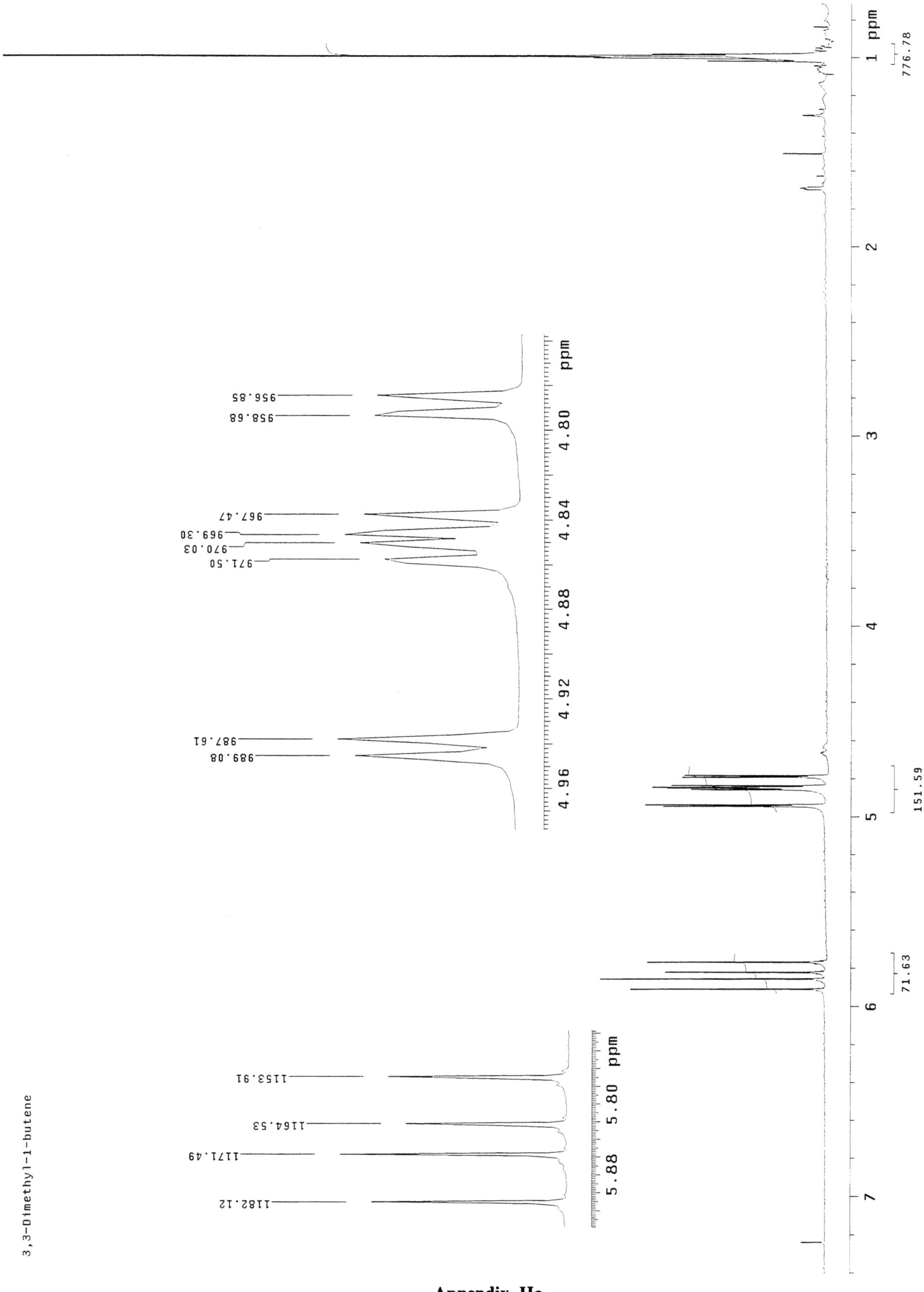

3,3-Dimethyl-1-butene

956.85
958.68

967.47
969.30
970.03
971.50

987.61
989.08

ppm
4.80
4.84
4.88
4.92
4.96

1153.91

1164.53

1171.49

1182.12

ppm
5.80
5.88

151.59

71.63

776.78

ppm
1
2
3
4
5
6
7

Appendix IIa

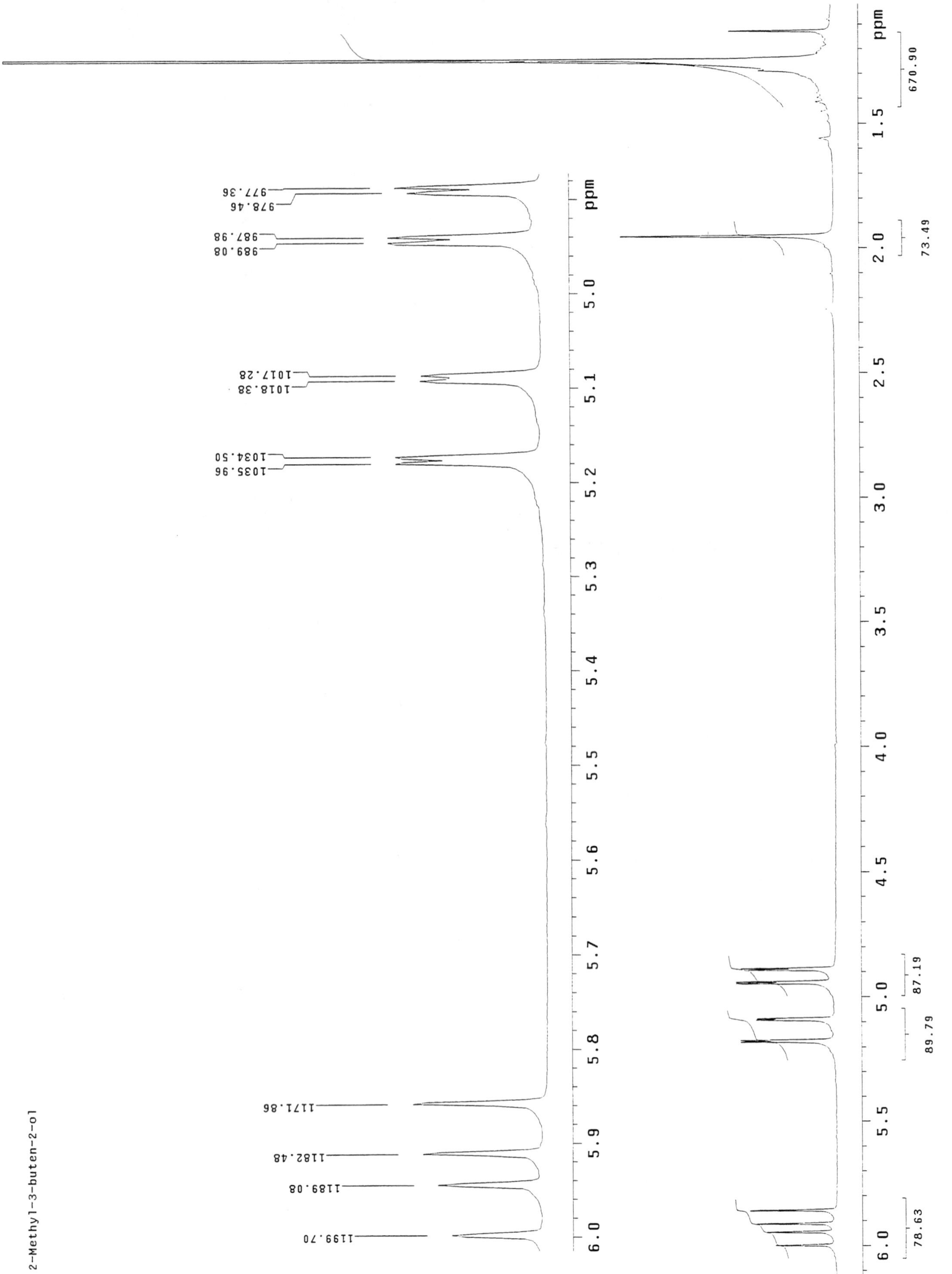

2-Methyl-3-buten-2-ol

977.36
978.46
987.98
989.08
1017.28
1018.38
1034.50
1035.96
1171.86
1182.48
1189.08
1199.70

ppm
6.0
5.9
5.8
5.7
5.6
5.5
5.4
5.3
5.2
5.1
5.0

ppm
1.5
2.0
2.5
3.0
3.5
4.0
4.5
5.0
5.5
6.0

670.90
73.49
87.19
89.79
78.63

Appendix IIb

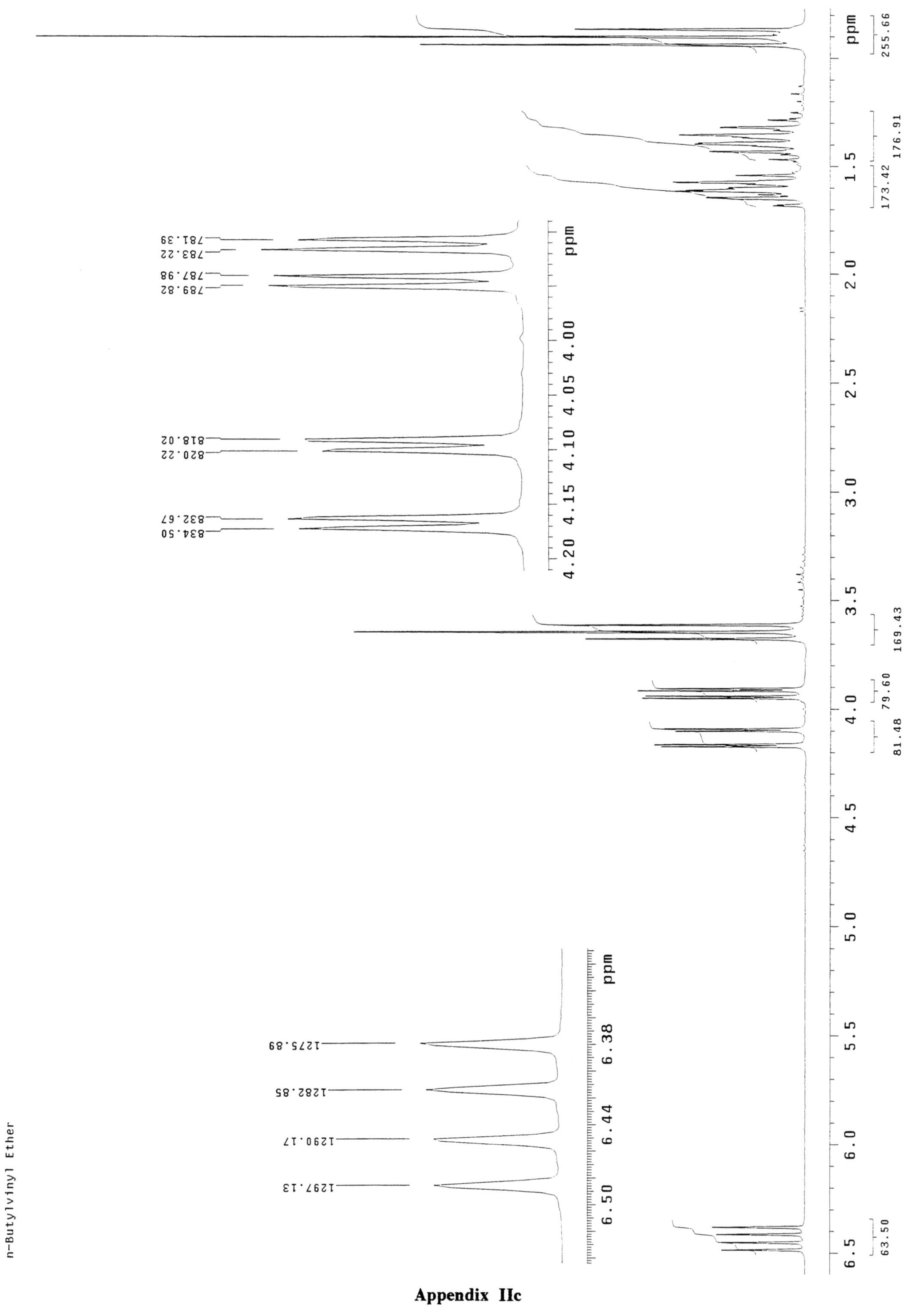

n-Butylvinyl Ether

255.66

176.91
173.42

781.39
783.22
787.98
789.82

ppm

4.00
4.05
4.10
4.15
4.20

818.02
820.22

832.67
834.50

169.43

79.60
81.48

ppm

6.38
6.44
6.50

1275.89

1282.85

1290.17

1297.13

63.50

ppm

1.5

2.0

2.5

3.0

3.5

4.0

4.5

5.0

5.5

6.0

6.5

Appendix IIc

Acrylonitrile

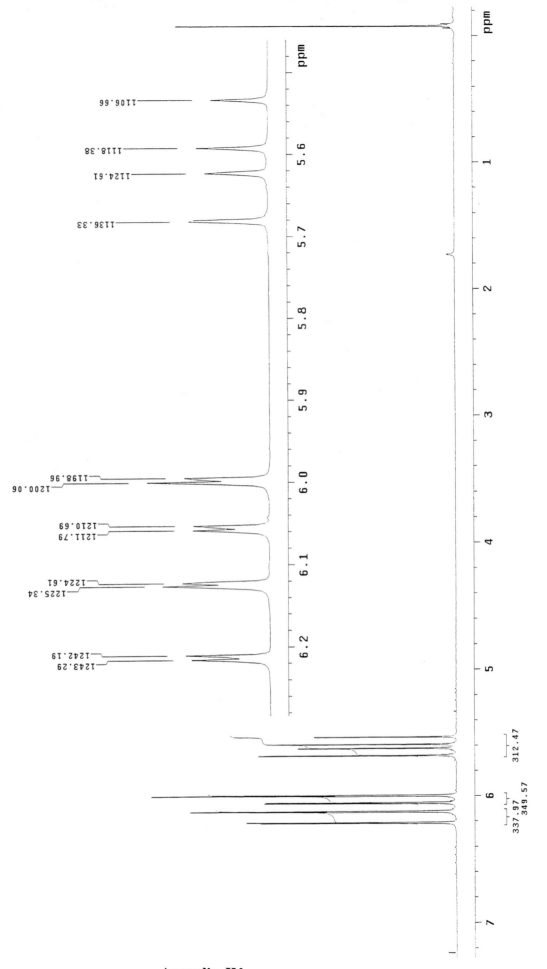

Appendix IId

ortho-Chlorophenol

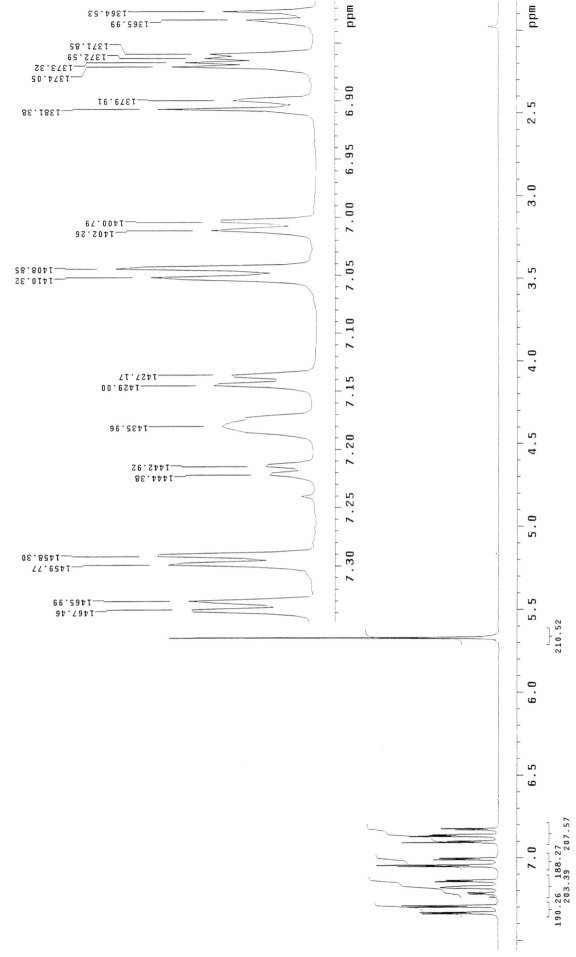

Appendix IIe

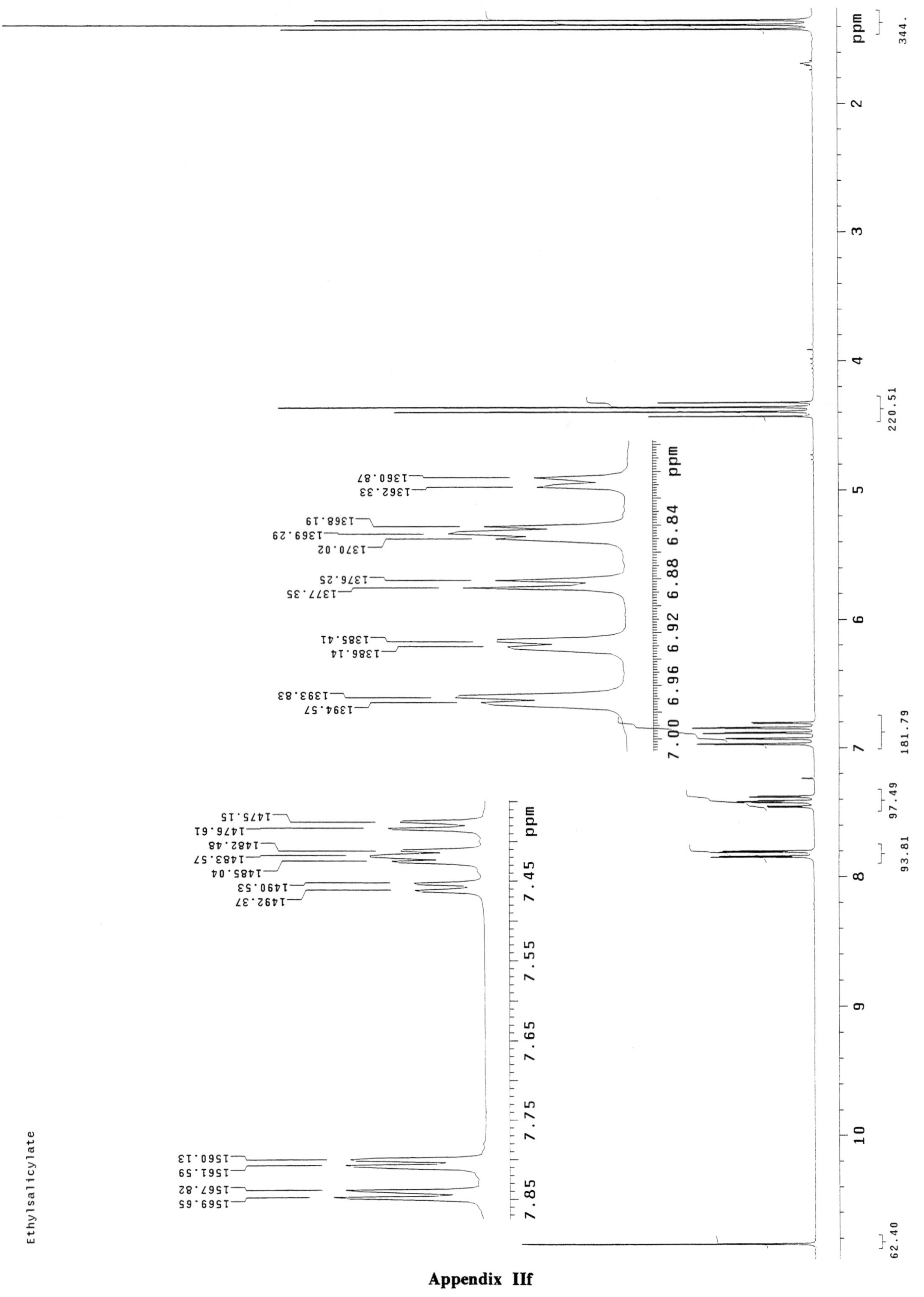

Ethylsalicylate

Appendix IIf

ppm
344.

220.51

181.79

97.49

93.81

62.40

1360.87
1362.33
1368.19
1369.29
1370.02
1376.25
1377.35
1385.41
1386.14
1393.83
1394.57

7.00 6.96 6.92 6.88 6.84 ppm

1475.15
1476.61
1482.48
1483.57
1485.04
1490.53
1492.37

7.45 7.55 7.65 7.75 7.85 ppm

1560.13
1561.59
1567.82
1569.65

2-Ethoxybenzamide

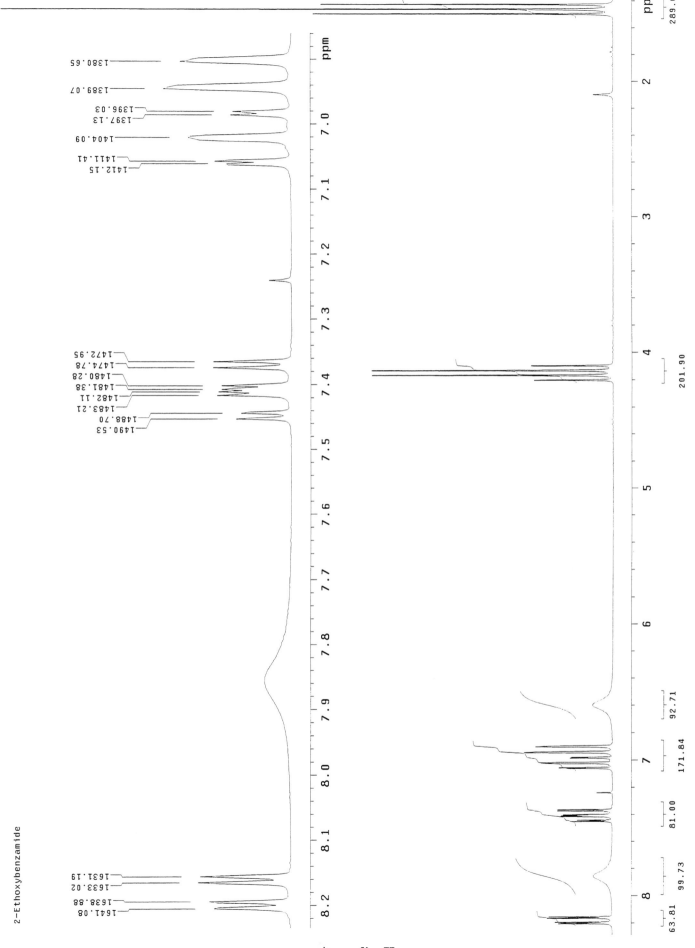

Appendix IIg

2,4-Dichlorophenol

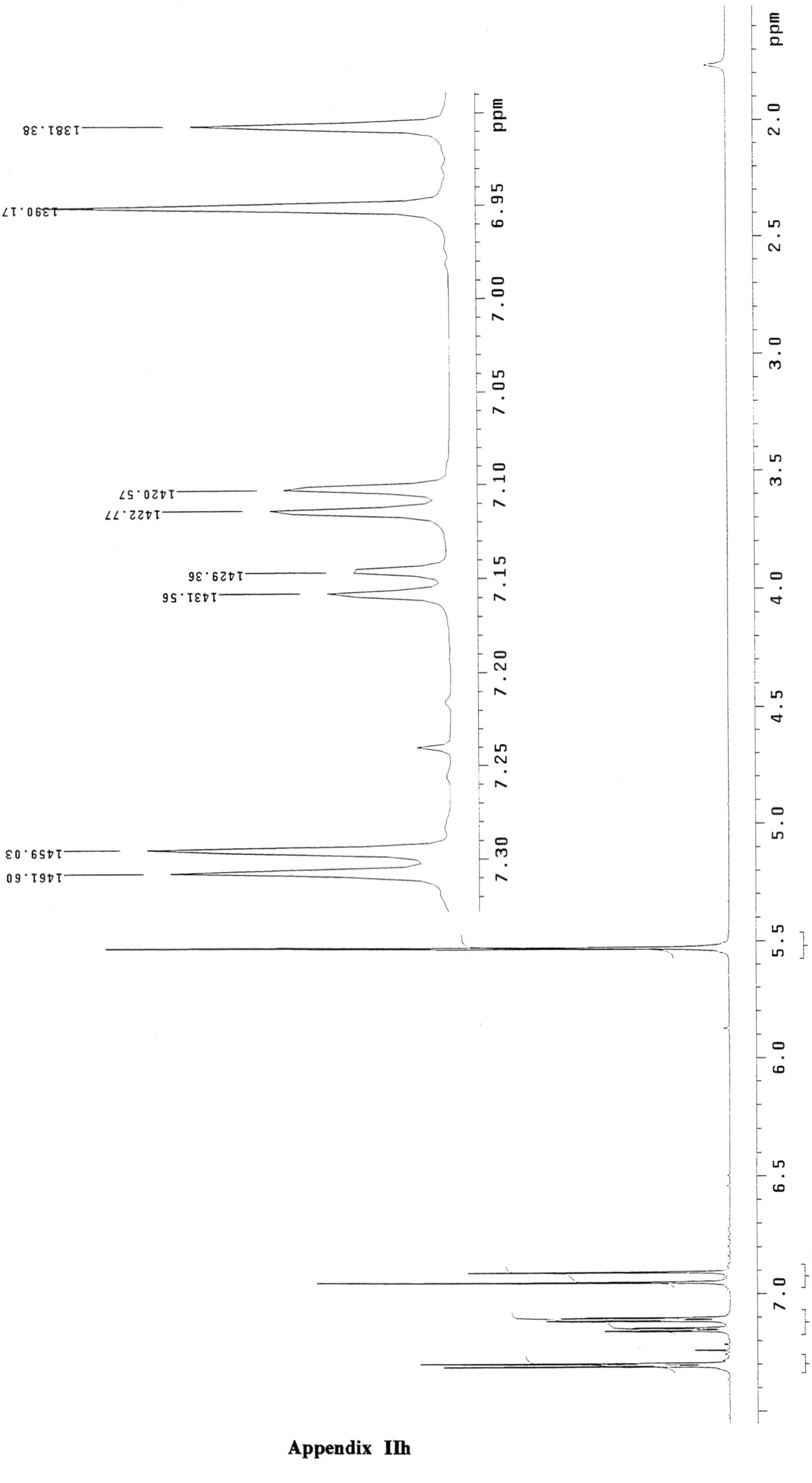

ppm
2.0
2.5
3.0
3.5
4.0
4.5
5.0
5.5
6.0
6.5
7.0
306.12
243.74
234.65
215.49
1381.38
1390.17
1420.57
1422.77
1429.36
1431.56
1459.03
1461.60
6.95
7.00
7.05
7.10
7.15
7.20
7.25
7.30

Appendix IIh

para-Nitrotoluene

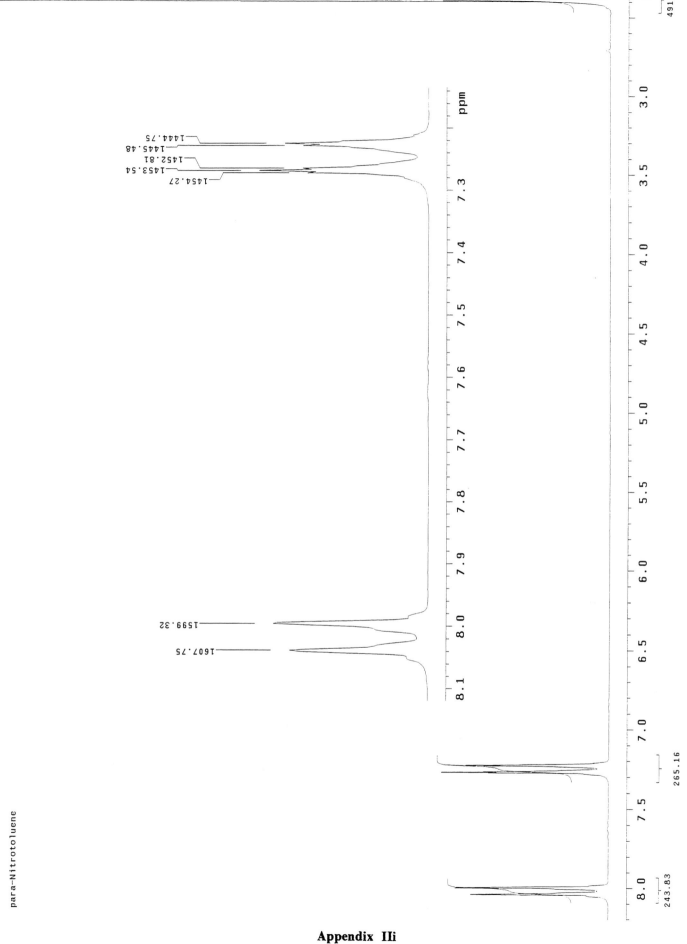

Appendix IIi

3,4-Methylenedioxybenzaldehyde

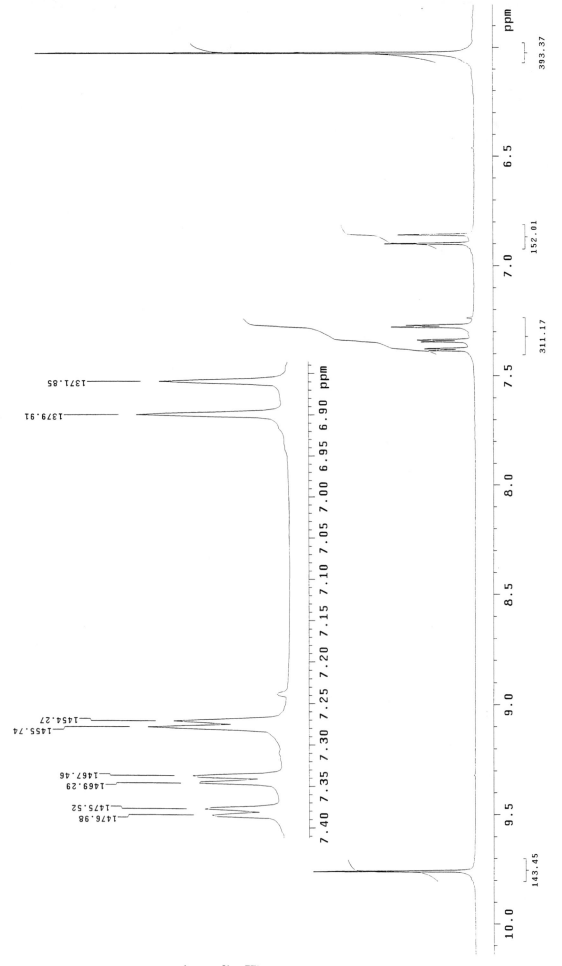

393.37

152.01

311.17

143.45

7.40 7.35 7.30 7.25 7.20 7.15 7.10 7.05 7.00 6.95 6.90 ppm

1371.85
1379.91
1454.27
1455.74
1467.46
1469.29
1475.52
1476.98

6.5 7.0 7.5 8.0 8.5 9.0 9.5 10.0 ppm

Appendix IIj

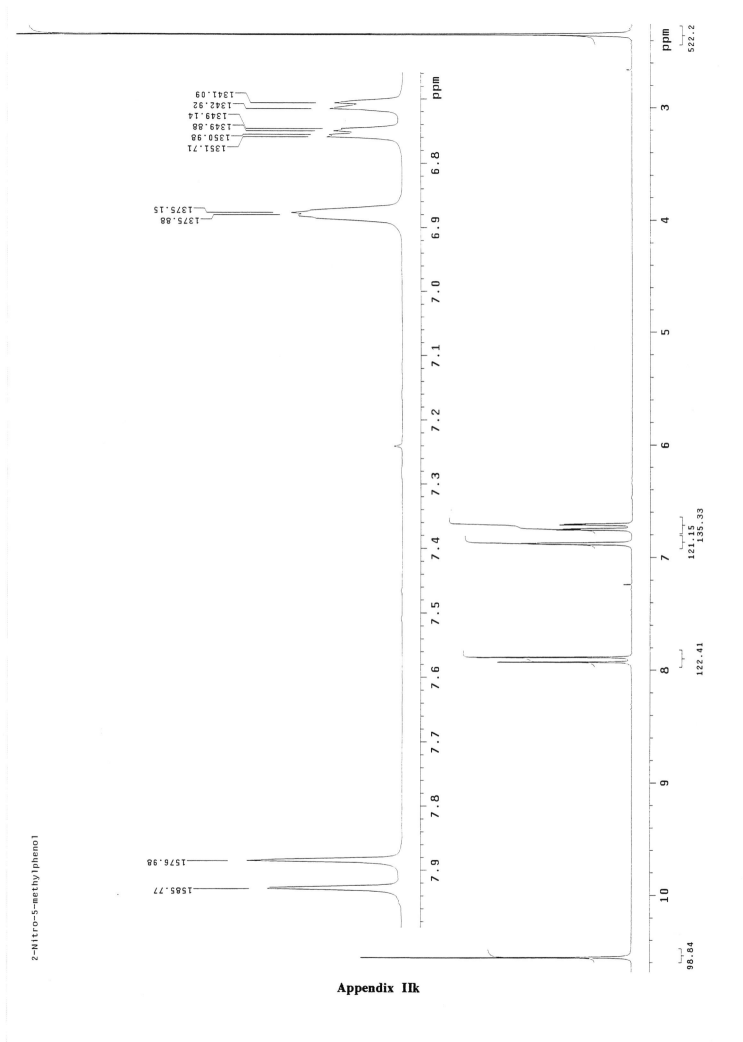

2-Nitro-5-methylphenol

Appendix IIk

Appendix III

^{1}H, ^{13}C, & IR Spectra for

Unknown Aldehyde Laboratory

Unknown Aldehyde #1

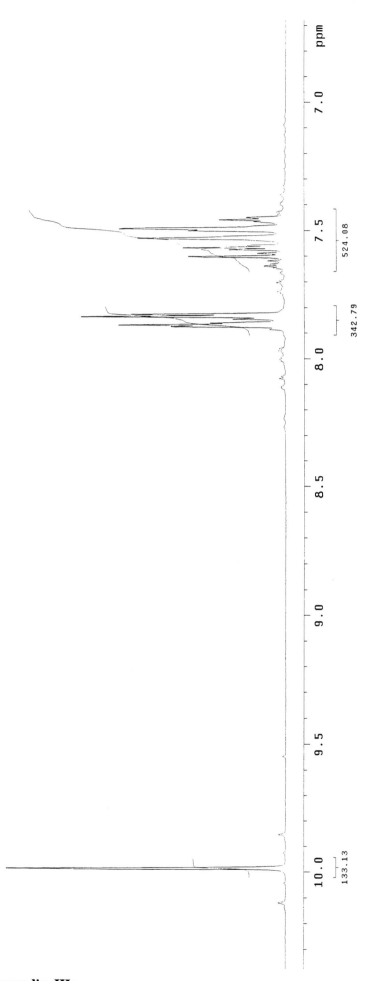

Appendix IIIa

Unknown Aldehyde #1

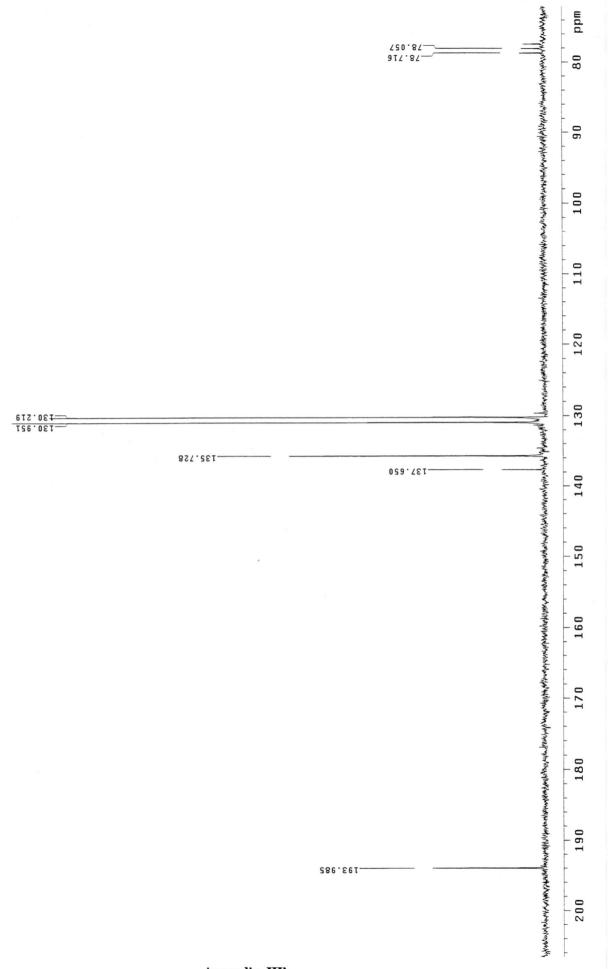

Unknown Aldehyde #1

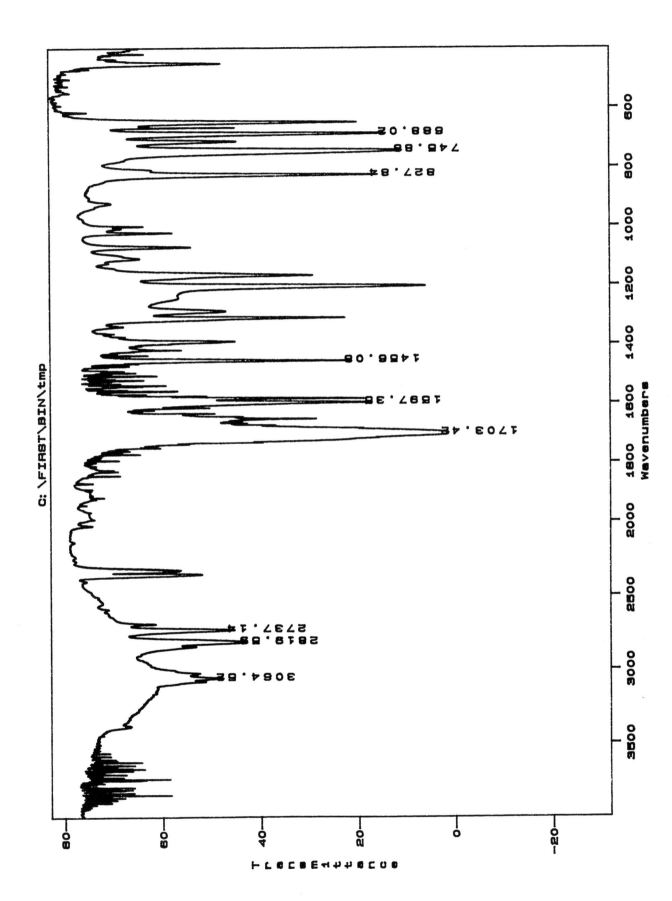

C: \FIRST\BIN\tmp

3064.62
2813.05
2737.1
1703.48
1597.36
1456.08
827.84
749.85
688.02

Wavenumbers

Appendix IIIc

Unknown Aldehyde #2

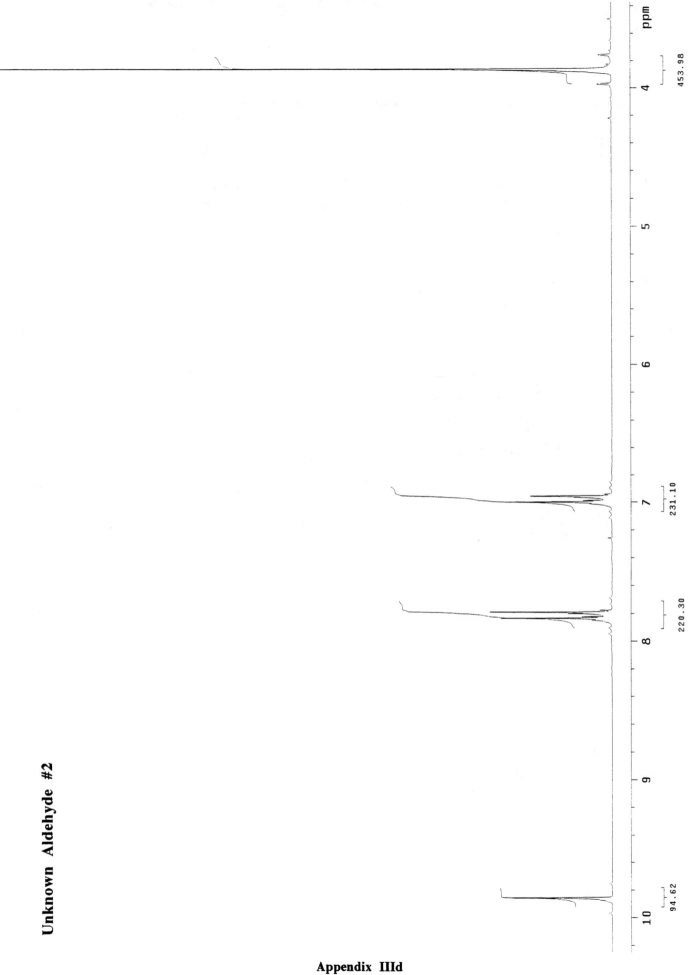

Unknown Aldehyde #2

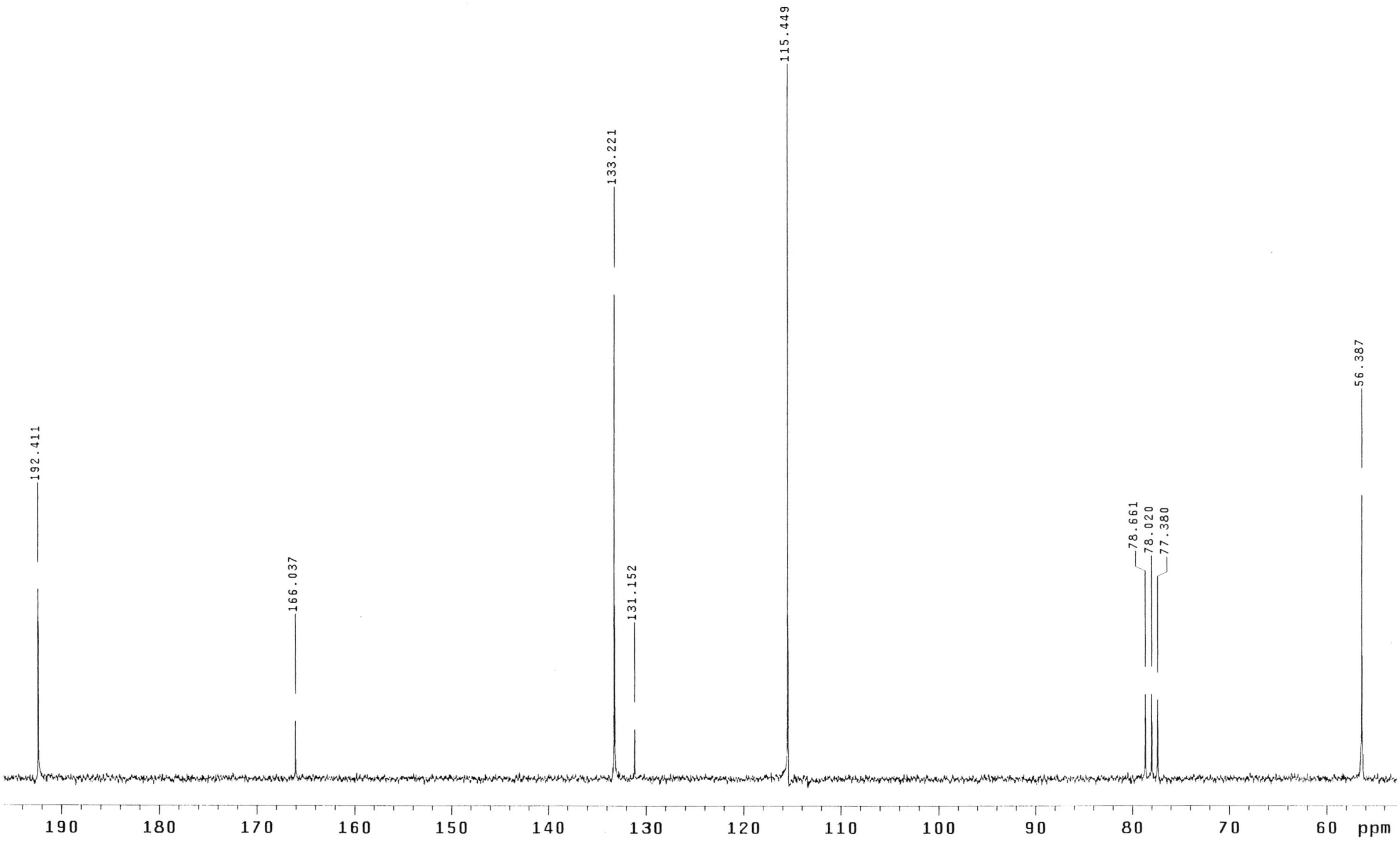

192.411
166.037
133.221
131.152
115.449
78.661
78.020
77.380
56.387

ppm
60
70
80
90
100
110
120
130
140
150
160
170
180
190

Appendix IIIe

Unknown Aldehyde #2

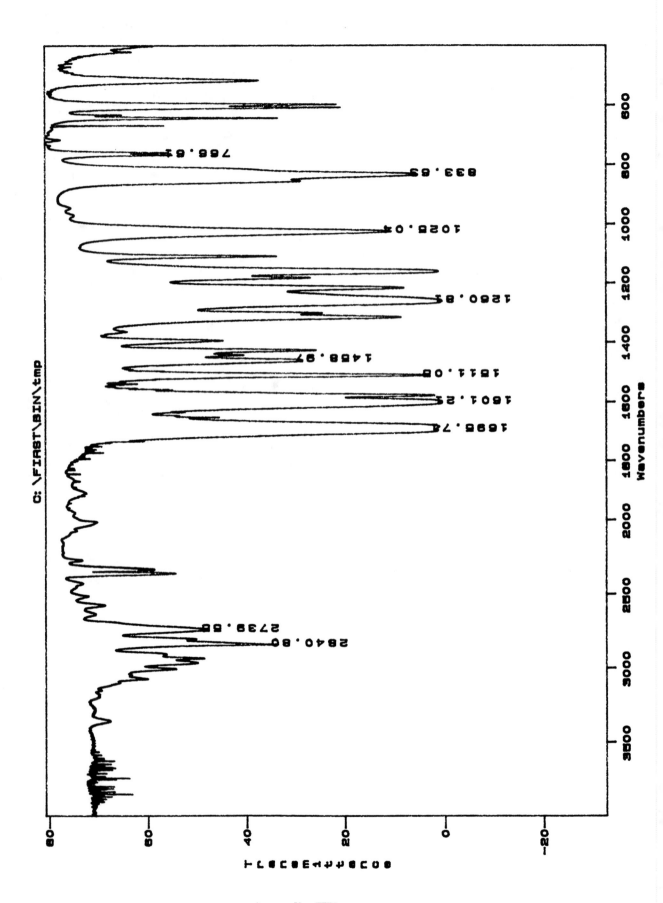

Appendix IIIf

Unknown Aldehyde #3

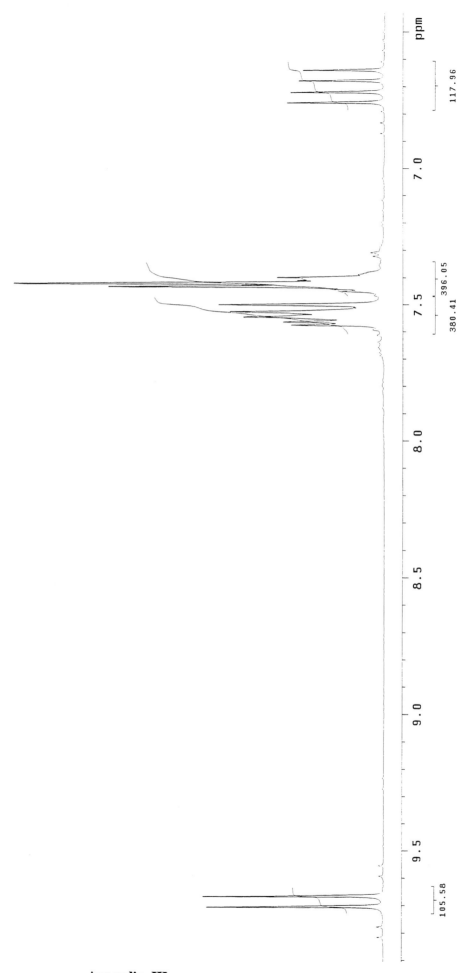

Unknown Aldehyde #3

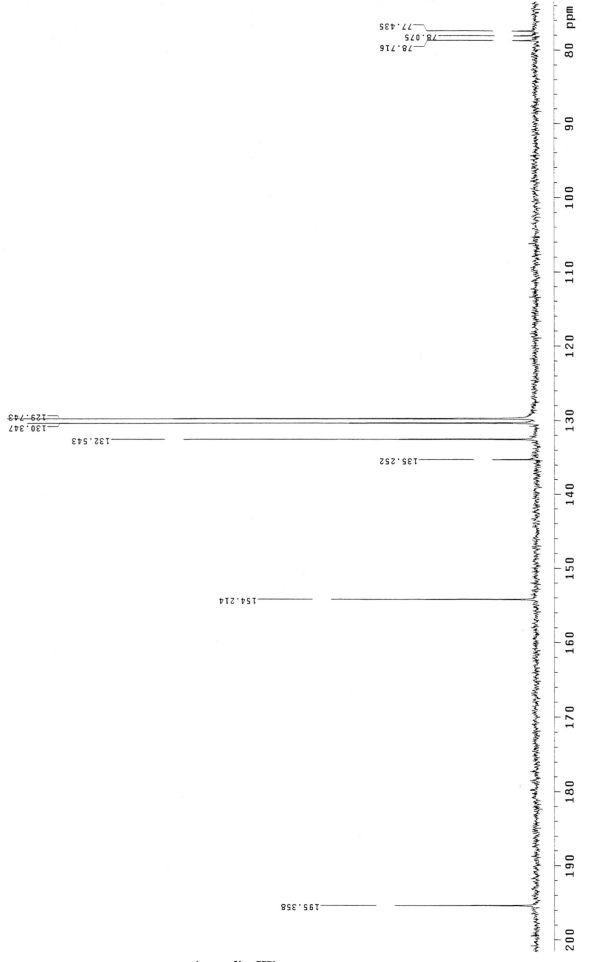

Unknown Aldehyde #3

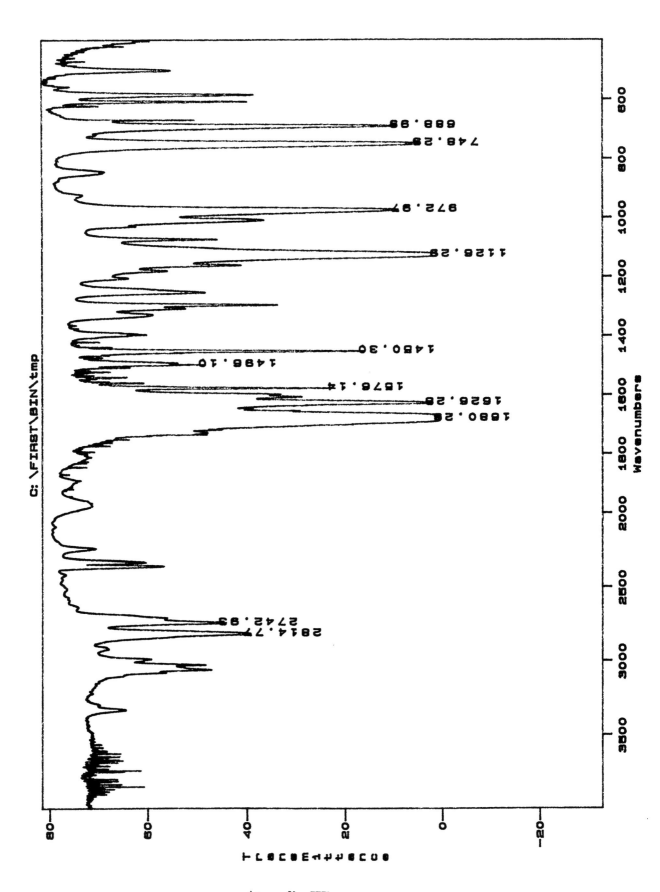

Appendix IIIi

Unknown Aldehyde #4

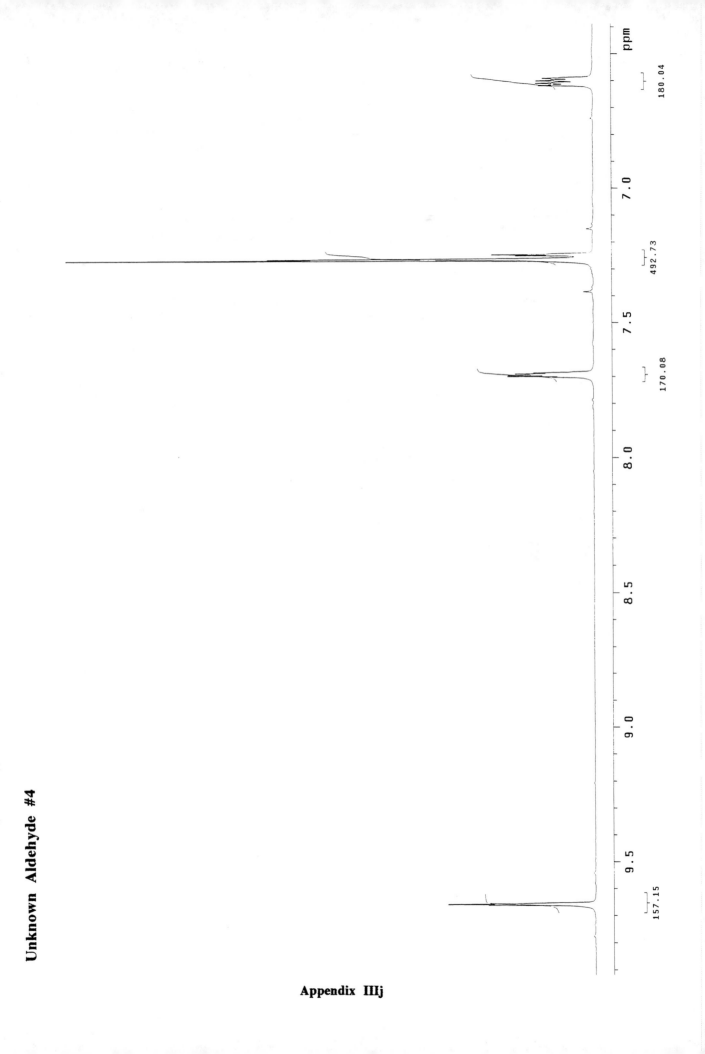

Appendix IIIj

Unknown Aldehyde #4

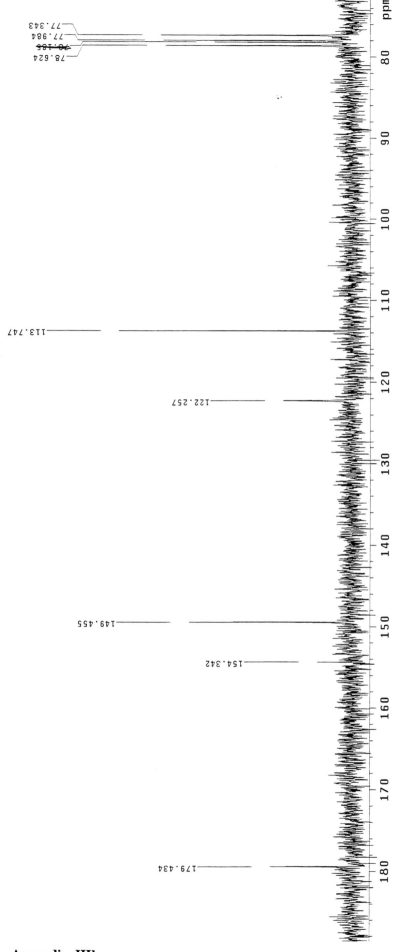

Appendix IIIk

Unknown Aldehyde #4

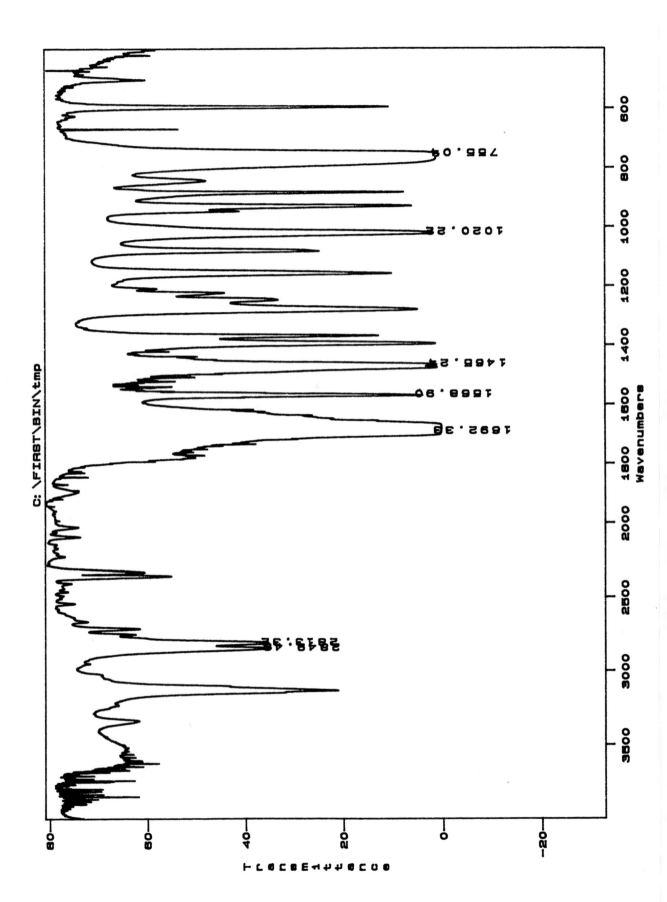

C:\FIRST\BIN\tmp

765.04

1050.22

1465.24

1558.90

1692.38

2819.35

Wavenumbers

Percent Transmittance

Appendix IIII

Unknown Aldehyde #5

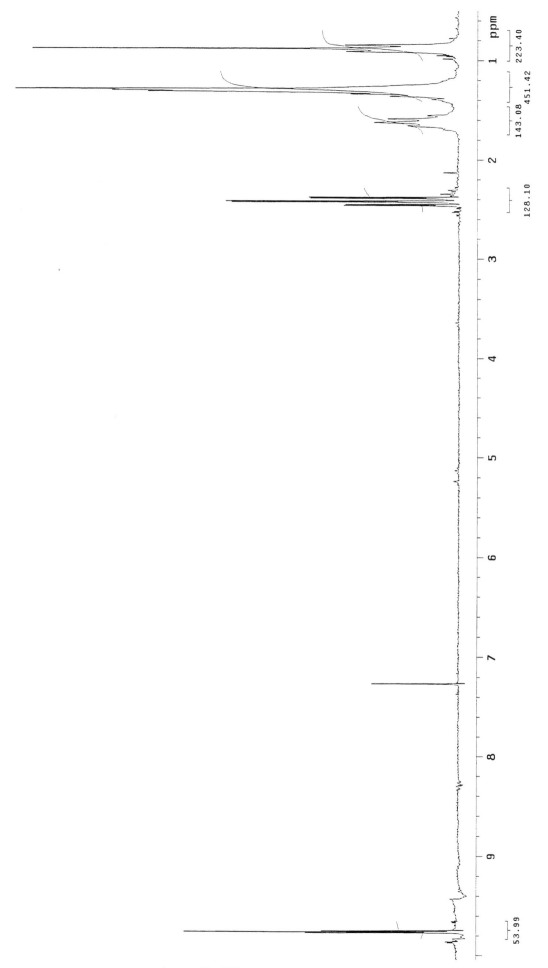

Unknown Aldehyde #5

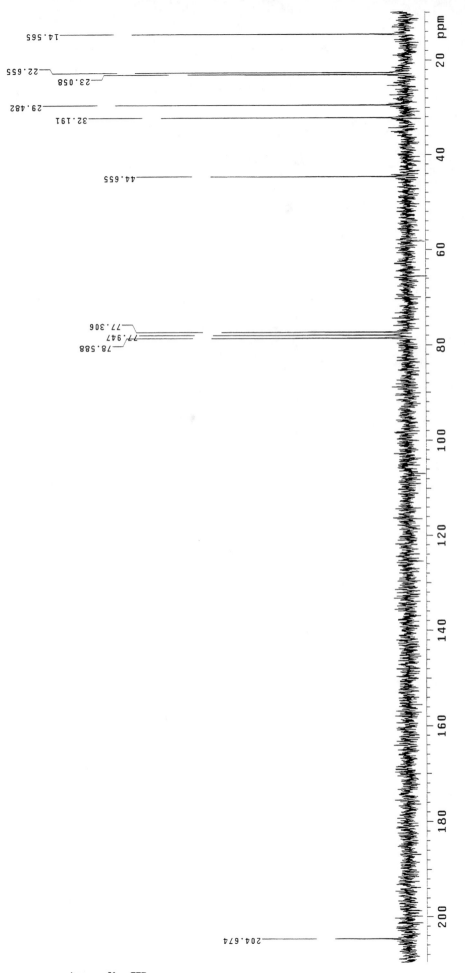

14.565

22.655
23.058

29.482
32.191

44.655

77.306
77.947
78.588

204.674

ppm

20

40

60

80

100

120

140

160

180

200

Appendix IIIn

Unknown Aldehyde #5

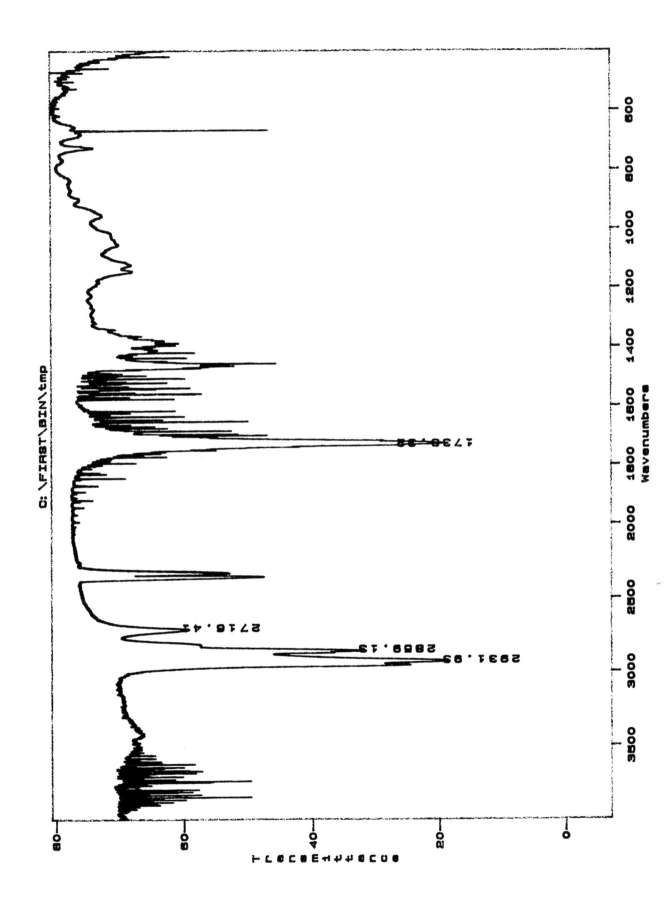

Appendix IIIo

Appendix IV

^{1}H, ^{13}C, & IR Spectra for

Unknown Organic Compound Laboratory

Unknown Organic Compound #1

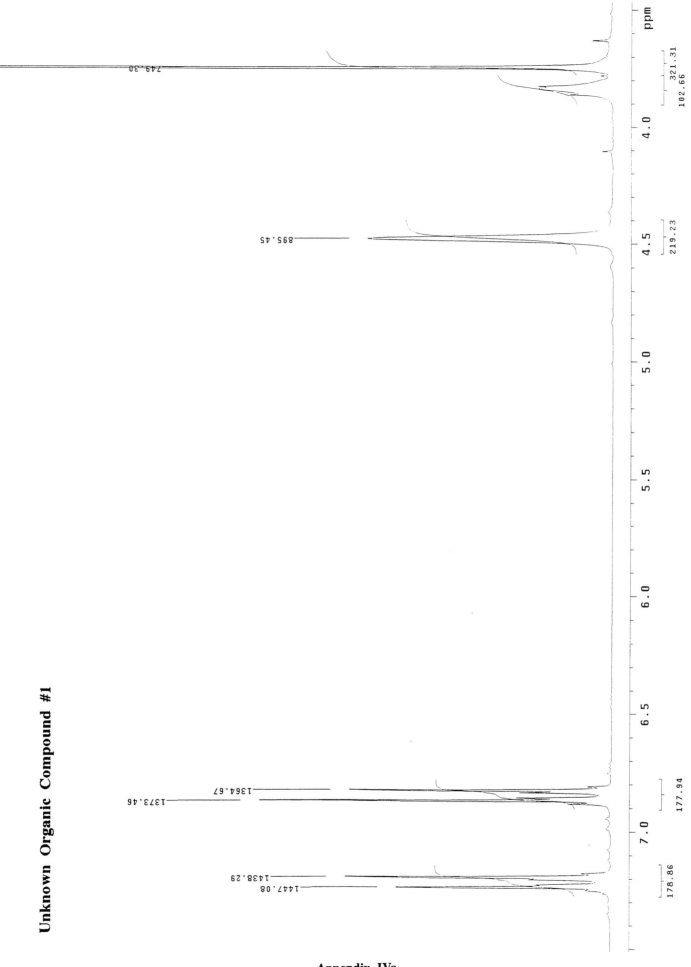

Unknown Organic Compound #1

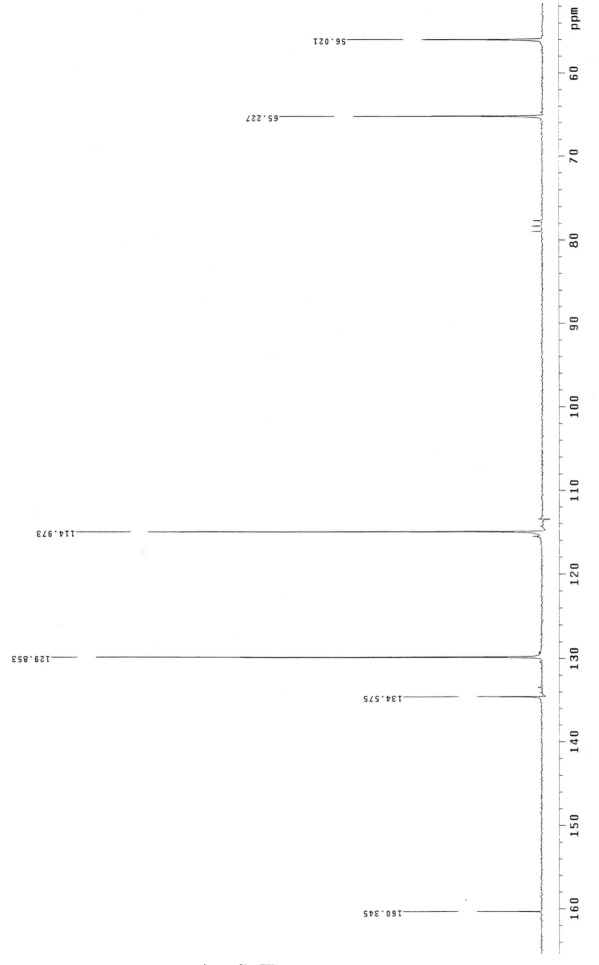

160.345
134.575
129.853
114.973
65.227
56.021
ppm

Appendix IVb

Unknown Organic Compound #1

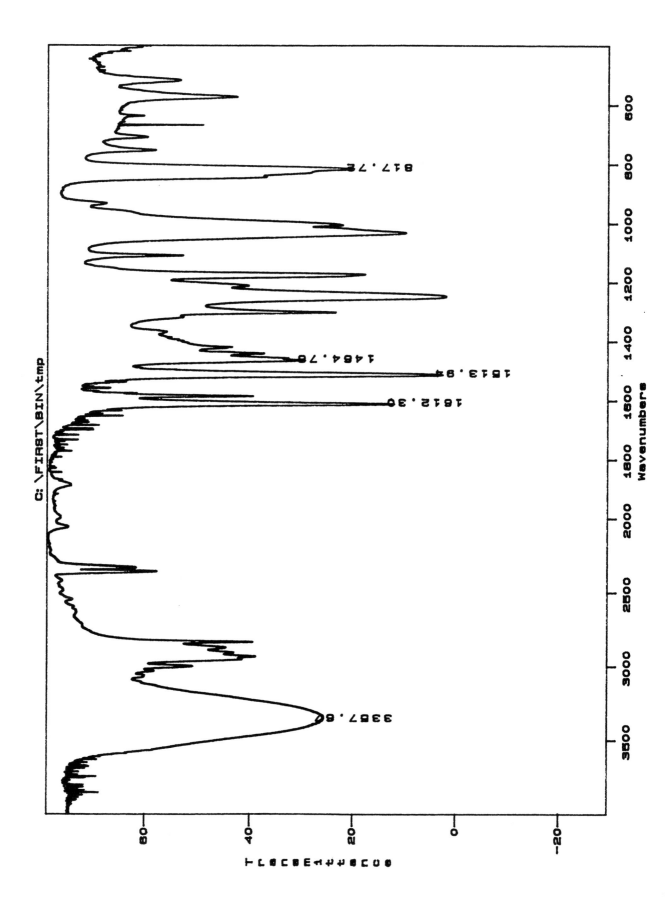

Unknown Organic Compound #2

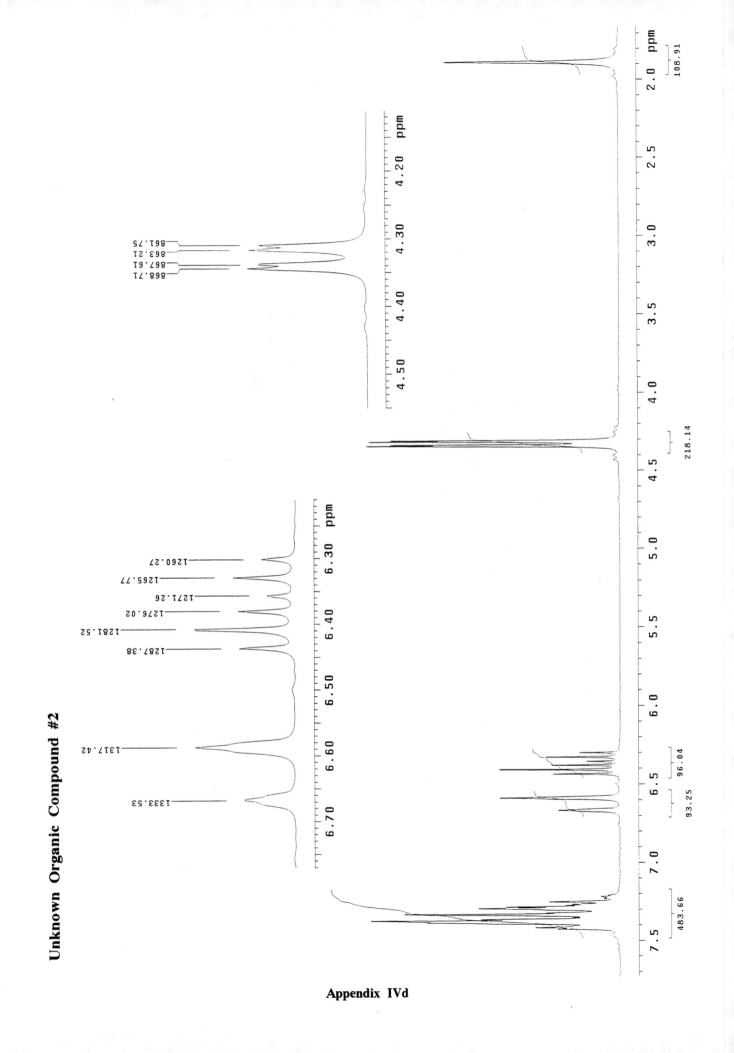

Appendix IVd

Unknown Organic Compound #2

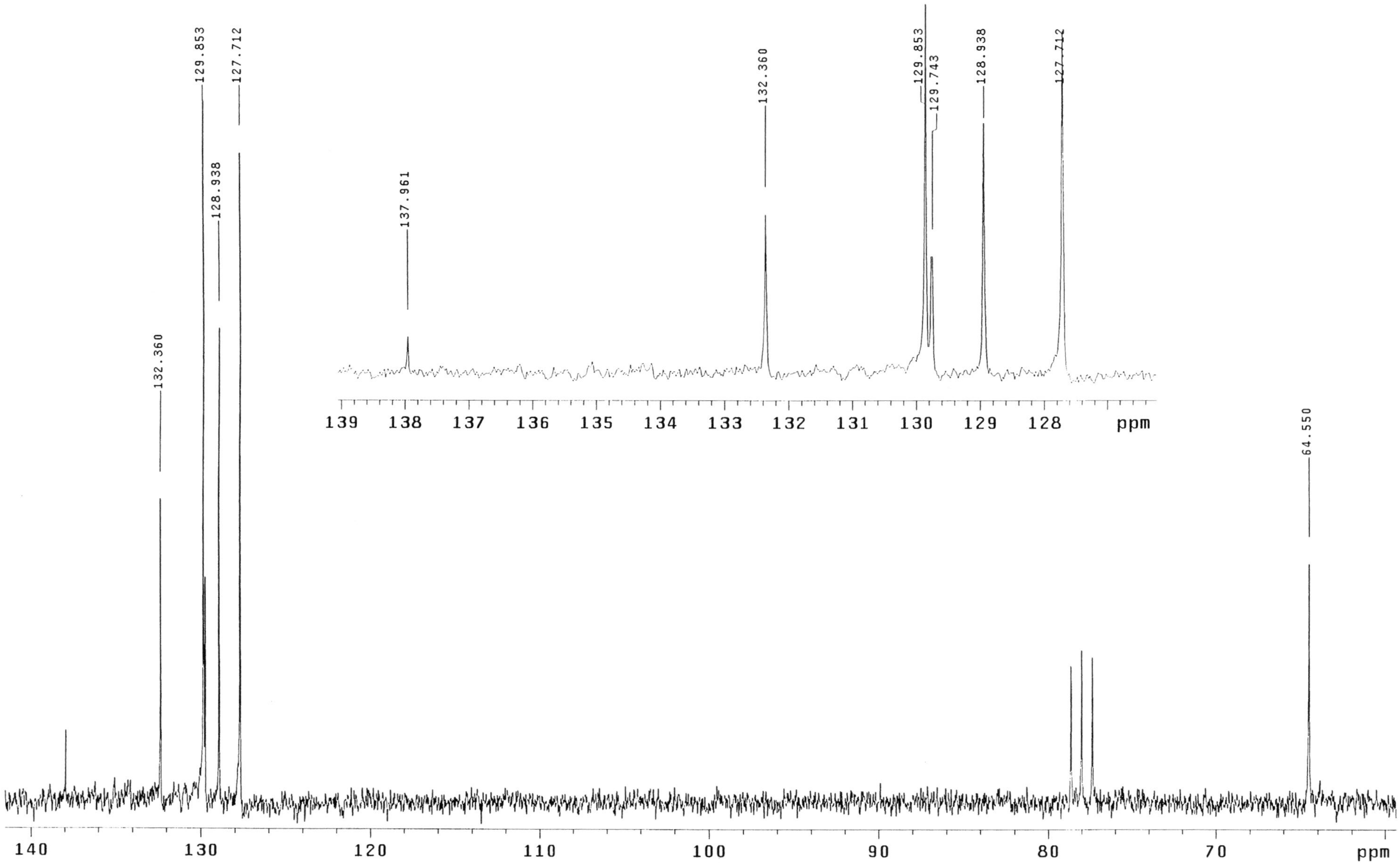

Appendix IVe

64.550

127.712
128.938
129.743
129.853
132.360
137.961

127.712
128.938
129.853
132.360

Unknown Organic Compound #2

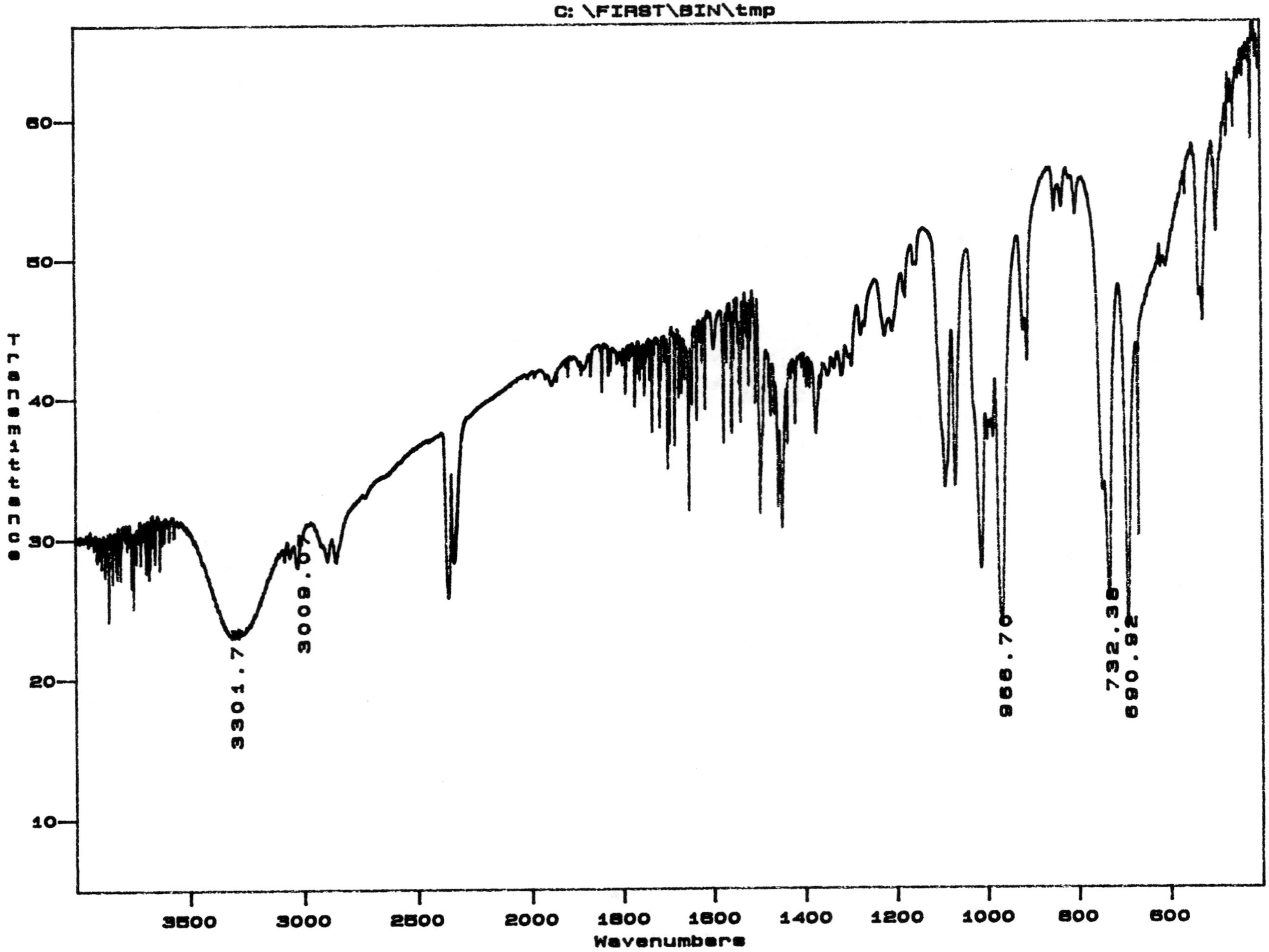

C:\FIRST\BIN\tmp

3301.73
3008.07
966.70
732.38
690.82

Wavenumbers

3500 3000 2500 2000 1800 1600 1400 1200 1000 800 600

Transmittance

60 50 40 30 20 10

Appendix IVf

Unknown Organic Compound #3

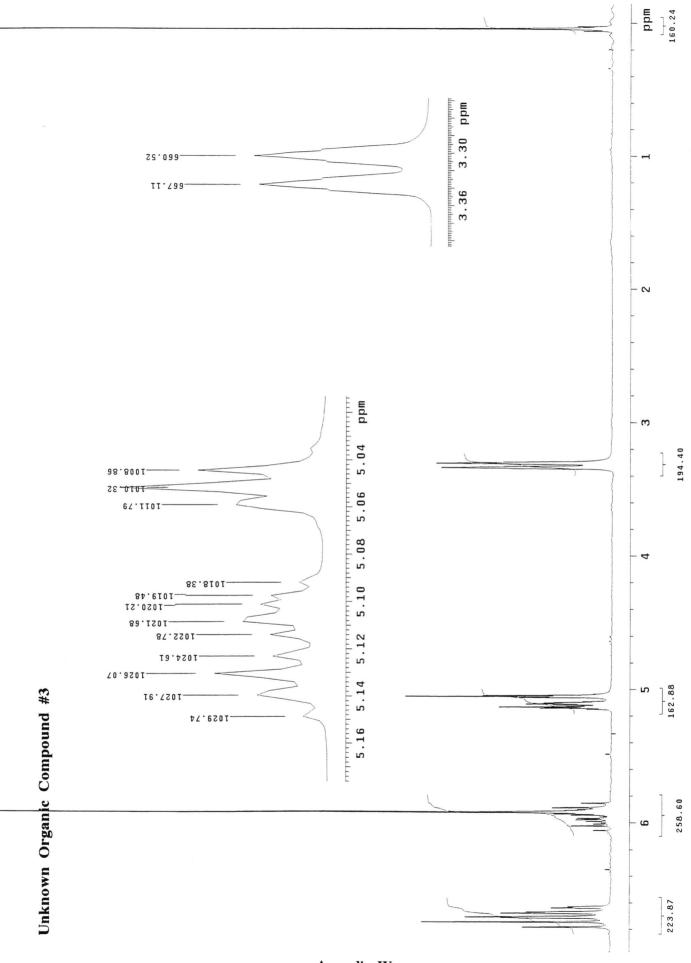

Appendix IVg

Unknown Organic Compound #3

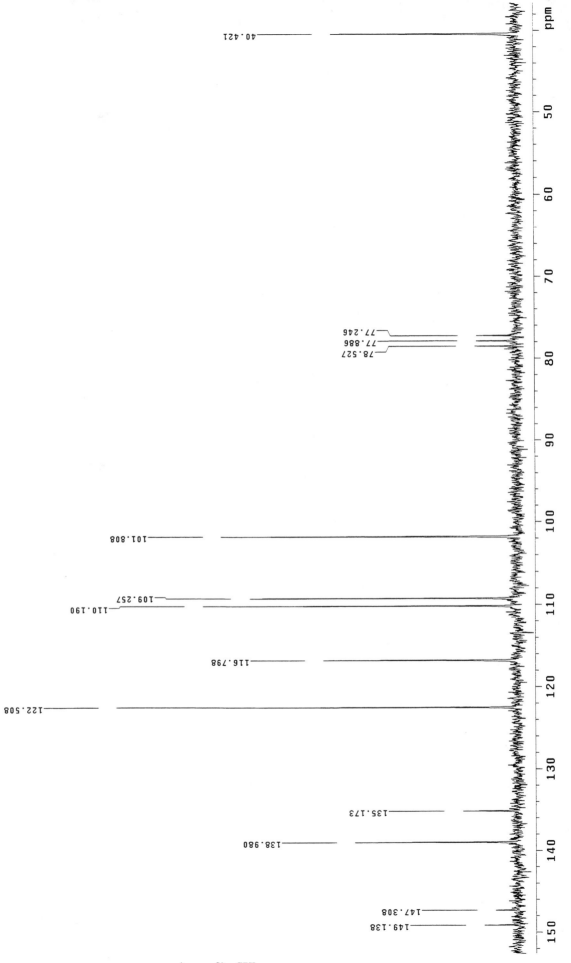

Appendix IVh

Unknown Organic Compound #3

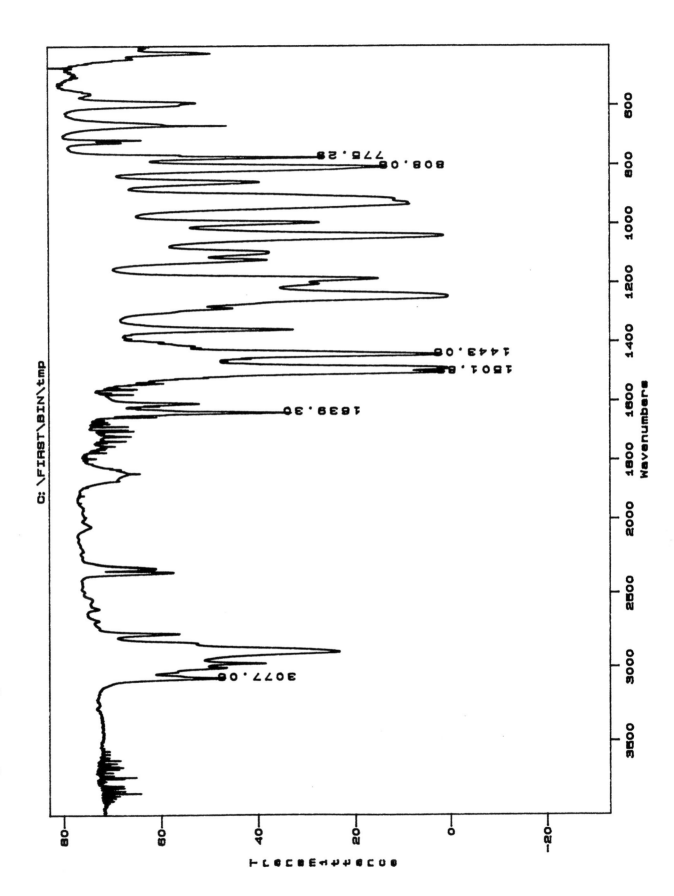

Unknown Organic Compound #4

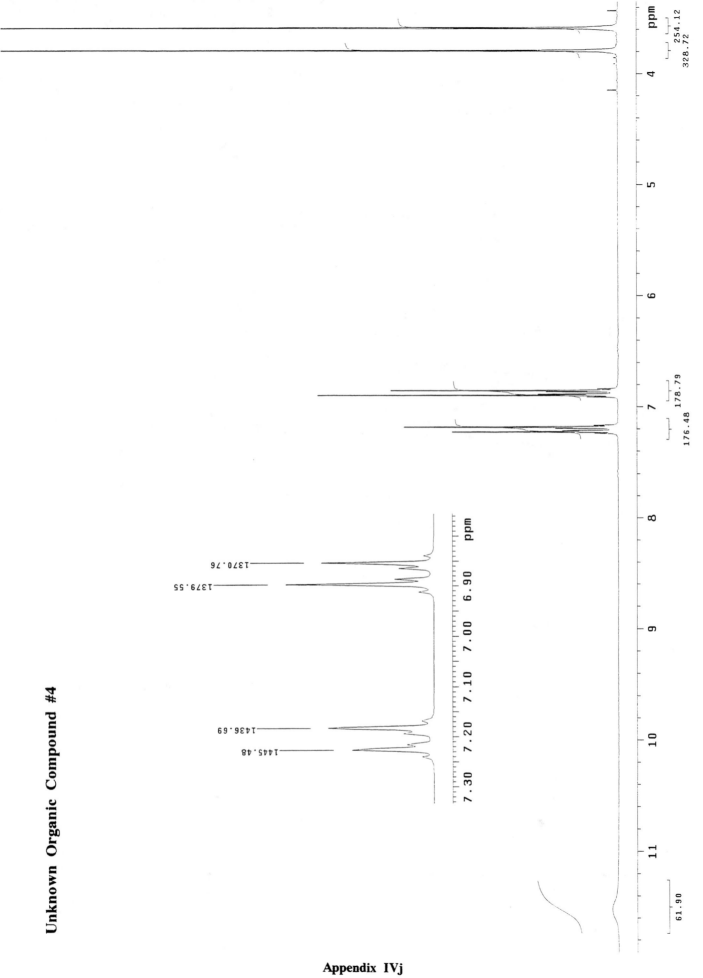

Unknown Organic Compound #4

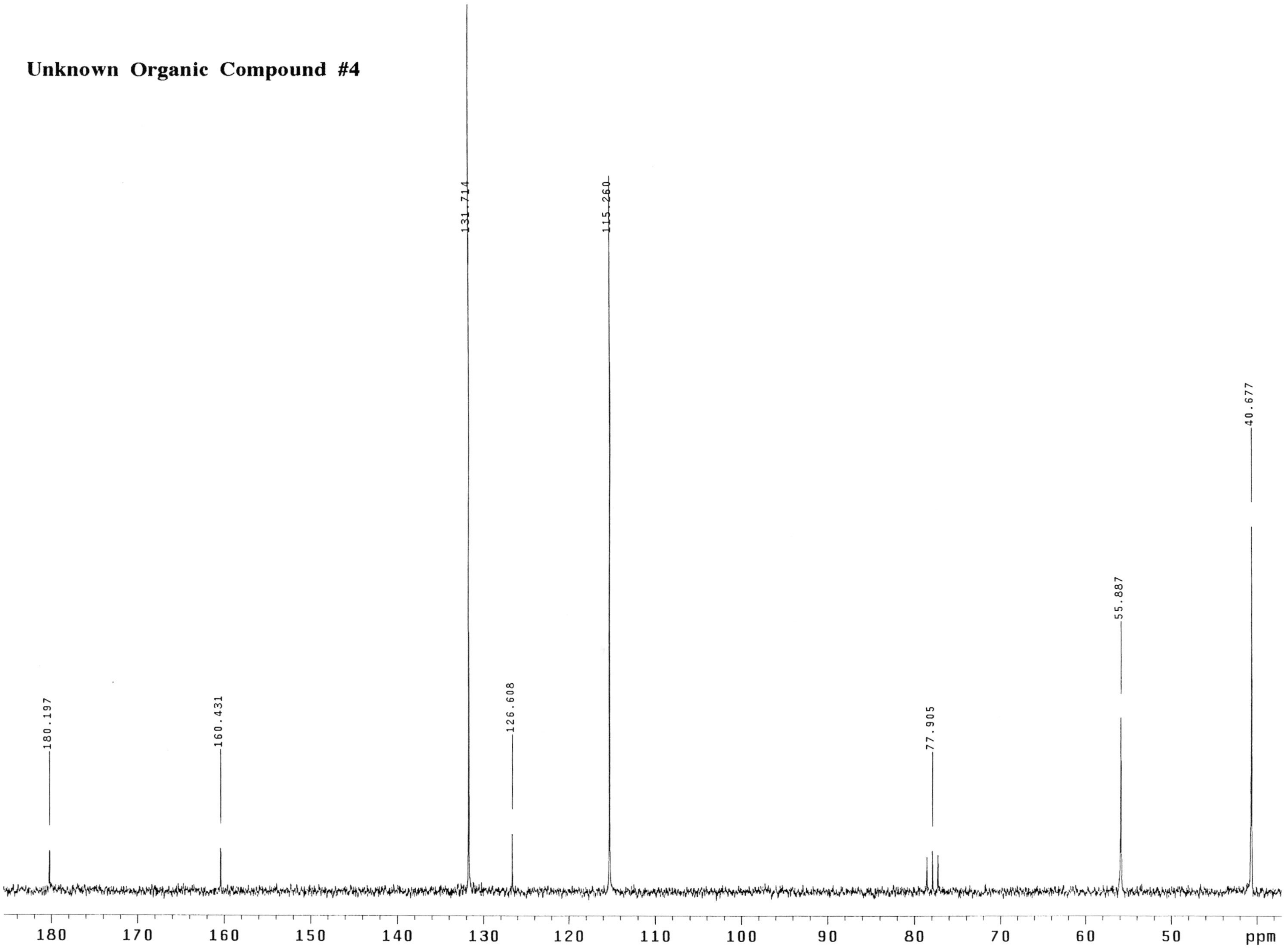

180.197

160.431

131.714

126.608

115.260

77.905

55.887

40.677

ppm

180   170   160   150   140   130   120   110   100   90   80   70   60   50

Appendix IVk

Unknown Organic Compound #4

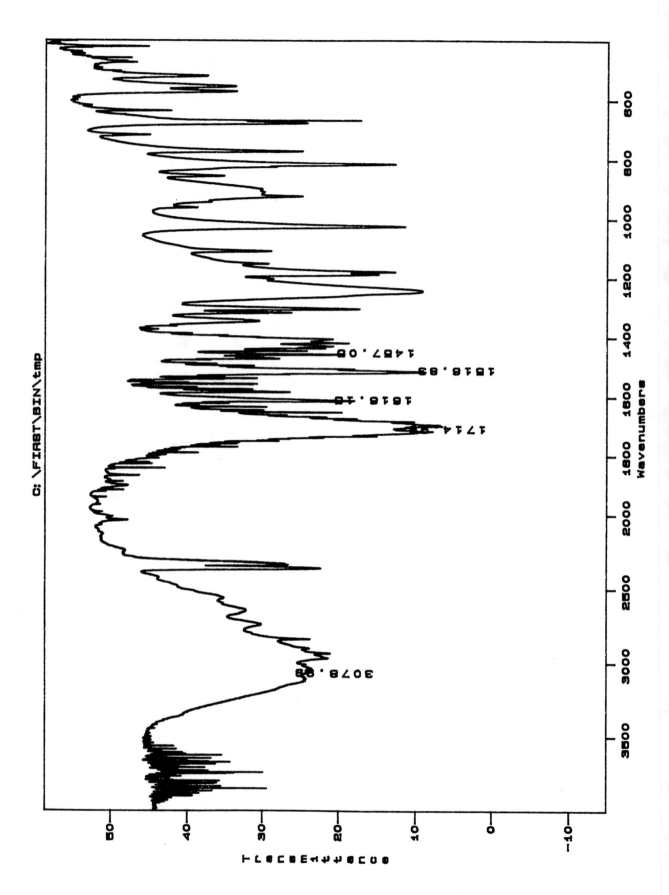

C: \FIRST\BIN\tmp

1714

1516.19

1516.83

1457.08

3078.88

Wavenumbers

Unknown Organic Compound #5

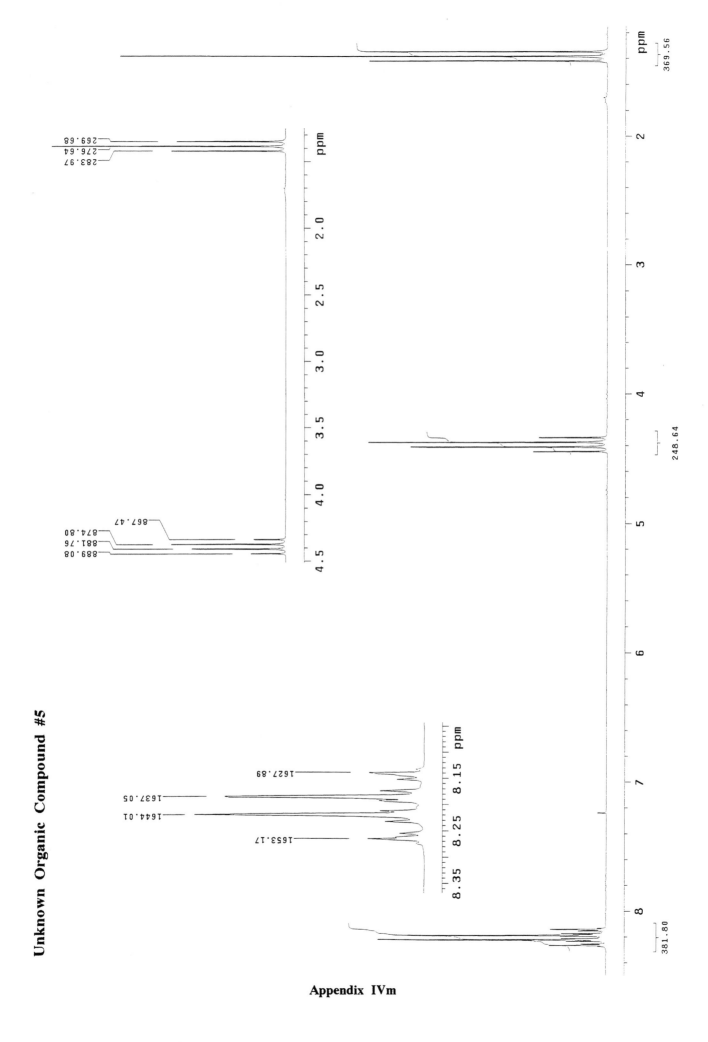

Appendix IVm

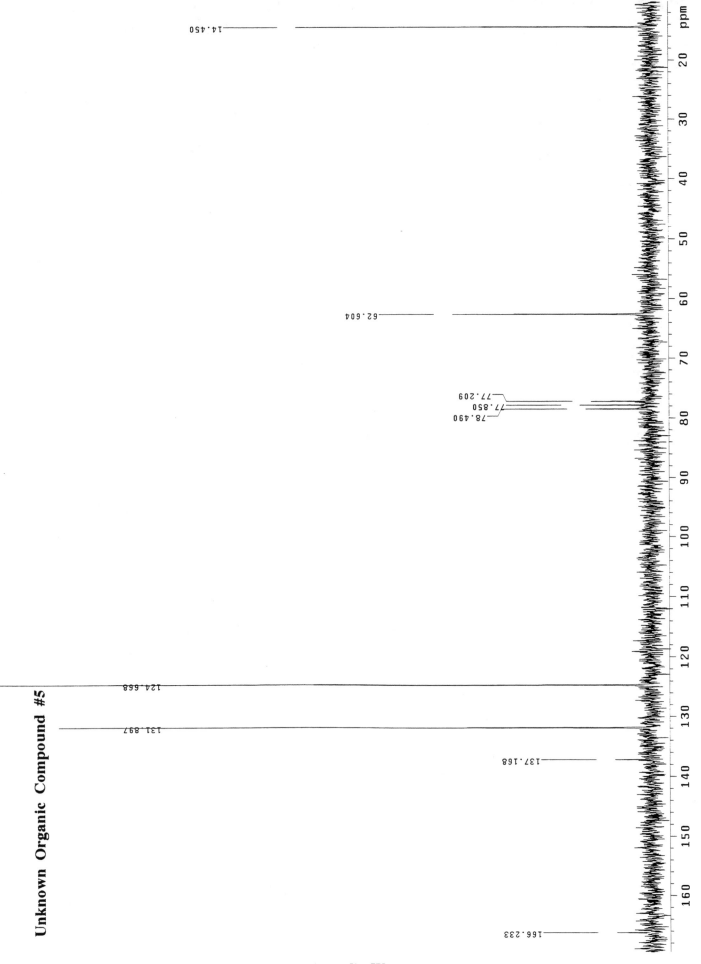

Unknown Organic Compound #5

166.233

137.168

131.897

124.668

78.490
77.850
77.209

62.604

14.450

ppm
20
30
40
50
60
70
80
90
100
110
120
130
140
150
160

Appendix IVn

Unknown Organic Compound #5

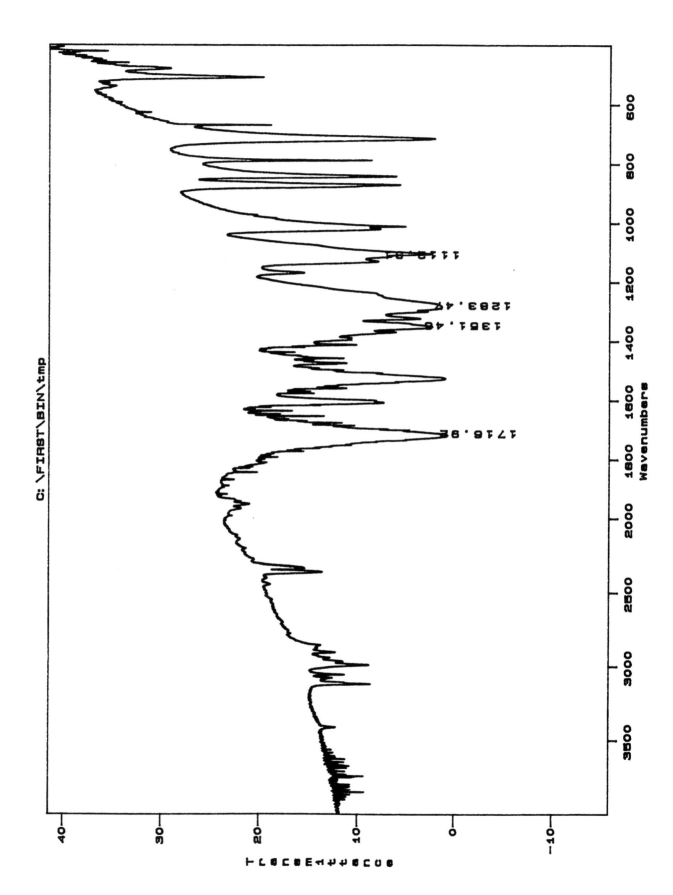

Unknown Organic Compound #6

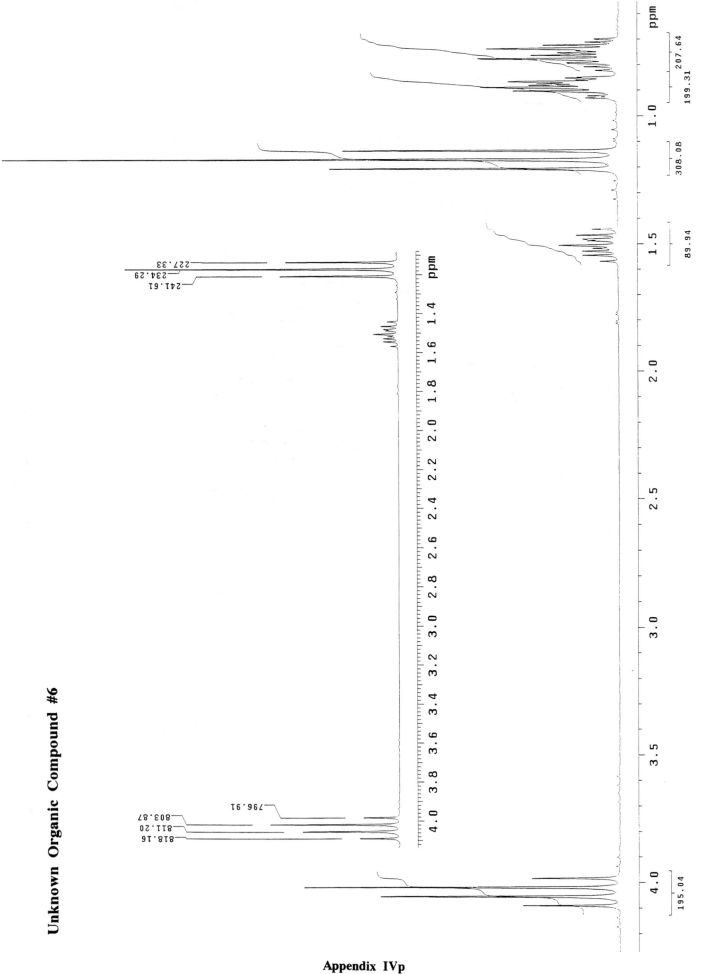

Unknown Organic Compound #6

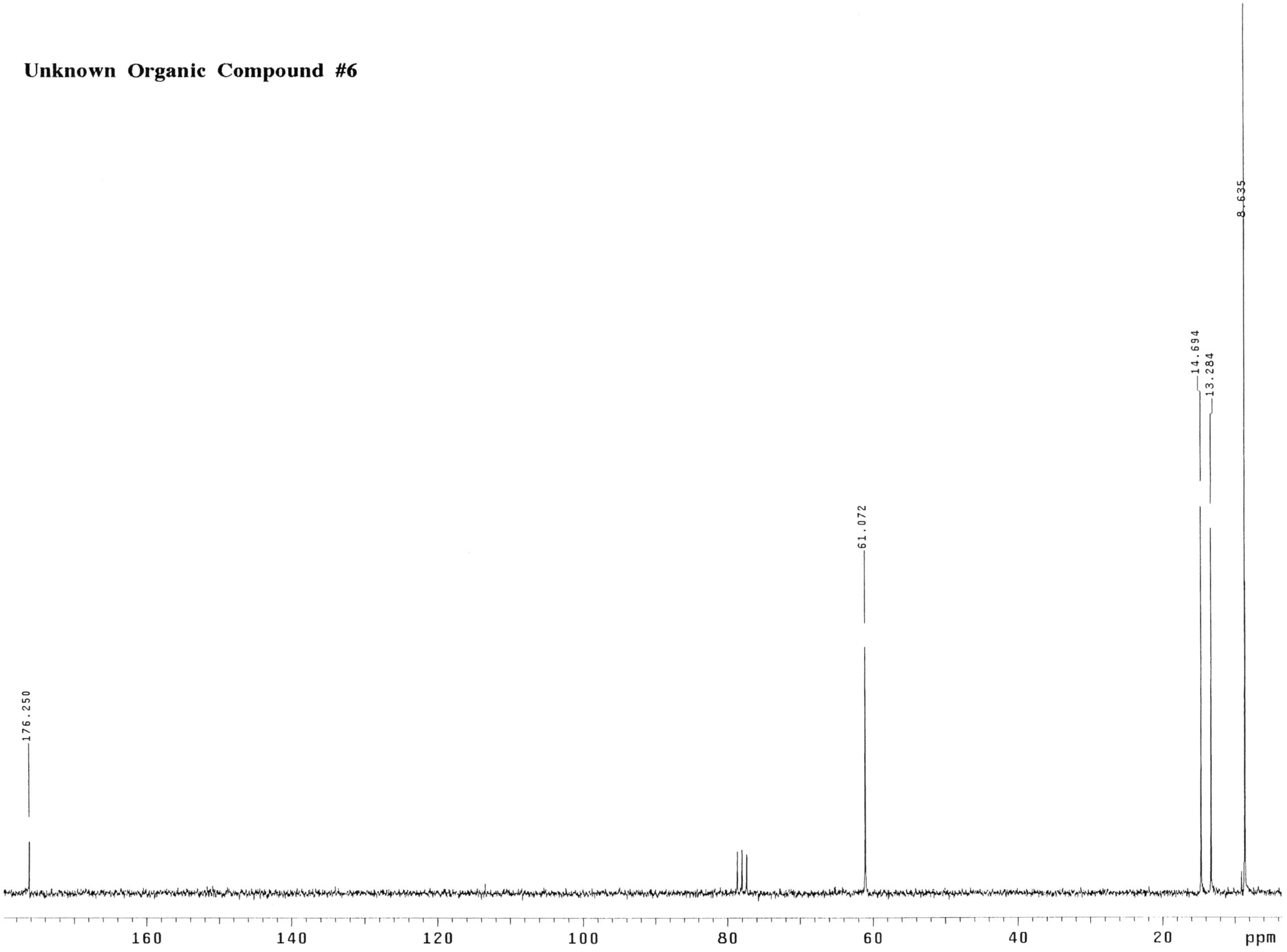

8.635

13.284

14.694

61.072

176.250

ppm
20
40
60
80
100
120
140
160

Appendix IVq

Unknown Organic Compound #6

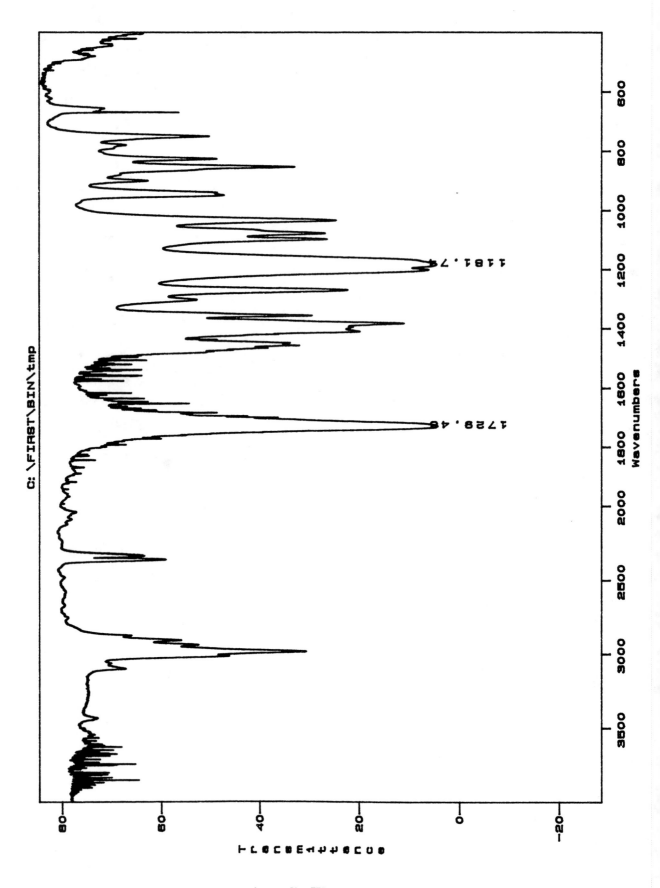

C:\FIRST\BIN\tmp

1729.46

1181.74

Wavenumbers

Appendix IVr

Unknown Organic Compound #7

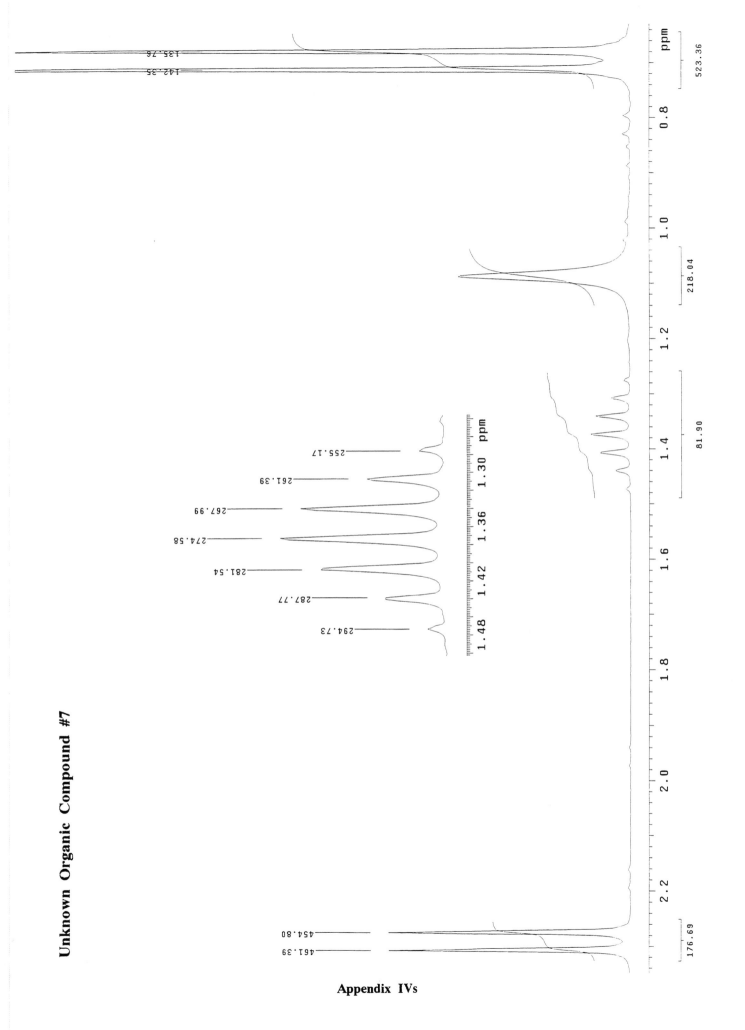

Unknown Organic Compound #7

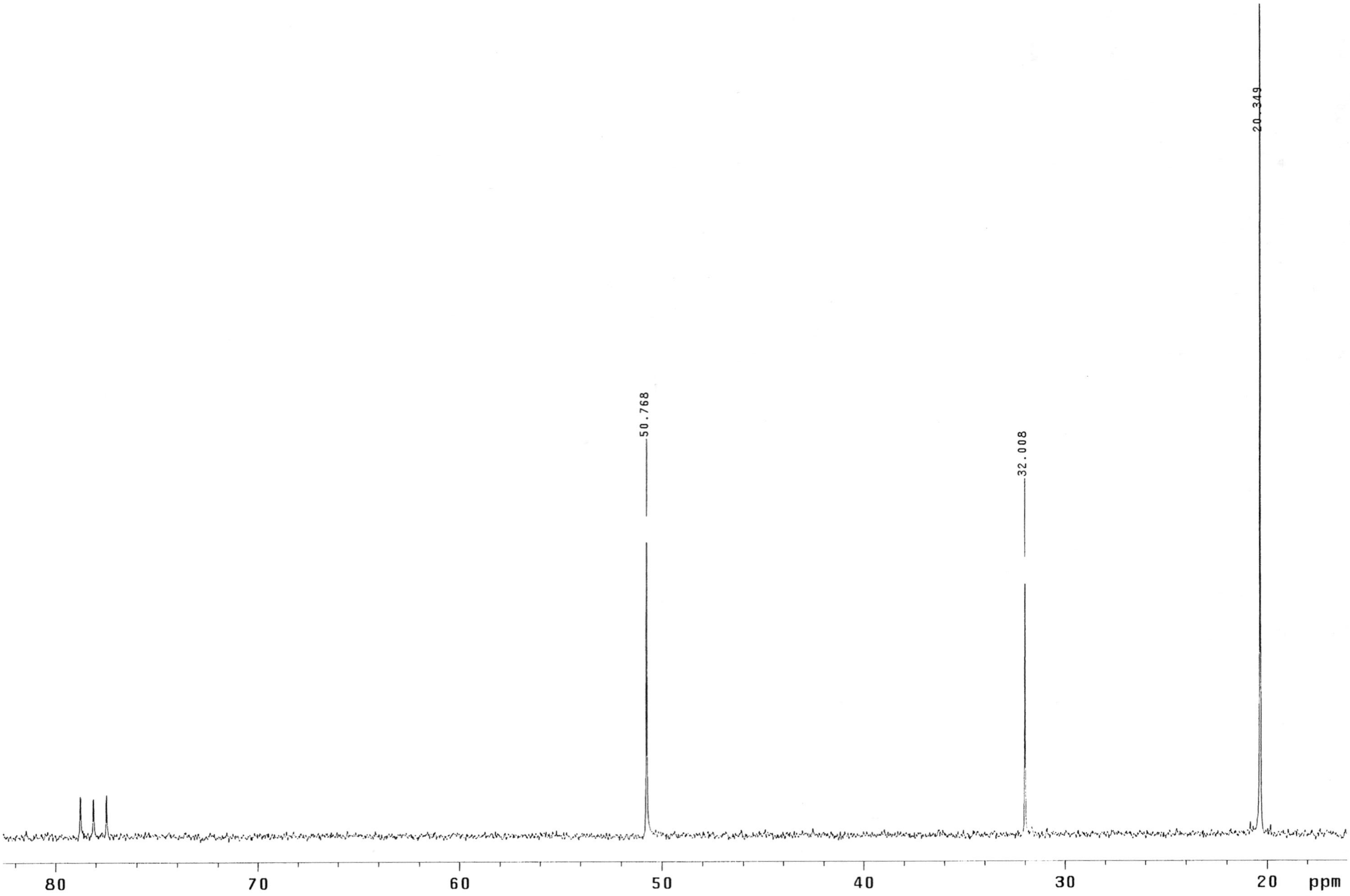

20.349

32.008

50.768

20	30	40	50	60	70	80

ppm

Appendix IVt

Unknown Organic Compound #7

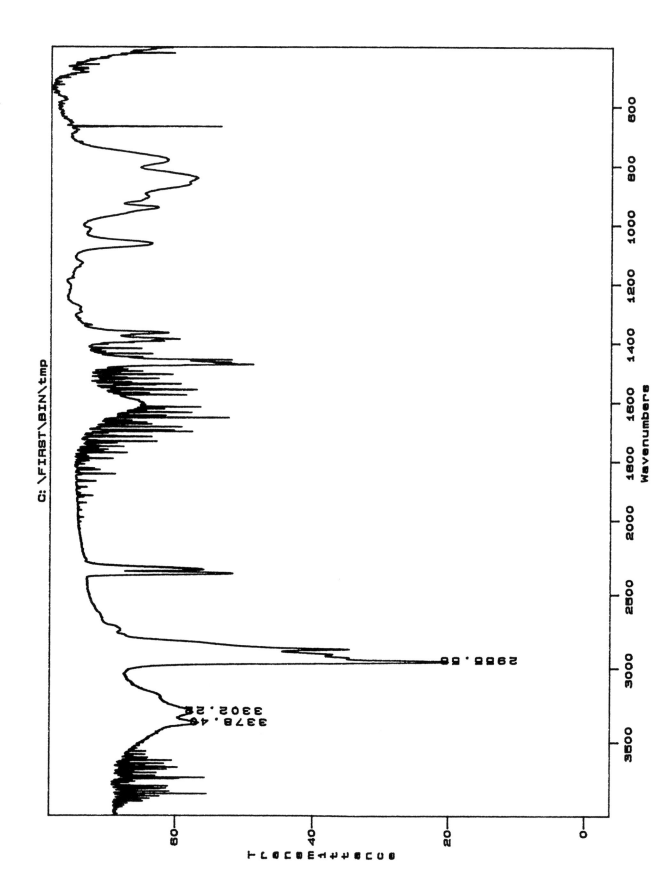

C:\FIRST\BIN\temp

2955.59

3378.40
3302.28

Wavenumbers

Appendix V

Qualitative Organic Analysis

Qualitative Identification of Organic Compounds

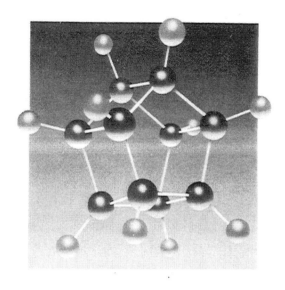

$C_{10}H_{10}$, Housane
Eaton, Or, Branca and Shankar (1968).

ORGANIC QUALITATIVE ANALYSIS

One of the exciting challenges that a chemist faces on a regular basis is the identification of organic compounds. To the introductory student this challenge is an excellent way to be initiated into the arena of chemical research. Millions of organic compounds are recorded in the chemical literature. At first glance it may seem a bewildering task to attempt to identify one certain compound from this vast array. However, it is important to realize that the majority of these substances can be grouped, generally by functional groups, into a comparatively small number of classes. In addition, chemists have an enormous database of chemical and spectroscopic information, which has been correlated and organized over the years, at their disposal. Determination of physical properties, of the functional groups present in a molecule, and of the reactions it undergoes, have allowed the chemist to establish a systematic, logical identification scheme.

Forensic chemistry, the detection of species causing environmental pollution, the development of new pharmaceuticals, progress in industrial research and development of polymers, to name a few, all depend to a large extent on the ability of the chemist to isolate, purify, and identify specific chemicals. The objective of organic qualitative analysis is to place a given compound, through screening tests, into one of a number of specific classes, which in turn greatly simplifies the *identification* of the compound. This screening is usually done by using a series of preliminary observations and chemical tests, in conjunction with the instrumental data that developments in spectroscopy have made available to the analyst. The advent of infrared (IR) and nuclear magnetic resonance (NMR) spectroscopy, and mass spectrometry (MS), have had a profound effect on the approach taken to identify a specific organic compound. Ultraviolet (UV) spectra may also be utilized to advantage with certain classes of materials.

The systematic approach taken in this text for the identification of an unknown organic compound is as follows:

1. Preliminary tests are performed to determine the physical nature of the compound.

2. The solubility characteristics of the unknown species are determined. This identification can often lead to valuable information related to the structural composition of an unknown organic compound.

3. Chemical tests, mainly to assist in identifying elements other than C, H, or O, may also be performed.

4. Classification tests to detect *common functional groups* present in the molecule, are carried out. The majority of these tests may be done using a few drops of a liquid or milligrams of a solid. There is an added benefit, especially in relation to the chemical detection of functional groups, that an introductory student in the organic chemistry laboratory may obtain. That is, a vast amount of chemistry can be *observed* and *learned* in performing these tests. The successful application of these tests requires that you develop the ability to think in a logical manner and based on your observations, that you learn to interpret the significance of each result. Later, as the *spectroscopic techniques* are introduced, *the number of chemical tests performed are usually curtailed.*

5. The spectroscopic method of analysis is utilized. As you develop further in your knowledge of chemistry, you will appreciate more and more the revolution that has taken place in chemical analysis over the past 25–30 years, and the powerful tools now at your disposal for the identification of organic compounds. For the introductory laboratory, the techniques of *IR, NMR,* and *UV–vis* spectroscopy are generally developed.

It is important to realize that *negative* findings are often as important as *positive* results in identifying a given compound. Cultivate the habit of following a *systematic pathway or sequence* so that no clue or bit of information is lost or overlooked along the way. It is important also to develop the *attitude* and *habit* of planning ahead. Outline a logical plan of attack, depending on the nature of the unknown, and follow it. As you gain more and more experience in this type of investigative endeavor, the planning stage will become easier.

At the *initial* phase of your training, the unknowns to be identified will be relatively pure materials and will all be known compounds. The properties of these materials are recorded in the literature, and/or in the tables in Appendix A. Later perhaps, mixtures of compounds or samples of commercial products will be assigned for separation, analysis, and identification of the component compounds.

Record all observations and results of the tests in your laboratory notebook. Review these data as you execute the sequential phases of your plan. This method serves to keep you on the path to success.

A large number of texts have been published on organic qualitative analysis. Several references are cited here.

BIBLIOGRAPHY

Cheronis, N. D.; Entrikin, J. B.; Hodnett, E. M. *Semimicro Qualitative Organic Analysis*, 3rd ed., Interscience: New York, 1965.

Cheronis, N. D.; Ma, T. S. *Organic Functional Group Analysis by Micro and Semimicro Methods;* Interscience: New York, 1964.

Feigl, F.; Anger, V. *Spot Tests in Organic Analysis*, 7th ed., Elsevier: New York, 1966.

Kamm, O. *Qualitative Organic Analysis*, 2nd ed., Wiley: New York, 1932.

Pasto, D. J.; Johnson, C. R.; Miller, M. J. *Experiments and Techniques in Organic Chemistry*; Prentice Hall, New Jersey, 1992.

Schneider, F. L. In *Qualitative Organic Microanalysis*, Vol. II of *Monographien aus dem Gebiete der qualitativen Mikroanalyse*; Benedetti-Pichler, Ed.; Springer-Verlag: Vienna, Austria, 1964.

Shriner, R. L.; Fuson, R. C.; Curtin, D. Y.; Morrill, T. C. *The Systematic Identification of Organic Compounds* 6th ed., Wiley: New York ,1980.

Vogel, A. I. *Qualitative Organic Analysis*, Part 2 of *Elementary Practical Organic Analysis*, Wiley: New York, 1966.

PRELIMINARY TESTS

Overview

The objective of preliminary tests is to assist you in selecting a route to follow in order to ultimately identify the unknown material at hand. It must be emphasized, however, that these tests frequently consume material. Given the amounts of material generally available at the micro- or semimicroscale level, judicious selection of the tests to perform must be made; however, in some tests, the material analyzed may be recovered. Each preliminary test that can be conducted with *little expenditure of time and material* can offer valuable clues as to which class a given compound belongs.

Physical State

Nonchemical Tests

If the material is a *solid*, a few milligrams of the sample may be viewed under a magnifying glass or microscope, which may give some indication as to the homogeneity of the material. Crystalline shape often is an aid in classifying the compound.

Determine the melting point, using a small amount of the solid material. If a narrow melting point range (1–2 °C) is observed, it is a good indication that the material is quite pure. If a broad range is observed, the compound must be recrystallized from a suitable solvent before proceeding. If the material undergoes decomposition on heating, it is worthwhile to try an evacuated (sealed-tube) melting point. If any evidence indicates that sublimation is occurring, an evacuated melting point should be run. Furthermore, this result indicates that sublimation might be used to purify the compound, if necessary.

If the material is a *liquid*, the boiling point is determined by the ultramicro method. If sufficient material is on hand, and the boiling point reveals that the material is relatively pure (narrow boiling point range), the *density* and the *refractive index* can provide valuable information for identification purposes.

Color

Since the majority of organic compounds are colorless, examination of the color can occasionally provide a clue as to the nature of the sample. Use caution, however, since tiny amounts of some impurities can color a substance. Aniline is a classic example. When freshly distilled it is colorless, but on standing a small fraction oxidizes and turns the entire sample a reddish-brown color.

Colored organic compounds contain a *chromophoric group*, usually indicating extended conjugation in the molecule. For example, 1,2-dibenzoylethylene (Experiments [3A] and [6]) is yellow; 5-nitrosalicylic acid

(Experiment [29C]) is light yellow; azobenzene (Experiment [35]) is red; tetraphenylcyclopentadienone (Experiment [A3ₐ]) is purple.

Can you identify the chromophores that cause these compounds to be colored? Note that a colorless liquid or white solid would *not contain* these units. Thus, compounds containing these groupings would be excluded from consideration as possible candidates in identification of a given substance.

Odor

Detection of a compound's odor can occasionally be of assistance, since the vast majority of organic compounds have no definitive odor. You should become familiar with the odors of the common compounds or classes. For example, aliphatic amines have a fishy smell; benzaldehyde (like nitrobenzene and benzonitrile) has an almond odor; esters have fruity odors (Experiments [8A–C]). Common solvents, such as acetone, diethyl ether, and toluene all have distinctive odors. Butyric and caproic acids have rancid odors. Low molecular weight mercapto (—SH) containing compounds have an intense smell of rotten eggs. In many cases, extremely small quantities of certain relatively high molecular weight compounds can be detected by their odor. For example, a C_{16} unsaturated alcohol released by the female silk worm moth elicits a response from male moths of the same species at concentrations of 100 molecules/cm^3. Odors are one extremely important facet of chemical communication between plants and animals and they can often result in a spectacular behavioral response (see also Experiment [8]).

Odor detection in humans involves your olfactory capabilities and thus can be considered a helpful lead, *but very rarely can this property be used to strictly classify or identify a substance.* As mentioned above, contamination by a small amount of an odorous substance is always a possibility.

CAUTION

CAUTION: You should be very cautious when detecting odors. Any odor of significance can be detected several inches from the nose. Do not place the container closer than this to your eyes, nose, or mouth. Open the container of the sample and gently waft the vapors toward you.

Ignition Test

CAUTION: Make sure you are wearing safety glasses.

Valuable information can be obtained by carefully noting the manner in which a given compound burns. The ignition test[1] is carried out by placing 1–2 mg of the sample on a spatula, followed by heating and ignition with a microburner flame. Do not hold the sample directly in the flame; heat the spatula about 1 cm from the flat end and move the sample slowly into the flame (see Fig. 10.1).

Important observations to be made concerning the ignition test are summarized in Table 10.1.

As the heating of the sample takes place, you should make the following observations.

---

[1] For an extensive discussion on examination of ignition residues see Feigl, F.; Anger, V. *Spot Tests in Organic Analysis*, 7th ed., Elsevier: New York; 1966, p. 51.

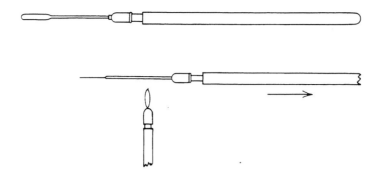

FIGURE 10.1 Heating on the microspatula *(Courtesy of Springer-Verlag, Vienna, Austria.)*

1. Any melting or evidence of sublimation: This observation gives an approximate idea of the melting point by the temperature necessary to cause melting.

2. Color of the flame as the substance begins to burn (see Table 10.1).

3. Nature of the combustion (flash, quiet, or an explosion). Rapid, almost instantaneous combustion indicates high hydrogen content. Explosion indicates presence of nitrogen, or nitrogen–oxygen, containing groups. For example, azo groups (Experiment [35]) or nitro groups (Experiment [29]).

4. Nature of the residue, if present, after ignition.

  a. If a black residue remains and disappears on further heating at higher temperature, the residue is carbon.

  b. If the residue undergoes swelling during formation, the presence of a carbohydrate or similar compound is indicated.

  c. If the residue is black initially but still remains after heating, an oxide of a heavy metal is indicated.

  d. If the residue is white, the presence of an alkali or alkaline earth carbonate, or SiO_2 from a silane or silicone is indicated.

TABLE 10.1 Ignition Test Observations[a]

Type of Compound	Example	Observation
Aromatic compounds, unsaturated, or higher aliphatic compounds	Toluene	Yellow, sooty flame
Lower aliphatic compounds	Hexane	Yellow, almost nonsmoky flame
Compounds containing oxygen	Ethanol	Clear bluish flame
Polyhalogen compounds	Chloroform	Generally do not ignite until burner flame applied directly to the substance
Sugars and proteins	Sucrose	Characteristic odor
Acid salts or organometallic compounds	Ferrocene	Residue

[a] Cheronis, N. D.; Entrikin, J. B. *Semimicro Qualitative Analysis*; Interscience: New York, 1947, p. 85.

Appendix Ve

SEPARATION OF IMPURITIES

If the preliminary tests outlined above indicate that the unknown in question contains impurities, it may be necessary to carry out one of several purification steps. These techniques are discussed in earlier chapters and are summarized below for correlation purposes.

1. For a liquid, distillation is generally used (see Techniques 2 and 3).
2. For a solid, recrystallization is generally used (see Technique 5).
3. Extraction is used especially if the impurity is insoluble in a solvent in which the compound itself is soluble (see Technique 4).
4. Sublimation is a very efficient technique, if the compound sublimes (see Technique 9).
5. Chromatography (gas, column, and thin-layer) is often used (see Techniques 1 and 6A).

It should be realized that these techniques may be applied to the separation of mixtures as well.

DETECTION OF ELEMENTS OTHER THAN CARBON, HYDROGEN, OR OXYGEN

The elements, other than C, H, and O, that are most often present in organic compounds are nitrogen, sulfur, and the halogens (F, Cl, Br, or I). To detect the presence of these elements, the organic compound is generally fused with metallic sodium. This reaction converts these heteroatoms to the water-soluble inorganic compounds, NaCN, Na_2S, and NaX. Inorganic qualitative analysis tests enable the investigator to determine the presence of the corresponding anions.

$$\text{Organic compound containing} \begin{Bmatrix} C \\ H \\ O \\ N \\ S \\ X \end{Bmatrix} \xrightarrow[\Delta]{Na} \begin{Bmatrix} NaCN \\ Na_2S \\ NaX \end{Bmatrix}$$

Sodium Fusion[2]

HOOD

IMPORTANT. *The fusion reaction is carried out in the **hood**. Make sure you are wearing safety glasses. All reagents must be of analytical grade, and deionized water must be used.*

CAUTION

CAUTION: Sodium metal can cause serious burns and it reacts *violently* with water.

In a small (10 x 75-mm) test tube (soft glass preferred), supported in a transite board (see Fig. 10.2), is placed about 25–30 mg of clean sodium metal (about one half the size of a pea).

[2] See Campbell, K. N.; Campbell, B. K. *J. Chem. Educ.* **1950,** *27,* 261 for a discussion of the procedure.

CAUTION: Use forceps to make this transfer, *never* touch sodium metal with your fingers.

CAUTION

Heat the tube with a flame until the sodium melts and sodium vapor is observed rising in the tube.

Mix a small sample of your unknown compound (1–2 drops of a liquid; 6–10 mg if a solid) with about 15–25 mg of *powdered* sucrose.[3] Gentle mixing of solids may be done on filter paper or glassine weighing paper and liquids on a watch glass. Then carefully add this mixture to the tube. During the transfer, be careful not to get any material on the sides of the test tube.

NOTE. *The addition of sucrose to the sample aids in the reduction of various nitrogen or sulfur compounds. Also, it absorbs volatile materials so that they may undergo the desired reaction before significant vaporization can occur.*

Now heat the tube gently to initiate the reaction with sodium. Remove the flame until the reaction subsides, and then heat to redness for 1–2 min. Allow the tube and contents to cool to room temperature. **Then**, *and only then*, **cautiously** add several drops of methanol (Pasteur pipet) to decompose any unreacted metallic sodium. Gently warm to drive off the excess methanol.

Reheat the tube to a bright red. While the tube is still red hot, lift the transite board and test tube from the iron ring and place the tube in a small beaker (30 mL) containing about 15 mL of deionized water (the transite board acts as a cover on the beaker).

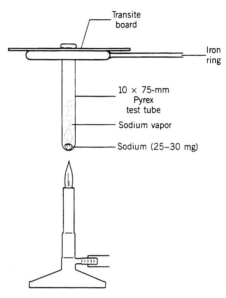

FIGURE 10.2 Apparatus for sodium fusion.

CAUTION: The soft-glass tube usually cracks and breaks during this operation.

CAUTION

Break up the tube with a glass rod, heat the solution to boiling and filter it by gravity into a clean 50-mL Erlenmeyer flask. Wash the filter paper with an additional 2.0 mL of distilled water and combine this wash with the original filtrate.

NOTE. *If a Pyrex test tube is used, after the unreacted sodium metal is completely destroyed by adding methanol, add 2 mL of deionized water directly to the tube and contents. Place a glass stirring rod in the tube and heat the solution to boiling with stirring and then filter as described above. Dilute the filtrate with deionized water to about 5 mL.*

Using the Fusion Solution

The clear, colorless fusion solution is used to test for the presence of CN^- (nitrogen), S^{-2} (sulfur), and X^- (halogens except F^-) as described in the following sections.

a. Place 2–3 drops (Pasteur pipet) of the fusion solution on a white spot plate, followed by 2 drops of water. Now add 1 drop of dilute

Sulfur

---

[3] Confectioner's sugar is used and can be purchased at the supermarket.

(2%) aqueous sodium nitroprusside solution. The formation of a deep blue-violet color is a positive test for sulfur.

$$Na_2S + Na_2Fe(CN)_5NO \rightarrow Na_4[Fe(CN)_5NOS]$$

Sodium nitroprusside   Blue-violet complex

b. Place 3–4 drops (Pasteur pipet) of the fusion solution on a white spot plate followed by 1–2 drops of acetic acid. Now add 1 drop of 1% lead(II) acetate solution. The formation of a black precipitate (lead sulfide) indicates the presence of sulfur.

Nitrogen[4]

Reagents

1. A 1.5% solution of *p*-nitrobenzaldehyde in 2-methoxyethanol.
2. A 1.7% solution of *o*-dinitrobenzene in 2-methoxyethanol.
3. A 2.0% solution of NaOH in distilled water.

NOTE. *All reagent drops are dispensed using Pasteur pipets.*

On a white spot plate, place together: 5 drops of Reagent **1**, 5 drops of Reagent **2**, and 2 drops of Reagent **3**. Stir this mixture gently with a glass rod.

Now add 1 drop of the fusion solution. The formation of a deep-purple color is a positive test for the presence of CN^- ion; a yellow or tan coloration is negative. If a positive result is obtained, nitrogen is present in the sample.

The test is valid in the presence of halogens (NaX) or sulfur (Na_2S). It is much more sensitive than the traditional Prussian Blue test.[5]

The Soda Lime Test

In a 10 × 75-mm test tube, mix about 50 mg of soda lime and 50 mg of MnO_2. Add 1 drop of a liquid unknown or about 10 mg of a solid unknown. Place over the mouth of the tube a moist strip of Brilliant Yellow paper (moist, red litmus paper is an alternative). Using a test tube holder, hold the tube at an incline (*pointing away from you and others*) and heat the contents gently at first and then quite strongly. Nitrogen-containing compounds will usually evolve ammonia.

A positive test for nitrogen is the deep red coloration of the brilliant yellow paper (or blue color of the litmus paper).

The Halogens (Except Fluorine)

Using the Fusion Solution

In a 10 × 75-mm test tube containing a boiling stone, place 0.5 mL (calibrated Pasteur pipet) of the fusion solution. Carefully acidify this solution by the dropwise addition of dilute HNO_3 acid, delivered from a Pasteur pipet (test acidity with litmus paper). If a positive test for nitrogen or sulfur was obtained, heat the resulting solution to a gentle boil (stir with a micro-

---

[4] Adapted from Guilbault, G. G.; Kramer, D. N. *Anal. Chem.* **1966,** *39,* 834. Idem. *J. Org. Chem.* **1966,** *31,* 1103. See also Shriner, R. L.; Fuson, R. C.; Morrill, T. C. *The Systematic Identification of Organic Compounds,* 6th ed., Wiley: New York, 1980, p. 80.

[5] See Vogel, A. I. *Elementary Practical Organic Chemistry,* Part 2, 2nd ed., Wiley: New York, 1966, p. 37.

spatula to prevent boilover) for 1 min over a microburner [**HOOD**] to expel   HOOD
any HCN or H_2S that might be present. Then cool the tube to room temperature.

To the resulting cooled solution, add 2 drops (Pasteur pipet) of aqueous 0.1 M $AgNO_3$ solution.

A heavy curdy-type precipitate is a positive test for the presence of Cl^-, Br^-, or I^- ion. A faint turbidity is a negative test.

AgCl precipitate is white.
AgBr precipitate is pale yellow.
AgI precipitate is yellow.
AgF is not detected by this test since it is relatively soluble in water.

The silver halides have different solubilities in dilute ammonium hydroxide solution.

Centrifuge the test tube and contents and remove the supernatant liquid using a Pasteur filter pipet. Add 0.5 mL (calibrated Pasteur pipet) of dilute ammonium hydroxide solution to the precipitate and stir with a glass rod to determine whether the solid is soluble.

AgCl is soluble in ammonium hydroxide due to the formation of the complex ion, $[Ag(NH_3)_2]^+$.
AgBr is slightly soluble in this solution.
AgI is insoluble in this solution.

Further Test
Once the presence of a halide ion has been established, a further test[6] is available to aid in distinguishing between Cl^-, Br^-, and I^- ion.

As described above, acidify 0.5 mL of the fusion solution with dilute HNO_3. To this solution, add 5 drops (Pasteur pipet) of a 1.0% aqueous $KMnO_4$ solution and shake the test tube for about 1 min.

Now add 10–15 mg of oxalic acid, enough to decolorize the excess purple permanganate, followed by 0.5 mL of methylene chloride solvent. The test tube is stoppered, shaken, vented, and the layers allowed to separate. Observe the color of the CH_2Cl_2 (lower) layer.

A clear methylene chloride layer indicates Cl^- ion.
A brown methylene chloride layer indicates Br^- ion.
A purple methylene chloride layer indicates I^- ion.

The colors may be faint and should be observed against a white background.

The Beilstein Test[7]
Organic compounds that contain chlorine, bromine, or iodine, and hydrogen decompose on ignition in the presence of copper oxide, to yield the corresponding hydrogen halides. These hydrogen halides react to form the volatile cupric halides that impart a green or blue-green color to a nonluminous flame. It is a very sensitive test, but some nitrogen-containing compounds and some carboxylic acids also give positive results.

---

[6] For a further test to distinguish between the three halide ions see Shriner, R. L.; Fuson, R. C.; Morrill, T. C. *The Systematic Identification of Organic Compounds*, 6th ed., Wiley: New York, 1980, p. 81. Also see this reference (p. 85) for a specific test for the F^- ion.
[7] Beilstein, F. *Berichte* **1872**, *5*, 620.

Pound the end of a copper wire to form a flat surface that can act as a spatula. The other end of the wire (~4 in. long) is stuck in a cork stopper to serve as an insulated handle.

Heat the flat tip of the wire in a flame until coloration of the flame is negligible.

On the **cooled** flat surface of the wire, place a drop (Pasteur pipet) of liquid unknown, or a few milligrams of solid unknown. Gently heat the material in the flame. The carbon present in the compound will burn first, and thus the flame will be luminous, but then the characteristic green or blue-green color may be evident. It may be fleeting, so watch carefully.

It is recommended that a known compound containing a halogen be tested so that you become familiar with the appearance of the expected color.

Fluoride ion is not detected by this test, since copper fluoride is not volatile.

SOLUBILITY CHARACTERISTICS

Determination of the solubility characteristics of an organic compound can often give valuable information as to its structural composition. It is especially useful when correlated with spectral analysis.

Several schemes have been proposed that place a substance in a definite group according to its solubility in various solvents. The scheme presented below is similar to that outlined in Shriner et al.[8]

There is no sharp dividing line between soluble and insoluble, and an arbitrary ratio of solute to solvent must be selected. We suggest that a compound be classified as soluble if its solubility is greater than 15 mg/500 μL of solvent.

Carry out the solubility determinations, at ambient temperature, in 10 × 75-mm test tubes. Place the sample (~15 mg) in the test tube and add a total of 0.5 mL of solvent in three portions from a graduated or calibrated Pasteur pipet. Between addition of each portion, stir the sample vigorously with a glass stirring rod for 1.5–2 min. If the sample is water soluble, test the solution with litmus paper to assist in classification according to the solubility scheme that follows.

NOTE. *To test with litmus paper, dip the end of a small glass rod into the solution and then gently touch the litmus paper with the rod. DO NOT DIP THE LITMUS PAPER INTO THE TEST SOLUTION.*

In doing the solubility tests follow the scheme in the order given. *Keep a record of your observations.*

Step I Test for water solubility. If soluble, test the solution with litmus paper.

Step II If water soluble, determine the solubility in diethyl ether. This test further classifies water-soluble materials.

Step III Water-insoluble compounds are tested for solubility in a 5% aqueous NaOH solution. If soluble, determine the solubility in 5% aqueous $NaHCO_3$. The use of the $NaHCO_3$ solution aids in distinguishing between strong (soluble) and weak (insoluble) acids.

Step IV Compounds insoluble in 5% aqueous NaOH are tested for solubility in a 5% HCl solution.

---

[8] Shriner, R. L.; Fuson, R. C.; Morrill, T. C. *The Systematic Identification of Organic Compounds*, 6th ed., Wiley: New York, 1980.

Step V Compounds insoluble in 5% aqueous HCl are tested with concentrated H_2SO_4. If soluble, further differentiation is made using 85% H_3PO_4, as shown in the scheme.

Step VI Miscellaneous neutral compounds containing sulfur or nitrogen are normally soluble in strong acid solution.

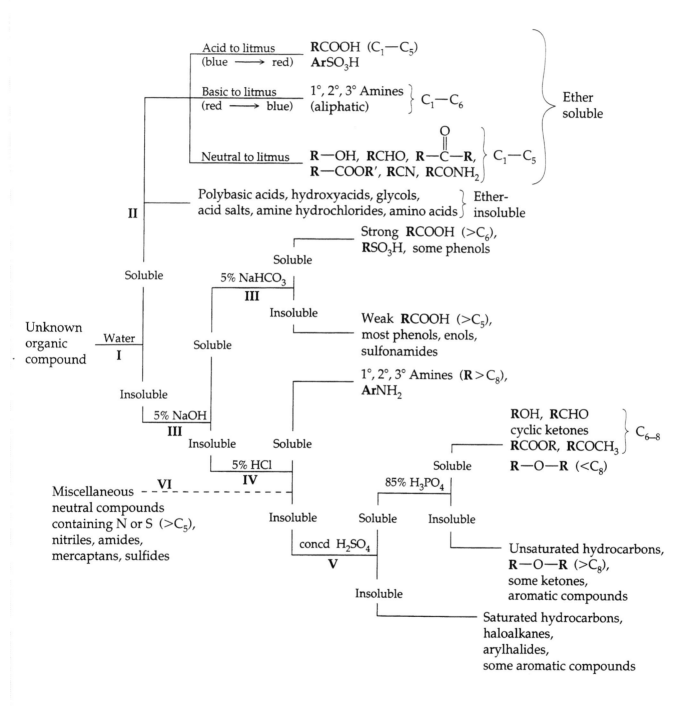

Note that to classify a given compound, it may not be necessary to test its solubility in every solvent. *Do only those tests that are required to place the compound in one of the solubility groups.* Make your observations with care, and proceed in a logical sequence as you make the tests.

THE CLASSIFICATION TESTS[9]

NOTE. *For all tests given in this section, drops of reagents are measured out using Pasteur pipets.*

Alcohols

Ceric Nitrate Test

INSTRUCTOR PREPARATION. *The reagent is prepared by dissolving 4.0 g of ceric ammonium nitrate [$(NH_4)_2Ce(NO_3)_6$] in 10 mL of 2 N HNO_3. Warming may be necessary.*

Primary, secondary, and tertiary alcohols having fewer than 10 carbon atoms give a positive test as indicated by a change in color from *yellow* to *red.*

$$(NH_4)_2Ce(NO_3)_6 + RCH_2OH \rightarrow [alcohol + reagent]$$
  Yellow   (Red complex)

Place 5 drops of test reagent on a white spot plate. Add 1–2 drops of the unknown sample (5 mg if a solid). Stir with a thin glass rod to mix the components and observe any color change.

1. If the alcohol is water insoluble, 3–5 drops of dioxane may be added, but run a blank to make sure the dioxane is pure. Efficient stirring gives positive results with most alcohols.

2. Phenols, if present, give a brown color or precipitate.

Chromic Anhydride Test: The Jones Oxidation

INSTRUCTOR PREPARATION. *The reagent is prepared by slowly adding a suspension of 1.0 g of CrO_3 in 1.0 mL of concentrated H_2SO_4 to 3 mL of water. Allow the solution to cool to room temperature before using.*

The Jones oxidation test is a rapid method to distinguish primary and secondary alcohols from tertiary alcohols. A positive test is indicated by a color change from *orange* (the oxidizing agent, Cr^{6+}) as the oxidizing agent is itself reduced to the *blue green* (Cr^{3+}).

$$\left.\begin{array}{c} RCH_2OH \\ or \\ R_2CHOH \end{array}\right\} + H_2Cr_2O_7 \xrightarrow{H_2SO_4} Cr_2(SO_4)_3 + \begin{array}{c} RCO_2H \\ or \\ R_2C{=}O \end{array}$$
                        Orange   Green

The test is based on oxidation of a primary alcohol to an aldehyde or acid, and of a secondary alcohol to a ketone.

On a white spot plate, place 1 drop of the liquid unknown (10 mg if a solid). Add 10 drops of acetone and stir the mixture with a thin glass rod. Add 1 drop of the test reagent to the resulting solution. Stir and observe any color change within a 2-second time period.

1. Run a blank to make sure the acetone is pure.

2. Tertiary alcohols, unsaturated hydrocarbons, amines, ethers, and ketones give a negative test within the 2-second time frame for observing

[9] For a detailed discussion of classification tests see (a) footnote 8, p. 138 or (b) Pasto, D. J.; Johnson, C. R.; Miller, M. J. *Experiments and Techniques in Organic Chemistry;* Prentice Hall: New Jersey, 1992.

the color change. Aldehydes, however, give a positive test since they are oxidized to the corresponding carboxylic acids.

The HCl/ZnCl₂ Test: The Lucas Test

INSTRUCTOR PREPARATION. *The Lucas reagent is prepared by dissolving 16 g of anhydrous ZnCl₂ in 10 mL of concd HCl while cooling in an ice bath.*

The Lucas test is used to distinguish between primary, secondary, and tertiary monofunctional alcohols having fewer than six carbon atoms.

$$R\text{—OH} + H^+ \xrightarrow{\text{ZnCl}_2} R^+ + H_2O$$

Soluble

$$\xrightarrow{\text{Cl}^-} \text{RCl}$$

Insoluble

The test requires that the alcohol initially be soluble in the Lucas test reagent solution. As the reaction proceeds, the corresponding alkyl chloride is formed, which is insoluble in the reaction mixture. As a result, the solution becomes cloudy. In some cases a separate layer may be observed.

1. Tertiary, allyl, and benzyl alcohols react to give an immediate cloudiness to the solution. You may be able to see a separate layer of the alkyl chloride after a short time.

2. Secondary alcohols generally produce a cloudiness within 3–10 min. The solution may have to be heated to obtain a positive test.

3. Primary alcohols having less than six carbon atoms dissolve in the reagent but react very, very slowly. Those having more than six carbon atoms do not dissolve to any significant extent, no reaction occurs, and the aqueous phase remains clear.

4. A further test to aid in distinguishing between tertiary and secondary alcohols is to run the test using concentrated hydrochloric acid. Tertiary alcohols react immediately to give the corresponding alkyl halide, whereas secondary alcohols do not react under these conditions.

In a small test tube prepared by sealing a Pasteur pipet off at the shoulder (■), place 2 drops of the unknown (10 mg if a solid) followed by 10 drops of the Lucas reagent.

Shake or stir the mixture with a thin glass rod and allow the solution to stand. Observe the results. Based on the times given above, classify the alcohol. Additional points to consider:

1. Certain polyfunctional alcohols also give a positive test.

2. If an alcohol having three or fewer carbons is expected, a 1-mL conical vial equipped with an air condenser should be used to prevent low molecular weight alkyl chlorides (volatile) from escaping and thus remaining undetected.

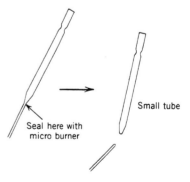

Seal here with micro burner

Small tube

Making a small test tube.

The Iodoform Test

This test is positive for compounds that on oxidation generate methyl ketones (or acetaldehyde) under the reaction conditions. For example, methyl carbinols (secondary alcohols having at least one methyl group attached to the carbon atom to which the —OH is attached), acetaldehyde, and ethanol give positive results.

For the test see Methyl Ketones and Methyl Carbinols (p. 715).

Periodic Acid: Vicinal Diols

INSTRUCTOR PREPARATION. *This reagent solution is prepared by dissolving 250 mg of periodic acid (H_5IO_6) in 50 mL of deionized water.*

Vicinal diols (1,2 diols) are differentiated from the simple alcohols by the characteristic reaction below. Metaperiodic acid (HIO_4) selectively oxidizes 1,2 diols to give carbonyl compounds.

$$\underset{\text{1,2 Diol}}{\overset{\displaystyle :\!\ddot{O}H \quad :\!\ddot{O}H}{\underset{|\quad\quad|}{C-C}}} \xrightarrow[H_2O]{HIO_4} 2 \underset{/}{\overset{\backslash}{C}}{=}\ddot{O} + H_2O + HIO_3$$

The test is based on the *instantaneous* formation of a white precipitate of silver iodate ($AgIO_3$) following addition of silver nitrate.

$$HIO_3 + AgNO_3 \rightarrow HNO_3 + AgIO_3 \downarrow$$

Place 2 mL of the periodic acid reagent solution in a small test tube.

Add 2 drops of concentrated nitric acid and mix the solution thoroughly. Add 2 drops of a liquid (~2–5 mg of a solid) and mix again. Now add 2–3 drops of 5% aqueous silver nitrate solution. An *instantaneous white precipitate* constitutes a positive test.

α-Hydroxyaldehydes, α-hydroxyketones, α-hydroxyacids, 1,2-diketones, and α-aminoalcohols, also give a positive test.

Aldehydes and Ketones

The 2,4-Dinitrophenylhydrazine Test

INSTRUCTOR PREPARATION. *The reagent solution is prepared by dissolving 1.0 g of 2,4-dinitrophenylhydrazine in 5.0 mL of concentrated sulfuric acid. This solution is slowly added, with stirring, to a mixture of 10 mL of water and 35 mL of 95% ethanol. After mixing, filter the solution.*

Aldehydes and ketones react rapidly with 2,4-dinitrophenylhydrazine to form 2,4-dinitrophenylhydrazones. These derivatives range in color from *yellow* to *red*, depending on the degree of conjugation in the carbonyl compound.

2,4-Dinitrophenylhydrazine   Yellow ⟶ red precipitate

On a white spot plate place 7–8 drops of 2,4-dinitrophenylhydrazine reagent solution.

Then add 1 drop of a liquid unknown. If the unknown is a solid, 1 drop of a solution prepared by dissolving 10 mg of the material in 10 drops of ethanol is added. The mixture is stirred with a thin glass rod. The formation of a red-to-yellow precipitate is a positive test.

NOTE: *The reagent, 2,4-dinitrophenylhydrazine, is orange-red and melts at 198 °C (dec). Do not mistake it for a derivative!*

Reactive esters or anhydrides react with the reagent to give a positive test. Allylic or benzylic alcohols may be oxidized to aldehydes or ketones, which in turn give a positive result. Amides do not interfere with the test. Be sure that your unknown is pure and does not contain aldehyde or ketone impurities.

Phenylhydrazine and *p*-nitrophenylhydrazine are often used to prepare the corresponding hydrazones. These reagents also yield solid derivatives of aldehydes and ketones.

Silver Mirror Test for Aldehydes: Tollens Reagent

This reaction involves the oxidation of aldehydes to the corresponding carboxylic acid, using an alcoholic solution of silver ammonium hydroxide. A positive test is the formation of a *silver* mirror, or a black precipitate of finely divided silver.

$$RC\overset{H}{=}\overset{..}{\underset{..}{O}} + 2\,Ag(NH_3)_2\overset{..}{\underset{..}{O}}H \longrightarrow 2\,Ag\downarrow + R-C\overset{\overset{..}{\underset{..}{O}}:}{\underset{\overset{..}{\underset{..}{O}}:^-,\,NH_4^+}{}} + H_2\overset{..}{\underset{..}{O}} + 3\,\overset{.}{N}H_3$$

The test should only be run after the presence of an aldehyde or ketone has been established.

In a small test tube prepared from a Pasteur pipet (see the Lucas test) place 1.0 mL of a 5% aqueous solution of $AgNO_3$, followed by 1 drop of aqueous 10% NaOH solution. Now add concentrated aqueous ammonia, drop by drop (2–4 drops) with shaking, until the precipitate of silver oxide just dissolves. Add 1 drop of the unknown (10 mg if a solid), with shaking, and allow the reaction mixture to stand for 10 min at room temperature. If no reaction has occurred, place the test tube in a sand bath at 40 °C for 5 min. Observe the result. Additional points to consider:

1. Avoid a large excess of ammonia.

2. Reagents must be well mixed. Stirring with a thin glass rod is recommended.

3. *This reagent is freshly prepared for each test. It should not be stored since decomposition occurs with the formation of* AgN_3, *which is explosive.*

4. This oxidizing agent is very mild and thus alcohols are not oxidized under these conditions. Ketones do not react. Some sugars, acyloins, hydroxylamines, and substituted phenols do give a positive test.

Chromic Acid Test

INSTRUCTOR PREPARATION. *The reagent is prepared by dissolving 1 g of chromium trioxide in 1 mL of concd* H_2SO_4, *followed by 3 mL of* H_2O.

Chromic acid in acetone rapidly oxidizes aldehydes to carboxylic acids. Ketones react very slowly, or not at all.

In a 3 mL vial or small test tube, place 2 drops of a liquid unknown (~10 mg if a solid) and 1 mL of spectral grade acetone. Now add several drops of the chromic acid reagent.

A green precipitate of chromous salts is a positive test. Aliphatic aldehydes give a precipitate within 30 seconds; aromatic aldehydes take 30–90 seconds.

The reagent also reacts with primary and secondary alcohols (see Chromic Anhydride Test: Jones Oxidation, p. 704).

Bisulfite Addition Complexes

INSTRUCTOR PREPARATION. *The reagent is prepared by mixing 1.5 mL of ethanol and 6 mL of a 40% aqueous solution of sodium bisulfite. Filter the reagent before use, if a small amount of the salt does not dissolve.*

Most aldehydes react with a saturated sodium bisulfite solution to yield a crystalline bisulfite addition complex.

The reaction is reversible and thus the carbonyl compound can be recovered by treatment of the complex with aqueous 10% $NaHCO_3$ or dilute HCl solution.

Place 50–75 μL of the liquid unknown in a small test tube and add 150 μL of the sulfite reagent and mix thoroughly.

A crystalline precipitate is a positive test.

Alkyl methyl ketones and unhindered cyclic ketones also give a positive test.

Alkanes and Cycloalkanes: Saturated Hydrocarbons

Iodine Charge-Transfer Complex

Alkanes exhibit a *negative* iodine charge-transfer complex test. Species containing π electrons or nonbonded electron pairs produce a brown colored solution. This color formation is due to the charge-transfer complex between iodine and the available electrons.

Solutions of iodine and nonparticipating compounds are violet in color.

On a white spot plate, place a small crystal of iodine. Now add 2–3 drops of a liquid unknown. Alkanes give a *negative* test (violet color).

The test is run only on liquid unknowns. Saturated hydrocarbons, fluorinated and chlorinated saturated hydrocarbons, and aromatic hydrocarbons and their halogenated derivatives all give violet colored solutions. All other species give a positive test (brown colored solution).

Concentrated Sulfuric Acid

Saturated hydrocarbons, halogenated saturated hydrocarbons, simple aromatic hydrocarbons, and their halogenated derivatives are insoluble in *cold* concentrated sulfuric acid.

CAUTION   In a small test tube place 100 μL of *cold* concentrated sulfuric acid [CAUTION]. Now add 50 μL of an unknown. A resulting heterogeneous solution (the unknown does *not* dissolve) is a positive test for a saturated hydrocarbon.

Alkenes, and compounds having a functional group containing a nitrogen or oxygen atom, are soluble in cold, concentrated acid.

Bromine in Methylene Chloride

Unsaturated hydrocarbons readily add bromine (Br$_2$). An example of this reaction is given in Experiment [F2].

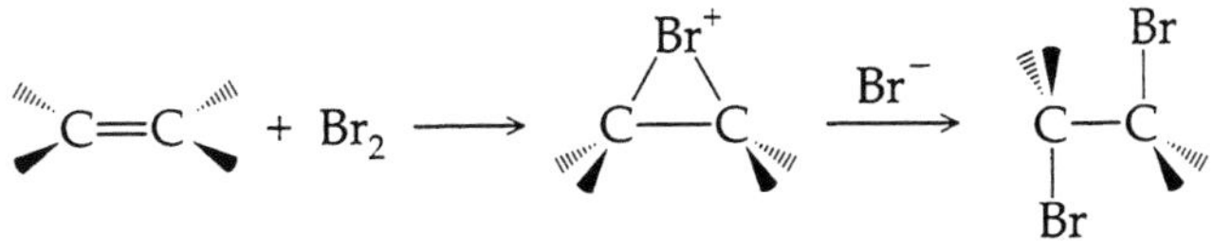

The test is based upon the decolorization of a red-brown bromine–methylene chloride solution.

CAUTION: Bromine is highly toxic and can cause burns.   CAUTION

In a 10 × 75-mm test tube, or in a small tube prepared from a Pasteur pipet (see Lucas test), place 2 drops of a liquid unknown (~15 mg if a solid) followed by 0.5 mL of methylene chloride. Add dropwise, with shaking, a 2% solution of bromine in methylene chloride solvent **[HOOD]**. The presence of an unsaturated hydrocarbon will require 2–3 drops of the reagent before the reddish-brown color of bromine persists in the solution. Additional points to consider:

1. Methylene chloride is used in place of the usual carbon tetrachloride (CCl$_4$) as it is less toxic.
2. Phenols, enols, amines, aldehydes, and ketones interfere with this test.

Permanganate Test: Baeyer Test for Unsaturation

Unsaturation in an organic compound can be detected by the decolorization of permanganate solution. The reaction involves the cis hydroxylation of the alkene to give a 1,2 diol (glycol).

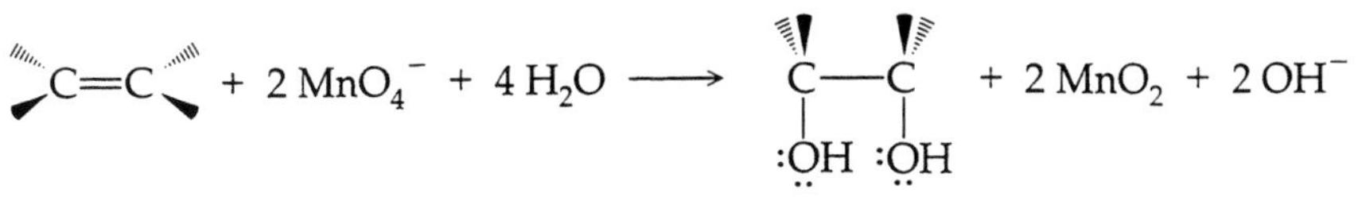

On a white spot plate, place 0.5 mL of *alcohol-free* acetone, followed by 2 drops of the unknown compound (~15 mg if a solid). Now add dropwise (2–3 drops), with stirring, a 1% aqueous solution of potassium permanganate (KMnO$_4$). A positive test for unsaturation is the discharge of purple permanganate color from the reagent and the precipitation of brown manganese oxides.

Any functional group that undergoes oxidation with permanganate interferes with the test (phenols, aryl amines, most aldehydes, primary and secondary alcohols, etc.).

Alkenes and Alkynes:
Unsaturated Hydrocarbons

HOOD

Appendix Vq

Alkyl Halides

Silver Nitrate Test

Alkyl halides that undergo the S_N1 substitution reaction react with alcoholic silver nitrate ($AgNO_3$) to form a precipitate of the corresponding silver halide.

Secondary and primary halides react slowly or not at all at room temperature. However, they do react at elevated temperatures. Tertiary halides react immediately at room temperature.

In a 1.0-mL conical vial place 0.5 mL of 2% ethanolic $AgNO_3$ solution and 1 drop of unknown (~10 mg if a solid). A positive test is indicated by the appearance of a precipitate within 5 min. If no reaction occurs, add a boiling stone and equip the vial with an air condenser. Heat the solution at *gentle* reflux for an additional 5 min using a sand bath. Cool the solution.

If a precipitate is formed, add 2 drops of dilute HNO_3. Silver halides will not dissolve in nitric acid solution. Additional points to consider:

1. The order of reactivity for R groups is allyl $\cong$ benzyl $>$ tertiary $>$ secondary $>>>$ primary. For the halide leaving groups: I $>$ Br $>$ Cl.

2. Acid halides, α-haloethers, and 1,2-dibromo compounds also give a positive test at room temperature. Only activated aryl halides give a positive test at elevated temperatures.

Sodium Iodide in Acetone

INSTRUCTOR PREPARATION.   *The reagent is prepared by dissolving 3 g of sodium iodide (NaI) in 25 mL of acetone. Store in a dark bottle.*

Primary alkyl chlorides and bromides can be distinguished from aryl and alkenyl halides by reaction with sodium iodide in acetone (Finkelstein reaction).

$$R-X + NaI \xrightarrow{\text{acetone}} R-I + NaX \downarrow$$
$$X = Cl, Br$$

Primary alkyl bromides undergo an S_N2 displacement reaction within 5 min at room temperature, primary alkyl chlorides only at 50 °C.

In a 1.0-mL conical vial, place 1 drop of a liquid unknown (~10 mg if a solid) and 3 drops of acetone. To this solution add 0.5 mL of sodium iodide–acetone reagent.

A positive test is the appearance of a precipitate of NaX within 5 min. If no precipitate is observed, add a boiling stone and equip the vial with an air condenser. Warm the reaction mixture in a sand bath at about 50 °C for 5 min. Cool to room temperature and determine whether a reaction has occurred. Additional points to consider:

1. Benzylic and allylic chlorides and bromides, acid chlorides and bromides, and α-haloketones, α-haloesters, α-haloamides, and α-halonitriles also give a positive test at room temperature.

2. Primary and secondary alkyl chlorides, and secondary and tertiary alkyl bromides, react at 50 °C under these conditions.

3. If the solution turns red brown in color, iodine is being liberated.

Amides, Ammonium Salts, and Nitriles

Hydroxamate Test for Amides

Unsubstituted (on nitrogen) amides, and the majority of substituted amides, will give a positive hydroxamate test.

where Q = NH_2, NHR', or NR'R''

The hydroxamic acid is identified by formation of a red-to-purple color in the presence of Fe^{3+} ion, as for the test with esters (see below).

In a 3.0-mL conical vial containing a boiling stone and equipped with an air condenser place 1 drop of a liquid unknown (~10 mg if a solid), followed by 0.5 mL of 1 M hydroxylamine hydrochloride–propylene glycol solution. Heat the resulting mixture to reflux temperature (~190 °C) using a sand bath, and reflux for 3–5 min. Cool the solution to room temperature, and add 2 drops of 5% aqueous $FeCl_3$ solution. The formation of a red-to-purple color is a positive test.

Ammonium salts, amides, and nitriles undergo hydrolysis in alkaline solution to form ammonia gas, or an amine.

Alkaline Hydrolysis

Detection of ammonia from ammonium salts, primary amides, and nitriles, by use of a color test using copper sulfate solution, constitutes a positive test for these functional groups. The same test may also be used for secondary and tertiary amides that can generate low molecular weight (volatile) amines upon hydrolysis.

In a 1.0-mL conical vial containing a boiling stone, and equipped with an air condenser, place 1–2 drops of the unknown liquid (~10 mg if a solid) and 0.5 mL of 20% aqueous NaOH solution. Heat this mixture to *gentle* reflux on a sand bath. Moisten a strip of filter paper with 2 drops of 10% aqueous copper sulfate solution and place it over the top of the condenser. Formation of a *blue* color [copper ammonia (or amine) complex] is a positive test.

The filter paper may be held in place using a small test tube holder or other suitable device.

Amines

Copper Ion Test

Amines will give a blue-green coloration or precipitate, when added to a copper sulfate solution. In a small test tube, place 0.5 mL of a 10% copper sulfate solution. Now add 1 drop of an unknown (~10 mg if a solid). The blue-green coloration or precipitate is a positive test. Ammonia will also give a positive test.

Hinsberg Test

The Hinsberg test is useful for distinguishing between primary, secondary, and tertiary amines. The reagent used is *p*-toluenesulfonyl chloride in alkaline solution.

Primary amines with fewer than seven carbon atoms form a sulfonamide that is soluble in the alkaline solution. Acidification of the solution results in the precipitation of the insoluble sulfonamide.

$$H_3C-\text{\textcircled{}}-SO_2Cl + R-NH_2 \xrightarrow{NaOH}$$

$$H_3C-\text{\textcircled{}}-SO_2\bar{N}R,\ Na^+ \underset{\text{excess base}}{\overset{\text{excess acid}}{\rightleftharpoons}} H_3C-\text{\textcircled{}}-SO_2NHR + NaCl + H_2O$$

       (soluble)   (insoluble)

Secondary amines form an insoluble sulfonamide in the alkaline solution.

$$H_3C-\text{\textcircled{}}-SO_2Cl + R_2NH \xrightarrow{NaOH} H_3C-\text{\textcircled{}}-SO_2NR_2 + NaCl + H_2O \xrightarrow{\text{excess base}} \text{no change}$$

                                               (insoluble)

Tertiary amines normally give no reaction under these conditions.

$$H_3C-\text{\textcircled{}}-SO_2Cl + R_3N \xrightarrow{NaOH} H_3C-\text{\textcircled{}}-SO_3^- + NR_3 + 2\,Na^+ + Cl^- + H_2O$$

                                       (soluble)   (oil)

HOOD   In a 1.0-mL conical vial containing a boiling stone, and equipped with an air condenser, place 0.5 mL of 10% aqueous sodium hydroxide solution, 1 drop of the sample unknown (~10 mg if a solid), followed by 30 mg of *p*-toluenesulfonyl chloride **[HOOD]**. Heat the mixture to reflux for 2–3 min on a sand bath, and then cool it in an ice bath. Test the alkalinity of the solution using litmus paper. If it is not alkaline, add additional 10% aqueous sodium hydroxide dropwise.

Using a Pasteur filter pipet, separate the solution from any solid that may be present. Transfer the solution to a clean 1.0-mL conical vial [SAVE].

SAVE

NOTE. *If an oily upper layer is obtained at this stage, remove the lower alkaline phase* [SAVE] *using a Pasteur filter pipet. To the remaining oil add 0.5 mL of cold water and stir vigorously to obtain a solid material.*

SAVE

If a solid is obtained, it may be (1) the sulfonamide of a secondary amine; (2) recovered tertiary amine, if the original amine was a solid; or (3) the insoluble salt of a primary sulfonamide derivative (if the original amine had more than six carbon atoms). Additional points to consider:

1. If the solid is a tertiary amine, it is soluble in aqueous 10% HCl.
2. If the solid is a secondary sulfonamide, it is insoluble in aqueous 10% NaOH.
3. If no solid is present, acidify the alkaline solution by addition of 10% aqueous HCl. If the unknown amine is primary, the sulfonamide will precipitate.

Bromine Water
Aromatic amines, since they possess an electron-rich aromatic ring, can undergo electrophilic aromatic substitution with bromine, to yield the corresponding arylamino halide(s). Therefore, if elemental tests indicate that an aromatic group is present in an amine, treatment with the bromine water reagent may indicate that the amine is attached to an aromatic ring.

For the test, see Phenols and Enols (p. 717).

Fuming Sulfuric Acid
Simple aromatic hydrocarbons are insoluble in sulfuric acid (H_2SO_4) but are soluble in fuming sulfuric acid. If these hydrocarbons contain more than two alkyl substituents, they may be sulfonated under these conditions.

Aromatic Hydrocarbons with NO Functional Groups

In a small test tube place 100 μL of fuming sulfuric acid [CAUTION]. Now add 50 μL of the unknown suspected to be aromatic. A resulting homogeneous solution is a positive test.

CAUTION

Azoxybenzene and Aluminum Chloride
This color test is run only on those aromatic compounds that are insoluble in sulfuric acid (see previous test). The color produced in this test results from the formation of a complex of $AlCl_3$ and a *p*-arylazobenzene derivative.

$$ArH + C_6H_5\overset{\overset{\displaystyle O}{\uparrow}}{N}{=}NC_6H_5 \xrightarrow{AlCl_3} \left[Ar{-}\!\!\underset{}{\bigcirc}\!\!{-}N{=}N{-}\!\!\underset{}{\bigcirc} \right] AlCl_3$$

Azoxybenzene   Colored complex

In a small dry test tube, place 250 μL of the aromatic unknown. Add a small crystal of azoxybenzene and about 12 mg of anhydrous aluminum chloride. If a color is not produced immediately, warm the mixture for a few min.

Aryl halides and other simple aromatic hydrocarbons give a deep-orange to dark-red color or precipitate. Polynuclear aromatic hydrocarbons, such as naphthalenes and anthracenes, give brown colors. Aliphatic hydrocarbons give no color, or at most a light yellow tint.

Appendix Vu

Carboxylic Acids

The presence of a carboxylic acid is detected by its solubility behavior. An aqueous solution of the acid will be acidic to litmus paper (or pH paper may be used). Since a sulfonic acid would also give a positive test, the test for sulfur (sodium fusion) is used to distinguish between the two types of acids. A water-soluble phenol is acidic toward litmus paper but also would give a positive ferric chloride test.

Carboxylic acids also react with a 5% solution of sodium bicarbonate (see Experiment [4B]).

Place 1–2 mL of the bicarbonate solution on a watch glass and add 1–2 drops of the acid (~10 mg if a solid). Gas bubbles of CO_2 constitute a positive test.

Esters

Hydroxamate Test

Carboxylic esters can be identified by conversion to hydroxamic acid salts. Acidification of this salt produces the corresponding hydroxamic acid (RCONHOH), which is identified by formation of a red-to-purple color in the presence of Fe^{3+} ion.

Red violet

In a 3.0-mL conical vial containing a boiling stone, and equipped with an air condenser, place 1 drop of the liquid unknown (~10 mg if a solid) followed by 0.5 mL of 1.0 M ethanolic hydroxylamine hydrochloride solution. Add 10% methanolic KOH to this solution (dropwise) until the resulting solution has pH ~10 (pH paper). Heat this mixture to reflux temperature using a sand bath for 5 min, cool to room temperature, and acidify to pH = 3–4 by dropwise addition of 5% aqueous HCl solution. Now add 2 drops of 5% aqueous $FeCl_3$ solution. The formation of a red-to-purple color is a positive test. Additional points to consider:

1. It is suggested that a blank be run for comparison purposes.
2. Acid chlorides, anhydrides, lactones, and imides also give a positive test.

Saponification

This well-known reaction of esters can often be used to classify these compounds. It also may lead to a useful derivative if the corresponding carboxylic acid is isolated.

In a 3.0-mL conical vial containing a magnetic spin vane, place 100 μL of the liquid unknown (~150 mg if a solid) and add 1 mL of 6 M NaOH solution. Attach the vial to a reflux condenser. Now place the vial in a sand bath on a magnetic stirring hot plate and, with stirring, heat the mixture at reflux for 0.5 hour, or until the solution becomes homogeneous.

A positive test is the disappearance of the organic layer (if the original unknown was water insoluble) or the lack of the usually pleasant aroma of the unknown ester.

High-boiling esters (bp > 200 °C) are usually not saponified under these conditions due to their low solubility in the aqueous solvent.

NOTE.   *Upon standing, ethers may form peroxides. Peroxides are very explosive. To test for the presence of these substances, use starch–iodide paper that has been moistened with 6 M HCl. Peroxides cause the paper to turn blue. To remove peroxides from ethers, pass the material through a short column of highly activated alumina (Woelm basic alumina, active grade 1, see p. 318 of the reference cited in footnote 9b).*

Ethers

Ferrox Test

The ferrox test is a color test sensitive to oxygen, which may be used to distinguish ethers from hydrocarbons that, like most ethers, are soluble in sulfuric acid.

In a dry 10 × 75-mm test tube using a glass stirring rod, grind a crystal of ferric ammonium sulfate and a crystal of potassium thiocyanate. The ferric hexathiocyanatoferrate that is formed adheres to the rod.

In a second clean 10 × 75-mm test tube, place 2–3 drops of a liquid unknown. If dealing with a solid, use about 10 mg and add toluene until a saturated solution is obtained. Now using the rod with the ferric hexathio-cyanatoferrate attached, stir the unknown. *If the unknown contains oxygen, the ferrate compound dissolves and a reddish-purple color is observed.*

Some high molecular weight ethers do not give a positive test.

Bromine Water

Aromatic ethers, since the aromatic ring is electron rich, can undergo electrophilic aromatic substitution with bromine to yield the corresponding aryl ether–halide(s). Therefore, if elemental tests indicate that an aromatic group is present in an ether, treatment with the bromine water reagent may substantiate the presence of an aryl ether.

For the test see Phenols and Enols (p. 717).

Iodoform Test

Methyl Ketones and Methyl Carbinols

INSTRUCTOR PREPARATION.   *Dissolve 3 g of KI and 1 g I$_2$ in 20 mL of water.*

The iodoform test involves hydrolysis and cleavage of methyl ketones to form a yellow precipitate of iodoform (CHI$_3$).

$$R-\overset{\ddot{O}}{\overset{\|}{C}}-CH_3 + 3\,I_2 + 3\,KOH \longrightarrow R-\overset{\ddot{O}}{\overset{\|}{C}}-CI_3 + 3\,KI + 3\,H_2O$$

$$\Big\downarrow {\scriptstyle KOH}$$

$$R-\overset{\ddot{O}}{\overset{\|}{C}}-\bar{O},\overset{+}{K} + CHI_3 \downarrow$$
$$\text{Yellow}$$

It is also a positive test for compounds that, upon oxidation, generate methyl ketones (or acetaldehyde) under these reaction conditions. For example, methyl carbinols (secondary alcohols having at least one methyl group attached to the carbon atom to which the OH unit is linked), acetaldehyde, and ethanol give positive results.

In a 3.0-mL conical vial equipped with an air condenser, place 2 drops of the unknown liquid (10 mg if a solid), followed by 5 drops of 10% aqueous KOH solution.

HOOD

NOTE. *If the sample is insoluble in the aqueous phase, either mix vigorously or add dioxane [HOOD] or bis(2-methoxyethyl) ether to obtain a homogeneous solution.*

Warm the mixture on a sand bath to 50–60 °C and add the KI–I$_2$ reagent dropwise until the solution becomes dark brown in color (~1.0 mL). Additional 10% aqueous KOH is now added (dropwise) until the solution is again colorless.

CAUTION: Iodine is highly toxic and can cause burns.

After warming for 2 min, cool the solution and determine whether a yellow precipitate (CHI$_3$, iodoform) has formed. If a precipitate is not observed, reheat as before for another 2 min. Cool and check again for the appearance of iodoform. Additional points to consider:

1. The iodoform test is reviewed elsewhere.[10]
2. An example of the general haloform reaction, using bleach to oxidize a methyl ketone, is given in Experiment [34].

Nitro Compounds

Ferrous Hydroxide Test

Many nitro compounds give a positive test based on the following reaction.

$$R{-}NO_2 + 4\ H_2O + 6\ Fe(OH)_2 \rightarrow R{-}NH_2 + 6\ Fe(OH)_3 \downarrow$$
$$\text{Red-brown}$$

The nitro derivative oxidizes the iron(II) hydroxide to iron(III) hydroxide, the latter is a red-brown solid.

In a 1.0-mL conical vial place 5–10 mg of the unknown compound, followed by 0.4 mL of freshly prepared 5% aqueous ferrous ammonium sulfate solution. After mixing, add 1 drop of 3 N sulfuric acid followed by 10 drops of 2 N methanolic KOH. Cap the vial, shake vigorously, vent, and then allow it to stand over a 5-min period. The formation of a red-brown precipitate, usually within 1 min, is a positive test for a nitro group.

Sodium Hydroxide Color Test

Treatment of an aromatic nitro compound with 10% sodium hydroxide solution may often be used to determine the number of nitro groups present on the aromatic ring system.

Mononitro compounds produce no color (a light yellow may be observed).
Dinitro compounds produce a bluish-purple color.
Trinitro compounds produce a blood-red color.

The color formation is due to formation of Meisenheimer complexes (for a discussion, see p. 321 of the text cited in footnote 9b).

[10] Fuson, R. C.; Bull, B. A. *Chem. Rev.* **1934,** *15,* 275.

To run the test, dissolve 10 mg of the unknown (1–2 drops if a liquid) in 1 mL of acetone in a small test tube. Now add about 200 μL of 10% NaOH solution and shake. Observe any color formation.

If amino, substituted amino, or hydroxyl groups are present in the molecule, a positive color test is not obtained.

Ferric Ion Test

Most phenols and enols form colored complexes in the presence of ferric ion, Fe^{3+}.

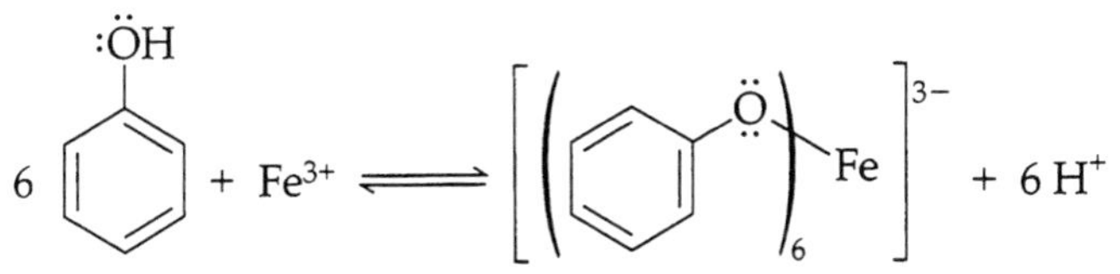

Phenols give red, blue, purple, or green colors. Sterically hindered phenols may give a negative test. Enols generally give a tan, red, or red-violet color.

On a white spot plate place 2 drops of water, or 1 drop of water plus 1 drop of ethanol, or 2 drops of ethanol, depending on the solubility characteristics of the unknown. To this solvent system add 1 drop (10 mg if a solid) of the substance to be tested. Stir the mixture with a thin glass rod to complete dissolution. Add 1 drop of 2.5% aqueous ferric chloride ($FeCl_3$) solution (light yellow in color). Stir and observe any color formation. If necessary, a second drop of the $FeCl_3$ solution may be added. Additional points to consider:

1. The color developed may be fleeting or it may last for many hours. A slight excess of the ferric chloride solution may or may not destroy the color.
2. An alternate procedure using $FeCl_3$–CCl_4 solution in the presence of pyridine is available.[11]

Bromine Water

Phenols, substituted phenols, aromatic ethers, and aromatic amines, since the aromatic rings are electron rich, undergo aromatic electrophilic substitution with bromine to yield substituted aryl halides. For example,

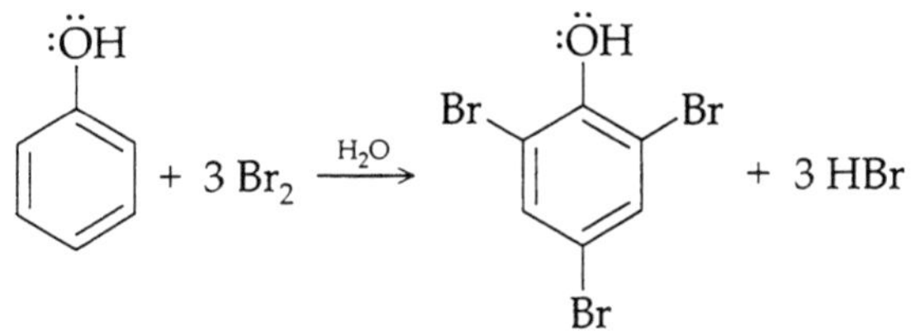

CAUTION: The test should be run in the *hood*.   HOOD

---

[11] Soloway, S.; Wilen, S. H. *Anal. Chem.* **1952**, *4*, 979.

In a small test tube, place 1–2 drops of the unknown (~20 mg if a solid) and add 1–2 mL of water. Check the pH of the solution with pH paper. In the **hood** add saturated bromine water dropwise until the bromine color persists. A precipitate generally forms.

A positive test is the decolorization of the bromine solution, and often the formation of an off-white precipitate. If the unknown is a phenol, this should cause the pH of the original solution to be less than 7.

PREPARATION OF DERIVATIVES

Based on the preliminary and classification tests carried out to this point, you should have established the type of functional group (or groups) present (or lack of one) in the unknown organic sample. The next step in qualitative organic analysis is to consult a set of tables containing a listing of known organic compounds sorted by functional group and/or by physical properties or by both. Using the physical properties data for your compound, you can select a few possible candidates that appear to "fit" the data you have collected. On a chemical basis, the final step in the qualitative identification sequence is to prepare one or two *crystalline derivatives* of your compound. Selection of the specific compound, and thus final confirmation of its identity, can then be made from the extensive derivative tables that have been accumulated. With the advent of spectral analysis, the preparation of derivatives is often not necessary, but the wealth of chemistry that can be learned by the beginning student in carrying out these procedures is extensive and important. The preparation of selected derivatives for the most common functional groups are given below. Condensed tables of compounds and their derivatives are summarized in Appendix A. For extensive tables and alternative derivatives that can be utilized, see the following Bibliography.

IMPORTANT.   *In each of the procedures outlined below, drops of reagents are measured using Pasteur pipets.*

BIBLIOGRAPHY

Pasto, D. J.; Johnson, C. R.; Miller, M. J. *Experiments and Techniques in Organic Chemistry*; Prentice Hall: Englewood Cliffs, NJ, 1992.

Rappoport, Z.; *Handbook of Tables for Organic Compound Identification*, 3rd ed., CRC Press: Boca Raton, FL, 1967.

Shriner, R. L.; Fuson, R. C.; Curtin; D. Y.; Morrill, T. C. *The Systematic Identification of Organic Compounds*, 6th ed., Wiley: New York, 1980.

CARBOXYLIC ACIDS[12]

Preparation of Acid Chlorides

$$R-\overset{\overset{\cdot\cdot}{O}}{\overset{\|}{C}}-\overset{\cdot\cdot}{\underset{\cdot\cdot}{O}}H + Cl-\overset{\overset{\cdot\cdot}{O}}{\underset{\cdot\cdot}{S}}-Cl \xrightarrow{DMF} R-\overset{\overset{\cdot\cdot}{O}}{\overset{\|}{C}}-Cl + HCl\uparrow + SO_2\uparrow$$

[12] See Tables A.1 and A.2.

Weigh and place 20 mg of the unknown acid in a dry 3.0-mL conical vial containing a boiling stone and fitted with a cap. Now add **[HOOD]** 4 drops of thionyl chloride and 1 drop of *N,N*-dimethylformamide (DMF). Immediately attach the vial to a reflux condenser that is protected by a calcium chloride drying tube.

HOOD

CAUTION: This reaction is run in the *hood* since hydrogen chloride and sulfur dioxide are evolved. Thionyl chloride is an irritant and is harmful to breathe. Immediately recap the vial after each addition until the vial is attached to the reflux condenser.

HOOD

Allow the mixture to stand at room temperature for 10 min, heat it at gentle reflux on a sand bath for 15 min, and then cool it to room temperature. Dilute the reaction mixture with 5 drops of methylene chloride solvent.

The acid chloride is not isolated but is used directly in the following preparations.

Amides

$$R-\overset{\overset{\displaystyle \cdot\overset{..}{O}\cdot}{\|}}{C}-Cl + 2\,\overset{..}{N}H_3 \longrightarrow R-\overset{\overset{\displaystyle \cdot\overset{..}{O}\cdot}{\|}}{C}-\overset{..}{N}H_2 + NH_4Cl$$

Cool the vial in an ice bath and add 10 drops of concentrated aqueous ammonia **[HOOD]** via Pasteur pipet, *dropwise*, with stirring. *It is convenient to make this addition down the neck of the air condenser.* The amide may precipitate during this operation. After the addition is complete, remove the ice bath and stir the mixture for an additional 5 min. Now add methylene chloride (10 drops) and stir the resulting mixture to dissolve any precipitate. Separate the methylene chloride layer from the aqueous layer using a Pasteur filter pipet and transfer it to another Pasteur filter pipet containing 200 mg of anhydrous sodium sulfate. Collect the eluate in a Craig tube containing a boiling stone. Extract the aqueous phase with an additional 0.5 mL of methylene chloride. Separate the methylene chloride layer as before and transfer it to the same column. Collect this eluate in the same Craig tube. Evaporate the methylene chloride solution using a warm sand bath **[HOOD]** under a gentle stream of nitrogen gas. Recrystallize the solid amide product using the Craig tube. Dissolve the material in about 0.5 mL of ethanol, add water (dropwise) until the solution becomes cloudy, cool the Craig tube in an ice bath, and collect the crystals in the usual manner. Dry the crystalline amide on a porous clay plate and determine the melting point.

HOOD

HOOD

Anilides

$$R-\overset{\overset{\displaystyle \cdot\overset{..}{O}\cdot}{\|}}{C}-Cl + 2\,H_2\overset{..}{N}-\!\!\bigcirc \longrightarrow R-\overset{\overset{\displaystyle \cdot\overset{..}{O}\cdot}{\|}}{C}-\underset{\underset{\displaystyle H}{|}}{\overset{..}{N}}-\!\!\bigcirc + \bigcirc\!\!-NH_3^+,\,Cl^-$$

In a 3.0-mL conical vial containing a magnetic spin vane, and equipped with an air condenser, place 5 drops of aniline and 10 drops of methylene chloride. Cool the solution in an ice bath and transfer the acid chloride

HOOD solution (prepared above) via Pasteur pipet, *dropwise*, with stirring, to the aniline solution **[HOOD]**. *It is convenient to make this addition down the neck of the condenser.* After the addition is complete, remove the ice bath and stir the mixture for an additional 10 min.

Transfer the methylene chloride layer to a 10×75-mm test tube, and wash it with 0.5 mL of H_2O, 0.5 mL of 5% aqueous HCl, 0.5 mL of 5% aqueous NaOH, and finally with 0.5 mL of H_2O. For each washing, shake the test tube and remove the top aqueous layer by Pasteur filter pipet. Transfer the resulting wet methylene chloride layer to a Pasteur filter pipet containing 200 mg of anhydrous sodium sulfate. Collect the eluate in a Craig tube containing a boiling stone. Rinse the original test tube with an additional 10 drops of methylene chloride. Collect this rinse and pass it through the same column. Both eluates are combined.

HOOD Evaporate the methylene chloride solvent on a warm sand bath under a gentle stream of nitrogen gas **[HOOD]**. Recrystallize the crude anilide from an ethanol–water mixture using the Craig tube. Dissolve the material in about 0.5 mL of ethanol, add water (dropwise) to the cloud point, cool in an ice bath, and collect the crystals in the usual manner. Dry the purified derivative product on a porous clay plate, and determine its melting point.

Toluidides

$$R-\overset{\overset{\displaystyle \cdot\cdot}{O}\cdot}{\underset{\|}{C}}-Cl + 2\,H_2\ddot{N}-\!\!\left\langle\ \right\rangle\!\!-CH_3 \longrightarrow R-\overset{\overset{\displaystyle \cdot\cdot}{O}\cdot}{\underset{\|}{C}}-\underset{\underset{\displaystyle H}{|}}{\ddot{N}}-\!\!\left\langle\ \right\rangle\!\!-CH_3 + CH_3-\!\!\left\langle\ \right\rangle\!\!-NH_3^+,\,Cl^-$$

The same procedure described for the preparation of anilides is used except that *p*-toluidine replaces the aniline.

ALCOHOLS [13]

Phenyl- and α-Naphthylurethanes (Phenyl- and α-Naphthylcarbamates)

$$Ar-\ddot{N}=C=\ddot{O}\colon + R-\ddot{O}-H \longrightarrow Ar-\underset{\underset{\displaystyle H}{|}}{\ddot{N}}-\overset{\overset{\displaystyle \ddot{O}\colon}{\|}}{C}-\ddot{O}-R$$

Isocyanate   Urethane

NOTE. *For the preparation of these derivatives, the alcohols must be anhydrous. Water hydrolyzes the isocyanates to produce arylamines that react with the isocyanate reagent to produce high-melting, disubstituted ureas.*

In a 3.0-mL conical vial containing a boiling stone and equipped with an air condenser protected by a calcium chloride drying tube place 15 mg of an anhydrous alcohol or phenol. Remove the air condenser from the vial and add 2 drops of phenyl isocyanate or α-naphthyl isocyanate. Replace the air condenser immediately. If the unknown is a phenol, add 1 drop of pyridine in a similar manner.

HOOD **CAUTION: This addition must be done in the *hood*. The isocyanates are lachrymators! Pyridine has the characteristic strong odor of an amine.**

[13] See Table A.3.

If a spontaneous reaction does not take place, heat the vial at about 80–90 °C, using a sand bath, for a period of 5 min. Then cool the reaction mixture in an ice bath. It may be necessary to scratch the sides of the vial to induce crystallization. Collect the solid product by vacuum filtration, using a Hirsch funnel, and purify it by recrystallization from ligroin. For this procedure, place the solid in a 10×75-mm test tube and dissolve it in 1.0 mL of warm (60–80 °C) ligroin. If diphenyl (or dinaphthyl) urea is present, (formed by reaction of the isocyanate with water), it is insoluble in this solvent. Transfer the warm ligroin solution to a Craig tube using a Pasteur filter pipet. Cool the solution in an ice bath and collect the resulting crystals in the usual manner. After drying the product on a porous clay plate, determine the melting point.

3,5-Dinitrobenzoates

3,5-Dinitrobenzoyl
chloride

NOTE. *The dinitrobenzoyl chloride reagent tends to hydrolyze on storage to form the corresponding carboxylic acid. Check its melting point before use (3,5-dinitrobenzoyl chloride, mp = 74 °C; 3,5-dinitrobenzoic acid, mp = 202 °C).*

In a 3.0-mL conical vial containing a boiling stone, and equipped with an air condenser protected by a calcium chloride drying tube, place 25 mg of pure 3,5-dinitrobenzoyl chloride and two drops of the unknown alcohol. Heat the mixture to about 10 °C below the boiling point of the alcohol (but not over 100 °C) on a sand bath for a period of 5 min. Cool the reaction mixture, add 0.3 mL of water, and then place the vial in an ice bath to cool. Collect the solid ester by vacuum filtration, using a Hirsch funnel, and wash the filter cake with three 0.5-mL portions of 2% aqueous sodium carbonate (Na_2CO_3) solution, followed by 0.5 mL of water. Recrystallize the solid product from an ethanol–water mixture using a Craig tube. Dissolve the material in about 0.5 mL of ethanol, add water (dropwise) until the solution is just cloudy, cool in an ice bath, and collect the crystals in the usual manner. After drying the product on a porous clay plate, determine the melting point.

ALDEHYDES AND KETONES[14]

2,4-Dinitrophenylhydrazones

2,4-Dinitrophenylhydrazine

A 2,4-dinitrophenylhydrazone

[14] See Tables A.4 and A.5.

Appendix Vcc

The procedure outlined in the Classification Test Section for aldehydes and ketones (p. 706) is used. Since the derivative to be isolated is a solid, it may be convenient to run the reaction in a 3-mL vial, or in a small test tube. Double the amount of the reagents used. If necessary, the derivative can be recrystallized from 95% ethanol.

The procedure is generally suitable for the preparation of phenylhydrazone and *p*-nitrophenylhydrazone derivatives of aldehydes and ketones.

Semicarbazones

Semicarbazide   A semicarbazone

In a 3.0-mL conical vial place 12 mg of semicarbazide hydrochloride, 20 mg of sodium acetate, 10 drops of water, and 12 mg of the unknown carbonyl compound. Cap the vial, shake vigorously, vent, and allow the vial to stand at room temperature until crystallization is complete (varies from a few min to several hours). Cool the vial in an ice bath if necessary. Collect the crystals by vacuum filtration, using a Hirsch funnel, and wash the filter cake with 0.2 mL of cold water. Dry the crystals on a porous clay plate. Determine the melting point.

AMINES[15]

Primary and Secondary Amines: Acetamides

In a 3.0-mL conical vial equipped with an air condenser, place 20 mg of the unknown amine, 5 drops of water, and 1 drop of concentrated hydrochloric acid.

In a small test tube, prepare a solution of 40 mg of sodium acetate trihydrate dissolved in 5 drops of water. Stopper the solution and set it aside for use in the next step.

Warm the solution of amine hydrochloride to about 50 °C on a sand bath. Then cool it, and add 40 μL of acetic anhydride in one portion
HOOD   [HOOD] through the condenser by aid of a 9-in. Pasteur pipet. In like manner, *immediately* add the sodium acetate solution (prepared previously). Swirl the contents of the vial to ensure complete mixing.

Allow the reaction mixture to stand at room temperature for about 5 min, and then place it in an ice bath for an additional 5–10 min. Collect the white crystals by vacuum filtration, using a Hirsch funnel, and wash the filter cake with two 0.1-mL portions of water. The product may be recrystallized from ethanol–water using the Craig tube, if desired. Dry the crystals on a porous clay plate and determine the melting point.

[15] See Tables A.6 and A.7.

Primary and Secondary Amines: Benzamides

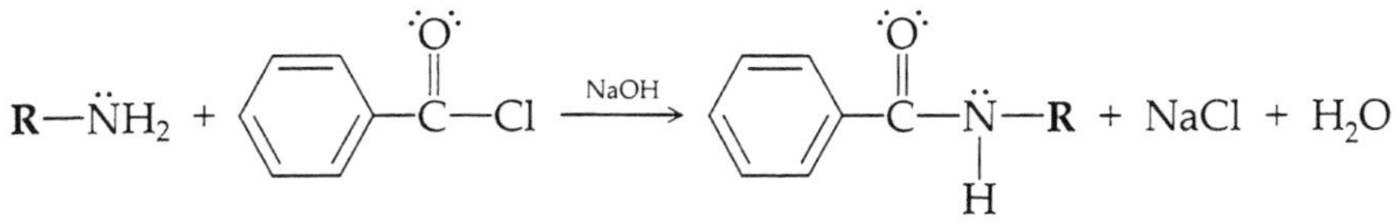

In a 3.0-mL conical vial place 0.4 mL of 10% aqueous NaOH solution, 25 mg of the amine, and 2–3 drops of benzoyl chloride [**HOOD**]. Cap and shake the vial over a period of about 10 min. Vent the vial periodically to release any pressure buildup.

HOOD

Collect the crystalline precipitate by vacuum filtration, using a Hirsch funnel, and wash the filter cake with 0.1 mL of dilute HCl followed by 0.1 mL of water. It is generally necessary to recrystallize the material from methanol or aqueous ethanol using the Craig tube. Dry the product on a porous clay plate and determine the melting point.

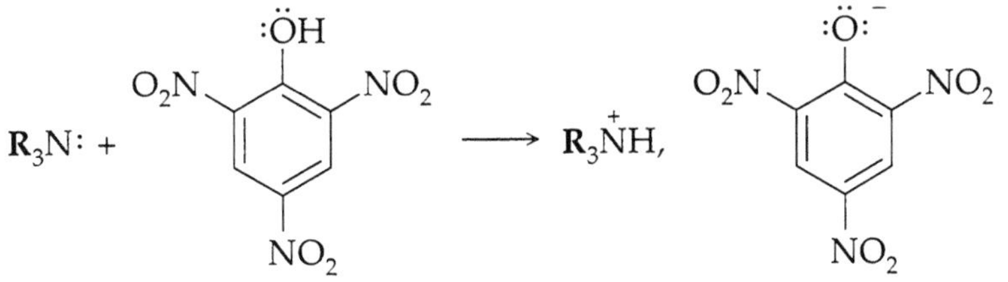

Picric acid   Picrate salt

Primary, Secondary, and Tertiary Amines: Picrates

In a 3.0-mL conical vial containing a boiling stone, and equipped with an air condenser, place 15 mg of the unknown amine and 0.3 mL of 95% ethanol.

NOTE. *If the amine is not soluble in the ethanol, shake the mixture to obtain a saturated solution and then transfer this solution, using a Pasteur filter pipet, to another vial.*

Now add 0.3 mL of a saturated solution of picric acid in 95% ethanol.

CAUTION: Picric acid explodes by percussion or when rapidly heated.

Heat the mixture at reflux, using a sand bath, for about 1 min and then allow it to cool slowly to room temperature. Collect the yellow crystals of the picrate by vacuum filtration, using a Hirsch funnel. Dry the material on a porous clay plate and determine the melting point.

ACID CHLORIDES AND ANHYDRIDES[16]

Amides

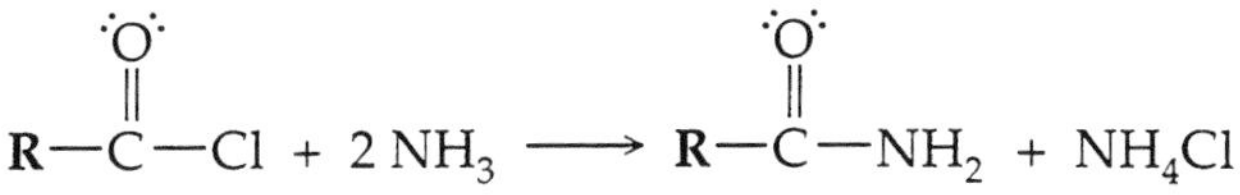

In a 10 × 75-mm test tube, place 0.4 mL of ice cold, concentrated ammonium hydroxide solution. To this solution is added slowly, [**HOOD**] with   HOOD

[16] See Table A.8.

Appendix Vee

shaking, about 15 mg of the unknown acid chloride or anhydride. Stopper the test tube and allow the reaction mixture to stand at room temperature for about 5 min. Collect the crystals by vacuum filtration, using a Hirsch funnel, and wash the filter cake with 0.2 mL of ice cold water. Recrystallize the material using a Craig tube, from water or an ethanol–water mixture. Dry the purified crystals on a porous clay plate and determine the melting point.

AROMATIC HYDROCARBONS[17]

Picrates

$$Ar\text{—}H + \text{Picric acid} \longrightarrow Ar\text{—}H \cdot \text{Picrate complex}$$

Picric acid   Picrate complex

The procedure outlined on page 723 is used to prepare these derivatives.

NITRILES[18]

Hydrolysis to Amides

$$\text{Ph—CN:} \xrightarrow[\text{NaOH}]{H_2O_2} \text{Ph—C(=O)—NH}_2 + O_2 + H_2O$$

Conversion of nitriles to water-insoluble amides, by hydrolysis with alkaline hydrogen peroxide, is a possible method of characterization for these compounds. It is especially useful for aromatic nitriles.

In a 5-mL conical vial containing a magnetic spin vane, weigh and place about 50 mg of the nitrile and 500 μL of a 1 M NaOH solution. Cool the mixture in a water bath and, with stirring, add dropwise 500 μL of 12% H_2O_2 solution. Attach the vial to an air condenser and warm the solution on a sand bath while stirring at 50–60 °C for approximately 45 min. To the cooled reaction mixture, add 1–2 mL of cold water, and then collect the solid amide by vacuum filtration. Wash the product with two 1-mL portions of cold water, and recrystallize the amide from aqueous ethanol using the Craig tube. Dry the solid and determine the melting point.

PHENOLS[19]

α-Naphthylurethanes (α-naphthylcarbamates)

The procedure outlined under Alcohols, Phenyl-, and α-Naphthylurethanes is used to prepare these derivatives (p. 720).

Bromo Derivatives

$$\text{PhOH} + 3\,Br_2 \xrightarrow{H_2O} \text{2,4,6-tribromophenol} + 3\,HBr$$

[17] See Table A.9.
[18] See Table A.13.
[19] See Table A.10.

INSTRUCTOR PREPARATION. *The brominating reagent is prepared by adding 1.0 mL (3 g) of bromine [HOOD] to a solution of 4.0 g of KBr in 25 mL of water.*   HOOD

In a 1.0-mL conical vial, place 10 mg of the unknown phenol followed by 2 drops of methanol and 2 drops of water. To this solution, add 3 drops [HOOD] of brominating agent from a Pasteur pipet.   HOOD

Continue the addition (dropwise) until the reddish-brown color of bromine persists. Now add water (4 drops), cap the vial, shake, vent, and then allow it to stand at room temperature for 10 min. Collect the crystalline precipitate by vacuum filtration using a Hirsch funnel and wash the filter cake with 0.5 mL of 5% aqueous sodium bisulfite solution. Recrystallize the solid derivative from ethanol, or from an ethanol–water mixture, using a Craig tube. Dissolve the material in about 0.5 mL of ethanol, add water until it becomes cloudy, cool in an ice bath, and collect the crystals in the usual manner. Dry the purified product on a porous clay plate and determine the melting point.

These compounds do not give derivatives directly, but are usually converted into another material that can then be derivatized. The procedures are, for the most part, lengthy, and frequently give mixtures of products. It is recommended that compounds belonging to these classes be primarily identified using spectroscopic methods. Measurement of their physical properties is also of utmost importance.

ALIPHATIC HYDROCARBONS, HALOGENATED HYDROCARBONS, AMIDES, NITRO COMPOUNDS, ETHERS, AND ESTERS[20]

QUESTIONS

10-1. The following six substances have approximately the same boiling point and are all colorless liquids. Suppose you were given six unlabeled bottles, each of which contained one of these compounds.

Explain how you would use simple chemical tests to determine which bottle contained which compound.

Ethanoic acid	Toluene
Propyl butanoate	Diisobutylamine
1-Butanol	Styrene

10-2. A colorless liquid (C_4H_6O) with a boiling point of 81 °C, was found to be soluble in water and also in ether. It gave a negative test for the presence of halogens, sulfur, and nitrogen. It did, however, give a positive test with the Baeyer reagent and also gave a positive test with the 2,4-dinitrophenylhydrazine reagent. It gave negative results when treated with ceric nitrate solution and with Tollens reagent. Treatment with ozone followed by hydrolysis in the presence of zinc gave formaldehyde as one of the products.

What is the structure and name of the colorless liquid?

10-3. A colorless liquid **A** (C_3H_6O) was soluble in water and ether, and had a boiling point of 94–96 °C. It decolorized a Br_2–CH_2Cl_2 solution and gave a positive ceric nitrate test. On catalytic hydrogenation it formed Compound **B** (C_3H_8O), which did not decolorize the above bromine solu-

[20] See Tables A.11, A.12, and A.14–A.17.

tion, but did give a positive ceric nitrate test. Treatment of Compound **A** with ozone, followed by hydrolysis in the presence of zinc, gave formaldehyde as one of the products. Compound **A** formed an α-naphthylurethane with a melting point of 109 °C.

What are the names and structures of Compounds **A** and **B**?

10-4. A compound of formula $C_{14}H_{12}$ gave a positive Baeyer test and burned with a yellow, sooty flame. Treatment with ozone followed by hydrolysis in the presence of zinc gave formaldehyde as one of the products. Also isolated from the ozonolysis reaction was a second compound, $C_{13}H_{10}O$, which burned with a yellow, sooty flame, and readily formed a semicarbazone with a melting point of 164 °C. The ^1H NMR spectrum of this compound ($C_{13}H_{10}O$) showed only complex multiplets near 7.5 ppm; the fully ^1H-decoupled ^{13}C NMR spectrum showed only 5 peaks.

What are the structures and names of the two compounds?

10-5. Compound **A** ($C_7H_{14}O$) burned with a yellow, nonsooty flame and did not decolorize a bromine–methylene chloride solution. It did give a positive 2,4-dinitrophenylhydrazine test, but a negative Tollens test. Treatment of the compound with lithium aluminum hydride followed by neutralization with acid, produced a Compound **B**, which gave a positive Lucas test in about 5 min. Compound **B** also gave a positive ceric nitrate test. The ^1H NMR spectrum for Compound **A** gave the following data:

1.02 ppm	9H, singlet
2.11 ppm	3H, singlet
2.31 ppm	2H, singlet

Give suitable structures for Compounds **A** and **B**.

10-6. A friend of yours who is a graduate student attempting to establish the structure of a chemical species from field clover, isolated an alcohol that was found to have an optical rotation of +49.5°. Chemical analysis gave a molecular formula of $C_5H_{10}O$. It was also observed that this alcohol readily decolorized Br_2–CH_2Cl_2 solution. On this basis, the alcohol was subjected to catalytic hydrogenation and it was found to absorb 1 mol of hydrogen gas. The product of the reduction gave a positive ceric nitrate test, indicating that it too was an alcohol. However, the reduced compound was optically inactive.

Your friend has come to you for assistance in determining the structures of the two alcohols. What do you believe the structures are?

10-7. An unknown compound burned with a yellow, nonsmoky flame and was found to be insoluble in 5% sodium hydroxide solution but soluble in concentrated sulfuric acid. Measurement of its boiling point gave a range of 130–131 °C. Combustion analysis gave a molecular formula of C_5H_8O. It was found to give a semicarbazone with a melting point of 204–206 °C. However, it gave a negative result when treated with Tollens reagent and it did not decolorize the Baeyer reagent. It also gave a negative iodoform test.

Identify the unknown compound.

10-8. An unknown organic carboxylic acid, mp = 139–141 °C, burned with a yellow, sooty flame. The sodium fusion test showed that nitrogen was present. It did not react with p-toluenesulfonyl chloride, but did give a positive test when treated with 5% aqueous ferrous ammonium sulfate solution, acidified with 3 N H_2SO_4, and then followed by methanolic KOH solution. A 200-mg sample of the acid neutralized 12.4 mL of 0.098 N sodium hydroxide solution.

Identify the acid.

Does your structure agree with the calculated equivalent weight?

10-9. An unknown organic liquid, **A**, was found to burn with a yellow, sooty flame and give a positive Lucas test (~5 min). Upon treatment with sodium dichromate–sulfuric acid solution it produced Compound **B**, which also burned with a yellow, sooty flame. Compound **B** gave a positive 2,4-dinitrophenylhydrazine test, but a negative result when treated with the Tollens reagent. However, **B** did give a positive iodoform test. The ^1H NMR spectrum for Compound **A** showed the following:

  1.4 ppm   3H (doublet)
  1.9 ppm   1H (singlet)
  4.8 ppm   1H (quartet)
  7.2 ppm   5H (complex multiplet)

Give the structures and suitable names for Compounds **A** and **B**.

10-10. A hydrocarbon **A** (C_6H_{10}) burned with a yellow, almost nonsmoky flame. On catalytic hydrogenation over platinum catalyst it absorbed 1 mol of hydrogen to form Compound **B**. It also decolorized a Br_2–CH_2Cl_2 solution to yield a dibromo derivative, **C**. Ozonolysis of the hydrocarbon gave only one compound, **D**. Compound **D** gave a positive iodoform test when treated with iodine–sodium hydroxide solution. On treatment of Compound **D** with an alcoholic solution of silver ammonium hydroxide, a silver mirror was formed within a few min.

Identify the hydrocarbon **A** and Compounds **B–D**.

10-11. A high-boiling liquid, bp = 202–204 °C, burns with a yellow, sooty flame. Sodium fusion indicates that halogens, nitrogen, and sulfur are not present. It is not soluble in water, dilute sodium bicarbonate solution, or dilute hydrochloric acid. However, it proved to be soluble in 5% aqueous sodium hydroxide solution. The compound gives a purple color with ferric chloride solution and a precipitate when reacted with bromine–water. Treatment with hydroxylamine reagent did not give a reaction, but a white precipitate was obtained when the compound was treated with α-naphthyl isocyanate. On drying, this white, solid derivative had a mp = 127–129 °C.

Identify the original liquid and write a structure for the solid derivative.

After identifying the unknown liquid, can you indicate what the structure of the precipitate obtained on reaction with bromine might be?

10-12. A colorless liquid, bp = 199–201 °C, burns with a yellow, sooty flame. The sodium fusion test proved negative for the presence of halogens, nitrogen, and sulfur. It was not soluble in water, 5% aqueous sodium hydroxide, or 5% hydrochloric acid. However, it dissolved in sulfuric acid with evolution of heat. It did not give a precipitate with 2,4-dinitrophenylhydrazine solution, and it did not decolorize bromine–methylene chloride solution. The unknown liquid did give a positive hydroxamate test and was found to have a saponification equivalent of 136.

Identify the unknown liquid.

10-13. Your friend of Question 10-5 still needs your help. A week later a low-melting solid **A** was isolated, which combustion analysis showed had composition $C_9H_{10}O$. The substance gave a precipitate when treated with 2,4-dinitrophenylhydrazine solution. Furthermore, when reacted with iodoform reagent, a yellow precipitate of CHI_3 was observed. Acidification of the alkaline solution from the iodoform test produced a solid material, **B**.

Reduction of Compound **A** with $LiAlH_4$ gave Compound **C** ($C_9H_{12}O$). This material, **C**, also gave Compound **B** when treated with iodoform reagent.

Vigorous oxidation of **A**, **B**, or **C** with sodium dichromate–sulfuric acid solution gave an acid having a mp = 121–122 °C.

Your friend needs your assistance in determining the structures for Compounds **A**, **B**, and **C**. Can you identify the three compounds?

10-14.   An organic compound ($C_9H_{10}O$) showed strong absorption in the IR spectrum at 1735 cm^{-1} and gave a semicarbazone having a melting point of 198 °C. It burned with a yellow, sooty flame and also gave a positive iodoform test. The ^{1}H NMR spectrum of the compound provided the following information:

2.11 ppm	3H (singlet)
3.65 ppm	2H (singlet)
7.20 ppm	5H (complex multiplet)

Identify the unknown organic compound.

10-15.   An unknown compound (**A**) was soluble in ether but only slightly soluble in water. It burned with a clear blue flame and combustion analysis showed it to have the molecular formula of $C_5H_{12}O$. It gave a positive test with the Jones reagent producing a new compound (**B**) with a formula of $C_5H_{10}O$. Compound **B** gave a positive iodoform test and formed a semicarbazone. Compound **A** on treatment with sulfuric acid produced a hydrocarbon (**C**) of formula C_5H_{10}. Hydrocarbon **C** readily decolorized a Br$_2$–CH$_2$Cl$_2$ solution, and on ozonolysis, produced acetone as one of the products.

Identify the structure of each of the lettered compounds.

10-16.   Compound **A** (C_7H_{14}) decolorized a Br$_2$–CH$_2$Cl$_2$ chloride solution. It reacted with BH$_3$•THF reagent, followed by alkaline peroxide solution, to produce Compound **B**. Compound **B**, on treatment with chromic acid–sulfuric acid solution, gave carboxylic acid **C**, which could be separated into two enantiomers. Compound **A**, on treatment with ozone, followed by addition of hydrogen peroxide, produced Compound **D**. Compound **D** was identical to that material isolated from the oxidation of 3-hexanol with chromic acid–sulfuric acid reagent.

Identify the structures of Compounds **A**, **B**, **C**, and **D**.

10-17.   Compound **A** (C_8H_{16}) decolorized a bromine–methylene chloride solution. Ozonolysis produced two compounds, **B** and **C**, which could be separated easily by GC. Both **B** and **C** gave a positive 2,4-dinitrophenylhydrazine test. Carbon–hydrogen analysis and molecular weight determination of **B** gave a molecular formula of $C_5H_{10}O$. The ^{1}H NMR spectrum revealed the following information for **B**:

0.92 ppm	3H, triplet
1.6 ppm	2H, pentet
2.17 ppm	3H, singlet
2.45 ppm	2H, triplet

Compound **C** was a low-boiling liquid (bp 56 °C). The ^{1}H NMR of this material showed only one singlet.

Identify Compounds **A**, **B**, and **C**.

Appendix VI

Tables of Derivatives

Tables of Derivatives

TABLE A.1 Derivatives of Carboxylic Acids (Liquids)

Acid	bp (°C)	Melting Point of Derivative (°C)[a]		
		Amide	Anilide	p-Toluidide
Methanoic (formic)	101	—	50	53
Ethanoic (acetic)	118	82	114	153
Propenoic (acrylic)	141	84	104	141
Propanoic	141	81	106	126
2-Methylpropanoic (isobutyric)	155	128	105	109
Butanoic (butyric)	163	115	96	75
2-Methylpentenoic (methacrylic)	163	102	87	—
Pyruvic	165	124	104	109
3-Methylbutanoic	177	135	110	106
Pentanoic (valeric)	186	106	63	74
2-Methylpentanoic	186	79	95	80
2,2-Dichloroethanoic	194	98	118	153
Hexanoic (caproic)	205	100	94	74
Heptanoic (enanthic)	223	96	65; 70	81
Octanoic (caprylic)	239	106; 110	57	70
Nonanoic (pelargonic)	254	99	57	84

[a] Two values are given for those derivatives that may exist in polymorphic forms.

TABLE A.2 Derivatives of Carboxylic Acids (Solids)

| Acid | bp (°C) | Melting Point of Derivative (°C)[a] | | |
		Amide	Anilide	p-Toluidide
Decanoic	31–32	108	70	78
Lauric	43–45	87	78	100
Myristic	54	103	84	93
Trichloroacetic	54–58	141	97	113
Chloroacetic	61	121	137	162
Palmitic	62	106	90	98
Octadecanoic (stearic)	70	109	95	102
Crotonic	72	158	118	—
3,3-Dimethyl acrylic	69	107	126	—
Phenylethanoic	77	156	65	117
2-Benzoylbenzoic	128	165	195	—
Pentandioic (glutaric)	97	175	223	218
Ethanedioic (oxalic)	101	219	148	169
2-Methylbenzoic (o-toluic)	105	143	125	144
3-Methylbenzoic (m-toluic)	112	94	126	118
Benzoic	122.4	130	160	158
Sebacic	131–134	170 (mono) 210 (di)	122 (mono) 200 (di)	201
trans-Cinnamic	133	147	153	168
2-Acetoxybenzoic (aspirin)	135	138	136	—
cis-Butenedioic (maleic)	137	172	198 (mono) 187 (di)	142 (di)
Malonic	137	—	132 (mono) 230 (di)	86 (mono) 253 (di)
2-Chlorobenzoic	140	—	118	131
3-Nitrobenzoic	140	143	154	162
2-Nitrobenzoic	146	176	155	—
Diphenylacetic	148	168	180	172
2-Bromobenzoic	150	155	141	—
Benzilic	150	153	175	190
Hexanedioic (adipic)	153	125 (mono) 230 (di)	151 (mono) 241 (di)	—
2-Hydroxybenzoic (salicylic)	158	142	136	156
2-Iodobenzoic	162	110	141	—
4-Methylbenzoic (p-toluic)	179	160	144	160; 165
4-Methoxybenzoic (p-anisic)	185	167	170	186
2-Naphthoic	186	192	171	192
Succinic	190	157 (mono) 260 (di)	143 (mono) 230 (di)	180 (mono) 255 (di)
Phthalic	211	149 (mono) 220 (di)	170 (mono) 254 (di)	150 (mono) 201 (di)
3,5-Dinitrobenzoic	205	183	234	—
4-Nitrobenzoic	241	198	204; 211	192; 204

[a] Two values are given for those derivatives that may exist in polymorphic forms.

TABLE A.3 Derivatives of Alcohols

Alcohol	bp (°C)	Phenyl-urethan	α-Naphthyl-urethan	3,5-Dinitro-benzoate
		Melting Point of Derivative (°C)		
Methyl (methanol)	65	47	124	108
Ethyl (ethanol)	78	52	79	93
Isopropyl (2-propanol)	82	88	106	122
tert-Butyl (tert-butanol)	83	136	101	142
Allyl	97	70	109	49
n-Propyl (1-propanol)	97	51	80	74
sec-Butyl (2-butanol)	99	65	97	76
tert-Pentyl (2-methyl-2-butanol)	102	42	71	116
Isobutyl (2-methyl-1-propanol)	108	86	104	87
3-Pentanol	116	48	71	101
n-Butyl (1-butanol)	118	63	71	64
2,3-Dimethyl-2-butanol	118	—	—	111
2-Pentanol	119	—	76	61
2-Methyl-2-pentanol	121	239	—	72
3-Methyl-3-pentanol	123	50	—	97
2-Methoxyethanol	125	—	113	—
2-Methyl-1-butanol	129	—	—	70
2-Chloroethanol	131	51	101	95
4-Methyl-2-pentanol	132	143	88	65
3-Methyl-1-butanol	132	55	—	61
2-Ethoxyethanol	135	—	67	75
3-Hexanol	136	—	—	77
2,2-Dimethyl-1-butanol	137	—	—	51
1-Pentanol	138	46	68	46
2-Hexanol	139	—	—	39
2,4-Dimethyl-3-pentanol	140	—	—	—
Cyclopentanol	141	132	118	115
2-Ethyl-1-butanol	148	—	—	52
2-Methyl-1-pentanol	148	—	—	51
4-Heptanol	156	—	80	64
1-Hexanol	158	42	59	58
2-Heptanol	159	—	54	49
Cyclohexanol	161	82	128	113
2-Furfuryl	172	45	129	81
1-Heptanol	177	68	—	47
Tetrahydrofurfuryl	178	61	—	84
2-Octanol	179	114	—	32
1-Octanol	195	74	—	61
Benzyl	205	78	—	113
2-Phenylethanol	221	79	—	108
1-Decanol	231	59	—	57
Cinnamyl	(mp 35)	90	—	121
Benzohydrol	(mp 67)	139	—	141
Cholesterol	(mp 147)	168	—	—

TABLE A.4   Derivatives of Aldehydes

| Aldehyde | bp (°C) | Melting Point of Derivative (°C)[a] | |
		Semi-carbazone	2,4-Dinitrophenyl-hydrazone
Acetaldehyde	21	162	168
Propionaldehyde	50	89 (154)	154
Isobutyraldehyde	64	125	187 (183)
n-Butyraldehyde	74	104	123
Isovaleraldehyde	92	107	123
n-Valeraldehyde	103	108	107
Crotonaldehyde	104	199	190
n-Hexaldehyde	131	106	104; 107
n-Heptaldehyde	153	109	108
2-Furaldehyde	161	202	212 (230)
Benzaldehyde	179	222	237
Salicylaldehyde	197	231	252 dec
p-Tolualdehyde	204	221	239
2-Chlorobenzaldehyde	215	146 (229)	213
Citral	228	164	116
4-Anisaldehyde	248	210	253
trans-Cinnamaldehyde	252	215	255
4-Chlorobenzaldehyde	(mp 47)	230	254

[a] Two values are given for those derivatives that may exist in polymorphic forms or as syn and anti geometrical isomers.

TABLE A.5   Derivatives of Ketones

Ketone	bp (°C)	Melting Point of Derivative (°C)[a]	
		Semi-carbazone	2,4-Dinitro-phenylhydrazone
Acetone	56	187	126
2-Butanone	80	146	117
3-Methyl-2-butanone	94	113	120
2-Pentanone	102	112	143
3-Pentanone	102	139	156
3,3-Dimethyl-2-butanone	106	157	125
4-Methyl-2-pentanone	119	134	95
2,4-Dimethyl-3-pentanone	124	160	88 (94)
2-Hexanone	129	122	106
Cyclopentanone	131	205	142
4-Heptanone	145	133	75
3-Heptanone	149	101	—
2-Heptanone	151	127	89
Cyclohexanone	155	166	162
2-Octanone	173	122	58
Acetophenone	200	198	240
Benzalacetone	(mp 41)	187	223
Benzophenone	(mp 48)	164	239
Benzalacetophenone	(mp 58)	168; 180	245
Benzil	(mp 95)	175 (182)	189
Benzoin	(mp 133)	206 (dec)	245

[a] Two values are given for those derivatives that may exists in polymorphic forms or as syn and anti geometrical isomers.

TABLE A.6   Derivatives of Primary and Secondary Amines

| Amine | bp (°C) | Melting Point of Derivative (°C)[a] | | |
		Acetamide	Benzamide	Picrate
Methylamine	−6	—	80	—
Ethylamine	17	—	71	—
Isopropylamine	33	—	71	165
tert-Butylamine	45	98	134	198
n-Propylamine	49	47	84	135
Allylamine	53	—	—	140
Diethylamine	55	—	42	155
sec-Butylamine	63	—	76	139
Isobutylamine	69	—	57	150
n-Butylamine	77	—	42	—
Diisopropylamine	84	—	—	140
Di-*n*-propylamine	109	—	—	75
Piperidine	106	—	48	152
Ethylenediamine	116	172 (di)	244 (di)	233
Cyclohexylamine	134	104	149	—
Diisobutylamine	139	86	—	121
Di-*n*-butylamine	159	—	—	59
Benzylamine	185	60	105	199
Aniline	185	114	163	198
N-Methylaniline	196	102	67	145
2-Methylaniline	199	110	144	213
4-Methylaniline	200 (mp 45)	148	158	—
3-Methylaniline	203	65	125	200
N-Ethylaniline	205	111	147	194
2-Chloroaniline	208	87	99	134
2,5-Dimethylaniline	215	139	140	171
2,6-Dimethylaniline	216	177	168	180
2,4-Dimethylaniline	217	133	192	209
N-Ethyl-3-methylaniline	221	—	72	—
2-Methoxyaniline	225	85	60 (84)	200
4-Chloroaniline	232 (mp 70)	179	192	178
4-Methoxyaniline	243 (mp 57)	130	154	170
2-Ethoxyaniline	229	79	104	—
4-Ethoxyaniline	254	135	173	—
Diphenylamine	(mp 54)	101	180	182
3-Nitroaniline	(mp 114)	152	155	—
4-Nitroaniline	(mp 147)	—	199	—

[a] Two values are given for those derivatives that may exist in polymorphic forms.

TABLE A.7   Derivatives of Tertiary Amines

Tertiary Amine	bp (°C)	Melting Point of Derivative (°C)[a]
		Picrate
Trimethylamine	3	216
Triethylamine	89	173
Pyridine	116	167
2-Methylpyridine (2-picoline)	129	169
2,6-Dimethylpyridine (2,6-lutidine)	142	168 (161)
3-Methylpyridine (3-picoline)	143	150
4-Methylpyridine (4-picoline)	143	167
Tripropylamine	157	116
N,N-Dimethylaniline	193	163
Tributylamine	216	105
N,N-Diethylaniline	216	142
Quinoline	237	203
Triisopentylamine	245	125

[a] Two values are given for those derivatives that may exist in polymorphic forms.

TABLE A.8   Derivatives of Acid Chlorides and Anhydrides

Acid Chloride or Anhydride	bp (°C)	mp (°C)	Melting Point of Derivative (°C)
			Amide
Acetyl chloride	52	—	82
Propionyl chloride	77–79	—	81
Butyryl chloride	102	—	115
Acetic anhydride	138–140	—	82
Propionic anhydride	167	—	81
Butyric anhydride	198–199	—	115
Benzoyl chloride	198	—	130
3-Chlorobenzoyl chloride	225	—	134
2-Chlorobenzoyl chloride	238	—	142
cis-1,2-Cyclohexanedicarboxylic anhydride	—	32	192d (acid)
Benzoic anhydride	—	39–40	130
Maleic anhydride	—	54–56	181 (mono) 266 (di)
4-Nitrobenzoyl chloride	—	72–74	201
Succinic anhydride	—	119–120	157 (mono) 260 (di)
Phthalic anhydride	—	131–133	149 (mono) 220 (di)

TABLE A.9 Derivatives of Aromatic Hydrocarbons

Aromatic Hydrocarbon	bp (°C)	mp (°C)	Melting Point of Derivative (°C)[a]
			Picrate
Benzene	80	—	84
Toluene	111	—	88
Ethylbenzene	136	—	96
p-Xylene	138	—	90
m-Xylene	138–139	—	91
o-Xylene	143–145	—	88
Mesitylene	163–166	—	97
1,2,4-Trimethylbenzene	168	—	97
1,2,3,4-Tetramethylbenzene	205	—	92
1-Methylnaphthalene	242	—	142
2-Methylnaphthalene	—	35	116
Pentamethylbenzene	—	51	131
Naphthalene	—	81	149
Acenaphthene	—	94	161
Phenanthrene	—	100	144 (133)
Anthracene	—	216	138

[a] Two values are given for those derivatives that may exist in polymorphic forms.

TABLE A.10   Derivatives of Phenols

| Phenol | mp (°C) | Melting Point of Derivative (°C) | |
		Bromo	α-Naphthylurethan
2-Chloro-	7 (bp 175)	48 (mono) 76 (di)	120
Phenol	42	95 (tri)	133
4-Methyl- (*p*-cresol)	35	49 (di) 108 (tetra)	146
3-Methyl- (*m*-cresol)	203 (bp)	84 (tri)	128
3,4-Dimethyl-	229 (bp)	171 (tri)	141
2-Methyl- (*o*-cresol)	33	56 (di)	142
4-Ethyl-	45	—	128
2-Nitro-	45	117 (di)	113
2,6-Dimethyl-	48	79	176
2-Isopropyl-5-methyl- (thymol)	50	55	160
3,5-Dimethyl-	64	166 (tri)	—
4-Bromo-	66	95 (tri)	168
2,5-Dimethyl-	73	178 (tri)	173
1-Naphthol	95	105 (di)	152
3-Nitro-	96	91 (di)	—
4-*tert*-Butyl-	98	50 (mono) 67 (di)	110
1,2-Dihydroxy- (catechol)	105	192 (tetra)	175
1,3-Dihydroxy- (resorcinol)	110	112 (tri)	275
4-Nitro-	112	142 (di)	150
2-Naphthol	123	84	157
Pyrogallol	134	158 (di)	173
1,4-Dihydroxy- (hydroquinone)	171	186 (di)	—

TABLE A.11   Aliphatic Hydrocarbons

Compound	bp (°C)	Compound	bp (°C)
Alkanes			
Pentane	36	2,2,4-Trimethyl-pentane	99
Cyclopentane	49		
2,2-Dimethylbutane	50	trans-1,4-Dimethyl-cyclohexane	119
2,3-Dimethylbutane	58		
2-Methylpentane	60	Octane	126
3-Methylpentane	63	Nonane	151
Hexane	69	Decane	174
Cyclohexane	81	Eicosane	343 (mp 37)
Heptane	98	Norbornane	(mp 87, subl)
		Adamantane	(mp 268, sealed)
Alkenes and Alkynes			
1-Pentene	30	3-Hexyne	82
2-Methyl-1,3-butadiene (isoprene)	34	Cyclohexene	84
		2-Hexyne	84
trans-2-Pentene	36	1-Heptene	94
cis-2-Pentene	37	1-Heptyne	100
2-Methyl-2-butene	39	2,4,4-trimethyl-1-pentene	102
Cyclopentadiene	41		
1,3-Pentadiene (piperylene)	41	2,4,4-Trimethyl-2-pentene	104
3,3-Dimethyl-1-butene	41	1-Octene	123
1-Hexene	63	Cyclooctene	146
cis-3-Hexene	66	1,5-Cyclooctadiene	150
trans-3-Hexene	67	d,l-α-Pinene	155
1-Hexyne	71	(−)-β-Pinene	167
1,3-Cyclohexadiene	80	Limonene	176
		1-Decene	181

TABLE A.12   Halogenated Hydrocarbons

Compound	bp (°C)	Compound	bp (°C)
Alkyl Halides			
Chlorides		**Bromides**	
n-Propyl	47	Ethyl	38
tert-Butyl	51	Isopropyl	60
sec-Butyl	68	Propyl	71
Isobutyl	69	*tert*-Butyl	72
n-Butyl	78	Isobutyl	91
Neopentyl	85	*sec*-Butyl	91
tert-Pentyl	86	Butyl	101
Cyclohexyl	143	*tert*-Pentyl	108
Hexachloroethane	185 (mp 187, subl)	Neopentyl	109
Triphenylmethyl	(mp 113)	1-Bromoheptane	178–179
		Iodides	
		Methyl	43
		Ethyl	72
		Isopropyl	90
		Propyl	102

Compound	bp (°C)	mp (°C)
Aryl Halides		
Chlorobenzene	132	—
Bromobenzene	156	—
2-Chlorotoluene	157–159	—
4-Chlorotoluene	162	—
1,3-Dichlorobenzene	172–173	—
1,2-Dichlorobenzene	178	—
2,4-Dichlorotoluene	196–203	—
3,4-Dichlorotoluene	201	—
1,2,4-Trichlorobenzene	214	—
1-Bromonaphthalene	279–281	—
1,2,3-Trichlorobenzene	—	51–53
1,4-Dichlorobenzene	—	54–56
1,4-Bromochlorobenzene	—	66–68
1,4-Dibromobenzene	—	87–89
1,2,4,5-Tetrachlorobenzene	—	138–140

TABLE A.13   Nitriles

Compound	bp (°C)	Compound	mp (°C)
Acrylonitrile	77	4-Chlorobenzylcyanide	30.5
Acetonitrile	81	Malononitrile	34
Propionitrile	97	Stearonitrile	40
Isobutyronitrile	108	2-Chlorobenzonitrile	41
n-Butyronitrile	117	Succinonitrile	48
Benzonitrile	191	Diphenylacetonitrile	75
2-Methylbenzonitrile	205	4-Cyanopyridine	80
3-Methylbenzonitrile	212		
4-Methylbenzonitrile	217		
Benzylcyanide	234		
Adiponitrile	295		

TABLE A.14   Amides[a]

Compound	bp (°C)	mp (°C)
N,N-Dimethylformamide	153	—
N,N-Diethylformamide	176	—
N-Methylformamide	185	—
N-Formylpiperidine	222	—
N,N-Dimethylbenzamide	—	41
N-Benzoylpiperidine	—	48
N-Propylacetanilide	—	50
N-Benzylacetamide	—	54
N-Ethylacetanilide	—	54
N,N-Diphenylformamide	—	73
N-Methyl-4-acetotoluidide	—	83
N,N-Diphenylacetamide	—	101
N-Methylacetanilide	—	102
Acetanilide	—	114
N-Ethyl-4-nitroacetanilide	—	118
N-Phenylsuccinimide	—	156
N-Phenylphthalimide	—	205

[a] Also see Tables A.1 and A.2 for amides prepared as derivatives of carboxylic acids.

TABLE A.15   Nitro Compounds

Compound	bp (°C)	mp (°C)
Nitrobenzene	211	—
2-Nitrotoluene	225	—
2-Nitro-*m*-xylene	225	—
3-Nitrotoluene	231	—
3-Nitro-*o*-xylene	245	—
4-Ethylnitrobenzene	246	—
2-Chloro-6-nitrotoluene	—	36
4-Chloro-2-nitrotoluene	—	38
3,4-Dichloronitrobenzene	—	42
1-Chloro-2,4-dinitrobenzene	—	50
4-Nitrotoluene	—	54
1-Nitronaphthalene	—	56
1-Chloro-4-nitrobenzene	—	84
m-Dinitrobenzene	—	90

TABLE A.16   Ethers

Compound	bp (°C)	mp (°C)
Furan	32	—
Ethyl vinyl ether	33	—
Tetrahydrofuran	67	—
n-Butyl vinyl ether	94	—
Anisole	154	—
4-Methylanisole	174	—
3-Methylanisole	176	—
4-Chloroanisole	203	—
1,2-Dimethoxybenzene	207	—
4-Bromoanisole	215	—
Anethole	234–237	—
Diphenyl ether	259	—
2-Nitroanisole	273	—
Dibenzyl ether	298	—
4-Nitroanisole	—	50–52
1,4-Dimethoxybenzene	—	56–60
2-Methoxynaphthalene	—	73–75

TABLE A.17   Esters

Compound	bp (°C)	Compound	bp (°C)
Liquids			
Methyl formate	32	Pentyl formate	132
Ethyl formate	54	Ethyl 3-methylbutanoate	135
Methyl acetate	57	Isobutyl propanoate	137
Isopropyl formate	68	Isopentyl acetate	142
Ethyl acetate	77	Propyl butanoate	143
Methyl propanoate	80	Ethyl pentanoate	146
Methyl propenoate	80	Butyl propanoate	147
Propyl formate	81	Pentyl acetate	149
Isopropyl acetate	91	Isobutyl 2-methylpropanoate	149
Methyl 2-methylpropanoate	93	Methyl hexanoate	151
sec-Butyl formate	97	Isopentyl propanoate	160
tert-Butyl acetate	98	Butyl butanoate	165
Ethyl propanoate	99	Propyl pentanoate	167
Propyl acetate	101	Ethyl hexanoate	168
Methyl butanoate	102	Cyclohexyl acetate	175
Allyl acetate	104	Isopentyl butanoate	178
Ethyl 2-methylpropanoate	110	Pentyl butanoate	185
sec-Butyl acetate	112	Propyl hexanoate	186
Methyl 3-methylbutanoate	117	Butyl pentanoate	186
Isobutyl acetate	117	Ethyl heptanoate	189
Ethyl butanoate	122	Isopentyl 3-methylbutanoate	190
Propyl propanoate	122	Ethylene glycol diacetate	190
Butyl acetate	126	Tetrahydrofurfuryl acetate	194
Diethyl carbonate	127	Methyl octanoate	195
Methyl pentanoate	128	Methyl benzoate	200
Isopropyl butanoate	128	Ethyl benzoate	213

Compound	mp (°C)	Compound	mp (°C)
Solids			
d-Bornyl acetate	29 (bp 221)	Ethyl 3,5-dinitrobenzoate	93
Ethyl 2-nitrobenzoate	30	Methyl 4-nitrobenzoate	96
Ethyl octadecanoate	33	2-Naphthyl benzoate	107
Methyl cinnamate	36 (bp 261)	Isopropyl 4-nitrobenzoate	111
Methyl 4-chlorobenzoate	44	Cyclohexyl 3,5-dinitrobenzoate	112
1-Naphthyl acetate	49	Cholesteryl acetate	114
Ethyl 4-nitrobenzoate	56	Ethyl 4-hydroxybenzoate	116
2-Naphthyl acetate	71	tert-Butyl 4-nitrobenzoate	116
Ethylene glycol dibenzoate	73	Hydroquinone diacetate	124
Propyl 3,5-dinitrobenzoate	74	tert-Butyl 3,5-dinitrobenzoate	142
Methyl 4-bromobenzoate	81	Hydroquinone dibenzoate	204